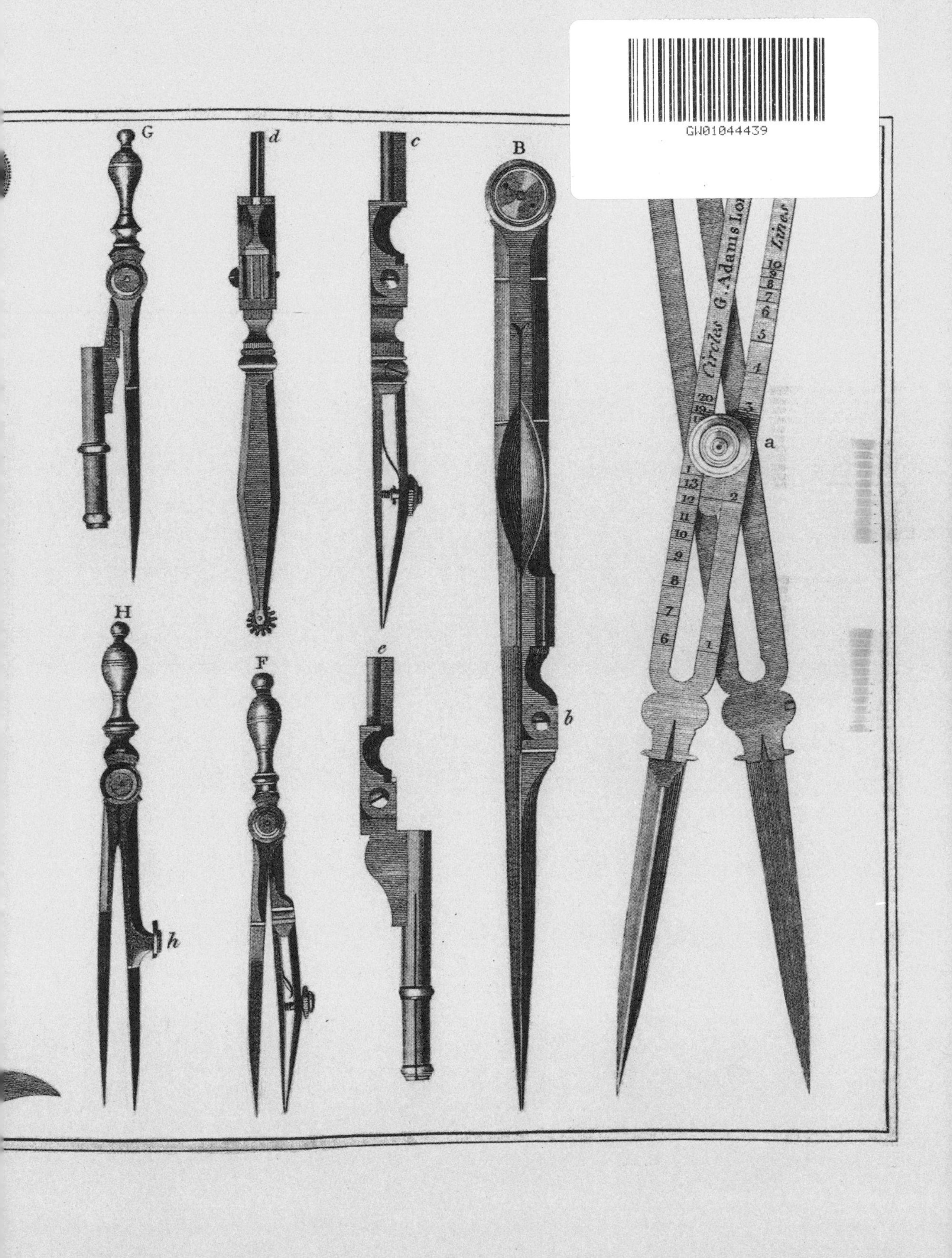
G
d
c
B
Circles G. Adams Lon
Lines
a
b
H
F
e
h

DRAWING INSTRUMENTS

Maya Hambly

Drawing Instruments
1580–1980

Sotheby's Publications

First published 1988
for Sotheby's Publications by
Philip Wilson Publishers Ltd
26 Litchfield Street
London WC2H 9NJ

Distributed in the USA by
Sotheby's Publications
Harper & Row, Publishers, Inc
10 East 53rd Street
New York
NY 10022

ISBN 0 85667 341 2
LC 88–060433

Designed by Alan Bartram
Printed and bound by
Butler and Tanner Ltd, Frome

ENDPAPERS
Engraved plate from the 1791 edition of George Adams the Younger's *Geometrical and Graphical Essays* which shows various patterns of compasses: (A) proportional compasses; (B) large compasses with (a) alternative inserts, (b) a point, (c) ink, (d) wheel pen, (e) pencil; (F) and (G) small bows for ink and pencil; (H) small dividers; (I) a pricker and (K) the drawing pen into which it is screwed; (L) dividers; (O) tracer/stylus; (P) and (Q) extension leg to compasses; (R) wholes and halves (fixed proportional compasses).

FRONTISPIECE
[1] Portrait of the American architect William Buckland by Charles Willson Peale (1789). *Yale University Art Gallery, Connecticut*

Contents

Foreword by John Harris 8

Preface 9

Acknowledgements 10

Introduction 11

1 **History of Drawing Instruments and their Makers** 19
Early civilizations to the Renaissance – the Renaissance and the era of exploration; 1400–1600 – the Age of Reason; 1600–1700 – the Age of Enlightenment; 1700–1800 – early industrialization; 1800–1900 – twentieth-century manufacturers

2 **Literary Evidence** 35
Early technical treatises on mathematical instruments – eighteenth-century treatises on mathematical instruments – seventeenth- and eighteenth-century handbooks and patternbooks – trade cards – London instrument makers' publications – encyclopaedias – nineteenth-century text-books – twentieth-century text-books

TYPES OF INSTRUMENT

3 **Straight Lines** 57
Styli – early ruling pens – eighteenth- and nineteenth-century ruling pens – specialist drawing pens – technical pens – pencils – technical pencils

4 **Circles and Dividing** 69
Compasses and dividers – dividers – callipers/cylindrical compasses

5 **Curves** 89
Ellipses (*elliptical trammels; ellipsographs; templates*) – spiral curves – parabola and hyperbola – conchoid curves – large radius curves – irregular curves – free curves

6 **Squaring and Ruling** 105
Squares (*triangle set squares; adjustable set squares*) – Rules (*parallel rules; rolling parallel rules; tee-squares; parallel motion rules*)

7 **Measurement** 115
Measuring to scale (*scale rules*) – measuring angles (*protractors; folding arm protractors*)

8 **Copying, Enlarging and Reducing** 125
Copying (*triangular compasses; prickers; tracers*) – enlarging and reducing (*proportional compasses; pantographs; eidographs*)

9 **Proportion and Ratio** 135
Sectors (*architectonic sectors; architectural proportional rods*)

10 **Perspective Aids** 144
Perspectographs – delineators

CASES OF DRAWING INSTRUMENTS

Introduction 153
Presentation cases 156
Magazine cases 161
Medium-sized cases 173
Pocket cases 185
Flat wallet cases 193

Select gazetteer of museum collections 195

Select bibliography 197

Photographic acknowledgements 200

Index 201

Colour Plates

		OPPOSITE PAGE
I	Wing-compasses by Christoph Trechsler. 1604. *Museum of the History of Science, Oxford*	32
II	Set of spring bows by W. F. Stanley. Late 19th century. *Andrew Alpern Collection, New York*	33
III	Set of beam compasses by a Milanese maker. *c.*1850. *Alessandro Ubertazzi Collection, Milan*	48
IV	Cased set of scales by W. F. Stanley. *Andrew Alpern Collection, New York*	48
V	Ellipsograph in case by John Farey. *c.*1815. *RIBA Collection, London*	49
VI	Presentation case of mathematical instruments by Domenicus Lusuerg. *c.*1701. *Science Museum, London*	64
VII	Magazine case by Giovanni Cattaneo. *c.*1850. *Alessandro Ubertazzi Collection, Milan*	65
VIII	French inlaid rosewood case. Late 19th century. *Andrew Alpern Collection, New York*	80
IX	Flat case by Kern of Aarau. *c.*1900. *Kern & Co Collection, Aarau*	81
X	Pocket case by Thomas Wright. *c.*1740. *National Maritime Museum, Greenwich*	81
XI	Pocket case by Benjamin Martin. Late 18th century. *Andrew Alpern Collection, New York*	128
XII	Pocket case probably by Peter Dollond. *c.*1800. *Andrew Alpern Collection, New York*	129
XIII	Small pocket case by Edward Nairne. *c.*1770. *Andrew Alpern Collection, New York*	144
XIV	Small pocket case by T. Whiford, 18th century. *Andrew Alpern Collection, New York*	145
XV	Pocket case by Troughton. Late 18th century. *Andrew Alpern Collection, New York*	145
XVI	Italian flat case. Mid-18th century. *Alessandro Ubertazzi Collection, Milan*	184
XVII	Flat case by W. F. Stanley. Late 19th century. *Andrew Alpern Collection, New York* BETWEEN PAGES	184–85
XVIII	Small flat case by Carlo Bordogna, Milan. *c.*1840. *Alessandro Ubertazzi Collection, Milan* BETWEEN PAGES	184–85
XIX	Set of miniature instruments contained in handle of a French walking-stick. 18th century. *Andrew Alpern Collection, New York*	185

Foreword

When I first joined the Library of the Royal Institute of British Architects in 1956, the Assistant Librarian took me through a round-up of those essential text-books that were in demand by architectural students. One such was W.F. Stanley's *Drawing and Mathematical Instruments* published by E. and F. N. Spon in 1925. Spon were publishers of basic text-books for the 'trade', and Stanley's text was written for the practitioner. There was no other, and as a student of architectural drawings I always had a nagging worry about the critical need for a book that would discuss the tools of the trade, and set them in an historical context.

As an inveterate traveller to the museums of Europe I have long been aware that drawing instruments have been collected and displayed as works of art. Hence they feature in vitrines with astronomical instruments and clocks, and frequently occur in the Wunderkammern of collectors, as in the Museum Fridericianum, in the Staatliche Kunstsammlungen, Cassel. This is not surprising because instrument making was one of the tasks of the greatest gold- and silversmiths, reaching a peak of artistic excellence in Augsburg in the seventeenth century.

Nevertheless, something was missing when museums displayed these instruments as works of art rather than as daily tools of a trade. The question 'What was their effect on paper?' was never answered.

This attitude of pure connoisseurship of form rather than function has been matched in the study of architectural drawings, and I would be the first to admit that I am guilty of this. Architectural drawings were long studied for the qualities of applied wash, style and presentation, rather than as products of drawing instruments and changing or evolving techniques. The pioneering study of Palladio's drawings by Professor Howard Burns, or of Inigo Jones's by Dr Gordon Higgott, has demonstrated that we cannot rely upon old-fashioned connoisseurship.

All this was brought home to me when Maya Hambly organised an exhibition in the Heinz Gallery of the Royal Institute of British Architects' Drawings Collection in 1982, titled *Drawing Instruments: their History, Purpose and Use for Architectural Drawings.* It attracted great attention for it was the first of its kind, and it coincided with the change in the way scholars were looking at architectural drawings. I remember reflecting at the time that until I understood the history of drawing instruments my study of the drawings would remain inadequate.

Since then Maya Hambly has not been inactive, for as all will recognise her book *Drawing Instruments 1580–1980* is a pioneering study of three centuries of these tools and instruments. No longer can one excuse one's inadequacies by having no text-book to describe the application of these tools by architects. Of course, although I write as an architectural historian, it will not escape the art historian that the same instruments were used by artists who made what are called 'Old Master' drawings. Similar criteria must apply, and I suggest that we shall witness radical changes in dating and attribution of these drawings when they are studied as the products of instruments in the hands of their makers.

John Harris
formerly Curator of the Drawings Collection
of the Royal Institute of British Architects

Preface

Interest in drawing instruments as a subject of study is a comparatively recent development, although many people, such as architects, engineers and graphic artists, whose occupation involves technical drawing, have long been fascinated by early drawing instruments. I developed a special interest in the subject as an architect whose work involved examining historical and modern architectural drawings. Curiosity prompted me to investigate the history of the various drawing instruments which might have been used in the preparation of such drawings, and in 1982 this resulted in the mounting of a small exhibition of drawing instruments, displayed according to their function and shown together with examples of drawings from the Royal Institute of British Architects Drawings Collection.

This book, the result of further research, provides a guide to the development of the numerous European drawing instruments and aids that have been produced over the past four hundred years. It is confined to those instruments used for carrying out geometrical drawing, whether by 'geometers' (as they were originally called), or by architects, surveyors, engineers and cartographers. It is not concerned with the history of the art of drawing; solely with the tools of draughtsmanship.

Throughout this book drawing instruments are defined according to their function, the first categories being those that can be distinguished as essential for drawing lines – ruling pens and pencils, compasses and other items incorporating a drawing point, such as ellipsographs, helicographs, pantographs and eidographs. These instruments are used in conjunction with indispensable drawing aids such as set squares, parallel rules, tee-squares and aids for accurate measurement such as protractors and scale rules. Some instruments whose prime function is calculation, such as proportional compasses used for enlarging and reducing to accurate ratios, and sectors, used to perform various ratio calculations, are included since they are often provided in cases of drawing instruments.

Different drawing instruments have differing histories. The ruling pen and the geometrical compass, for example, have retained their basic form since Classical times, becoming more sophisticated in their design from 1550 onwards. However, in the case of parallel rulers, rolling parallel rules and sectors for example, changing methods of draughtsmanship since 1850 have led to their gradually becoming obsolete.

The most extensive chapter, on cases of drawing instruments, provides a survey of the many varied kinds. Most museum collections display magnificent presentation sets made of costly materials showing the maker's technical virtuosity and the beauty of fine workmanship. While impressive, such cases were manufactured as symbols of prestige, for a ruler or patron. They were kept for display seldom, if ever, being used for any practical purpose. It is in the range of medium-sized cases and pocket cases that one finds prime examples of sets which served the needs of the practitioners of geometrical drawing.

Examples illustrated in this book have been gathered from a wide selection of European museums and private collectors. Other important sources of drawing instruments, where items may be examined closely, are the salerooms where interesting items now regularly appear.

It is hoped that this book will stimulate an increased interest in all the different instruments used for drawing, and will lead to the location of additional material of value. There are still many specialist drawing devices requiring detailed study lingering in the obscurity of attics and basement cupboards. How rewarding it would be if more of the excellent drawing instruments at present held in reserve collections of major European museums could be put on permanent display.

M. H.

Acknowledgements

As the result of my being an enthusiast rather than an expert I am indebted to guidance in this subject from experts in scientific instruments who shared a special interest in drawing instruments. These included Derek de Sola Price, whom I met only a few days before his sudden death; I was given repeated advice by Dr Gerard L'E. Turner and encouraged to continue with my work by Silvio Bedini. I owe particular thanks to David Bryden who offered constructive criticism based on his wide knowledge of the subject.

In carrying out my research I have appreciated the generous help received from many museums and their specialist curators, in particular Dr M. Miniati and Franca Principe of the Museum of the History of Science in Florence; Dr Alto Brachner and Dr Joachim Fischer of the Deutsches Museum, Munich; Professor Dr Ludolf von Mackensen, Staatliche Kunstsammlungen, Cassel; Dr. F. A. Dreier of the Kunstgewerbemuseum, Berlin; Dr Klaus Schillinger; Mathematisch-Physikalisher Salon, Dresden; Dr Jon Darius, Science Museum, London; F. R. Maddison and his colleagues at the Museum of the History of Science, Oxford; Olivia Brown of the Whipple Museum of the History of Science, Cambridge; Dr A. D. Simpson, the Royal Scottish Museum, Edinburgh.

I have had the opportunity of examining cases as well as individual instruments, and photos have been supplied to me with the help of the London salerooms: Jon Baddeley of Sotheby's Bond Street; Jeremy Collins of Christie's, South Kensington; Hugo Marsh of Phillips, Blenheim Street; and in Paris, Anthony Turner of Herve-Chayette, Laurence-Calmels.

I must also thank those specialist private collectors who have allowed me access to and use of photographs of items in their collections: in particular, Andrew Alpern of New York who has loaned me his material since 1983; Alessandro Ubertazzi of Milan who with Italo Rota mounted a definitive exhibition of drawing instruments in Milan in 1979; Gustav Thorban of West Germany who loaned photos of German early works; Dr Berthold Wolpe, David Gray and Paul Breman of London; Michael Scott-Scott of Dartmouth.

Finally, several people and firms have allowed me to use their reference material, mainly regarding instrument-makers and the detailed history of individual instrument-makers. These include Dr M. A. Crawforth and the Project Simon, Kiddlington, Oxford; John R. Millburn, Aylesbury; Dr J. A. Chaldecott, Eastbourne; Peter Delahar, London; Victor Burness, Sevenoaks; Clemens Riefler and Gebrüder Haff, Bavaria; Kern & Co, Aarau, Switzerland; Keuffel & Esser, New Jersey; and Hearlihy & Co, Ohio.

M.H.

Introduction

The drawing instruments discussed in this book, many with their origins in Antiquity, were developed to satisfy the needs of those engaged in technical drawing from 1500 onwards. With the introduction of paper into Europe during the fourteenth century, drawings began to be prepared using quill pens, metal point, charcoal and crayon. Prior to this 'drawings' of proposed or existing buildings or machines, maps or charts were prepared using a scoring instrument, such as a stylus, on a prepared waxed surface or on vellum or a sheet of parchment. The term 'dead drawing' is sometimes used for this method, which dates from the Roman period. The incised lines were filled in using a goose-quill pen and some form of ink, probably iron-gall ink, known since Classical times. The sketch-books of the medieval master builder Villard de Honnecourt were prepared *c.*1235 using this method, and some of the surviving designs in the lodge books of later medieval architects are clearly also scored lines filled with ink.

The practice continued with early hand-made paper, and the sixteenth-century Italian architect Andrea Palladio used both incised lines and lines drawn with a ruling pen and ink. In the same period the Elizabethan architect Robert Smythson prepared most of his drawings with the main lines incised [2A, 2B]. Several sixteenth-century instrument cases contain styli for producing incised lines, together with compasses for drawing that are provided with one scoring point. The general use of ruling pens with ink was gradual, and a stylus was still provided in some cases of drawing instruments after 1700.

The surviving drawings of such fifteenth-century engineers as Francesco di Giorgio Martini [3] are in the main free-hand sketches depicting diagrammatic ideas which are not drawn to scale. The need for more accurate drawings coincided with the introduction, during the sixteenth century, of the use of exact measurements by pioneer scientists involved in astronomy, navigation, military engineering and land-surveying. This resulted in the emergence of technical drawing as we understand it. Scale measures, the plane-table (a field drawing table), protractors, set squares and parallel rules were all necessary for carrying out surveys by the triangulation method. Use of these instruments became common practice by 1600 for land-surveyors and for military engineers in the design of fortifications. At this time, also, orthogonal drawing became the established method of depicting building and architectural works. This is a system of drawing in which all the elements are drawn to scale in plan, section and elevation. This convention soon began to be used for most technical drawings, the principle common to all being that they were to scale, that is, they were a proportional reduction of the proposed or actual size. This type of drawing involves ruling straight lines, parallel lines and lines at given angles to others as well as measuring all parts of lines to scale.

Although the ruling pens in use until the seventeenth century were crude – that is, they had no screw to adjust the two blades (see Chapter 3) – conventions were soon evolved with regard to the thickness of the lines used. A thicker line indicated that the view or cut taken was through a solid, or represented a plane which projected in front of another; a thin line depicted an element in the distance or at a lower level (such as a window-sill or steps of a staircase). The thickness of the lines was achieved by varying the distance between the blades. Later, several pens were included in instrument cases, each giving different ranges of line thickness. From 1600 onwards wheel-pens were included, usually as inserts to compasses, for the purpose of providing dotted lines to indicate something hidden below or above the level at which the plan or section was drawn. (In the case of sun-dialling, imaginary lines were shown as dotted.)

Rules, parallel rules and triangular set squares were also used for carrying out hatching, a system of shading in which parallel lines are drawn close

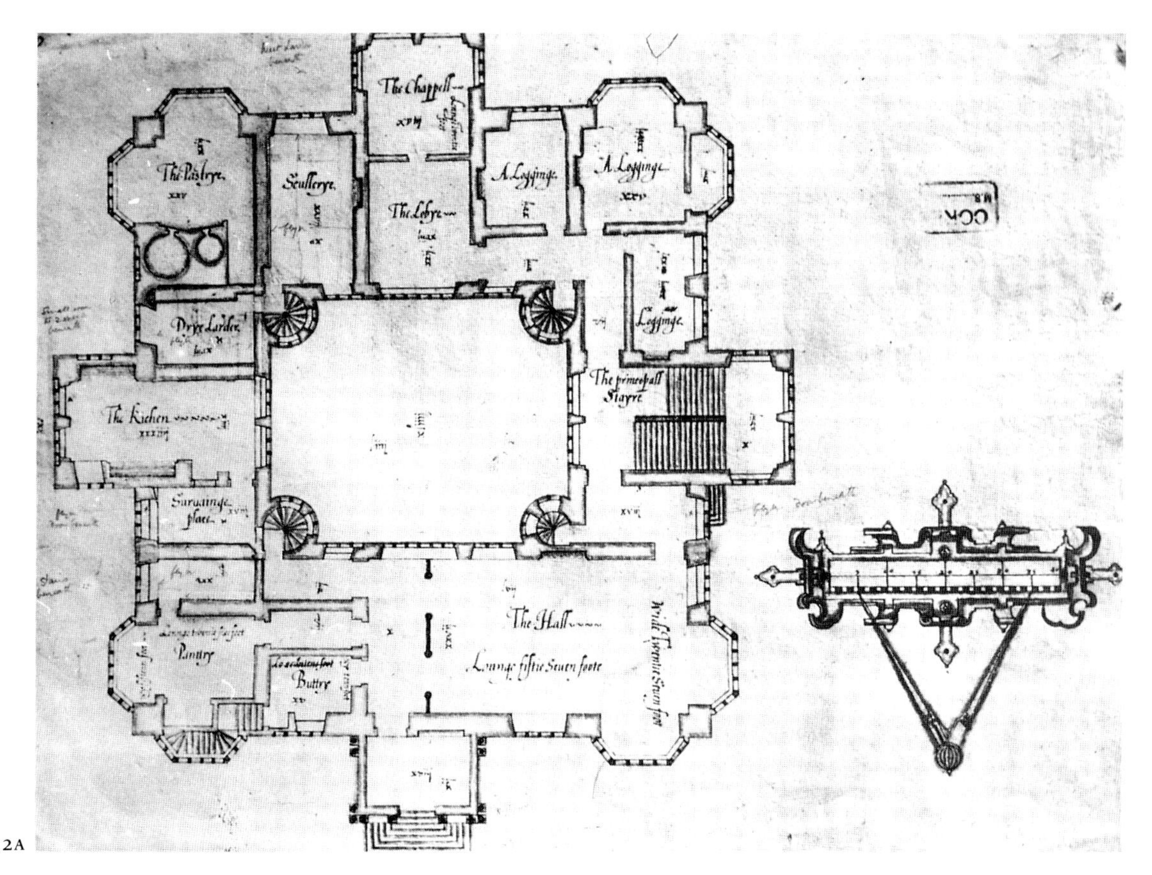

2A

together, usually at 45° or 60°, to emphasize solids when shown in plan and section, or an opening in elevation. This technique was used by such sixteenth-century architects as Palladio and Smythson and was widely adopted by wood-engravers and later by copperplate-engravers, to form part of their technique for creating contrast. (Perspective drawings by Vredeman de Vries *c.*1600 [6] show the rich possibilities of this technique.) Hatching was also to become one of the conventions used in technical drawing.

The popular early treatises on drawing and perspective that appeared from the seventeenth century onwards included mathematics and the rules of elementary geometry necessary for setting up technical drawings [5]. These subjects, together with a knowledge of the system of proportion required in the design and use of the five Classical orders of architecture, formed part of the education of most cultivated people. The general quality of architectural draughtsmanship had improved by the eighteenth century, and this advance is particularly noticeable in the drawings prepared for such publications as *Vitruvius Britannicus* (1715–27) by the Scottish architect Colen Campbell. Clarity and an even line were of

[2A] Plan of Lord Bedford's house at Twickenham by Robert Smythson, which includes an elaborate scale and a pair of dividers, *c.*1590. *RIBA Drawings Collection, London.*

[2B] Design for a round window in stone by Robert Smythson, 1599. *RIBA Drawings Collection, London.*

[3] Drawing for an 'automobile' vehicle by Francesco di Giorgio Martini. Late 15th century.

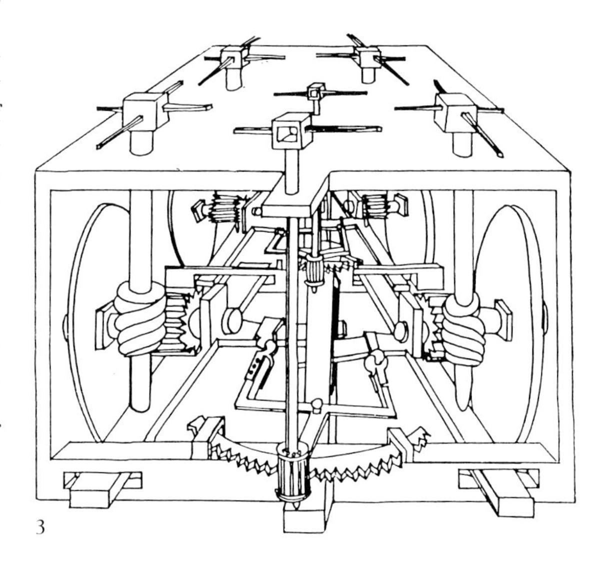

3

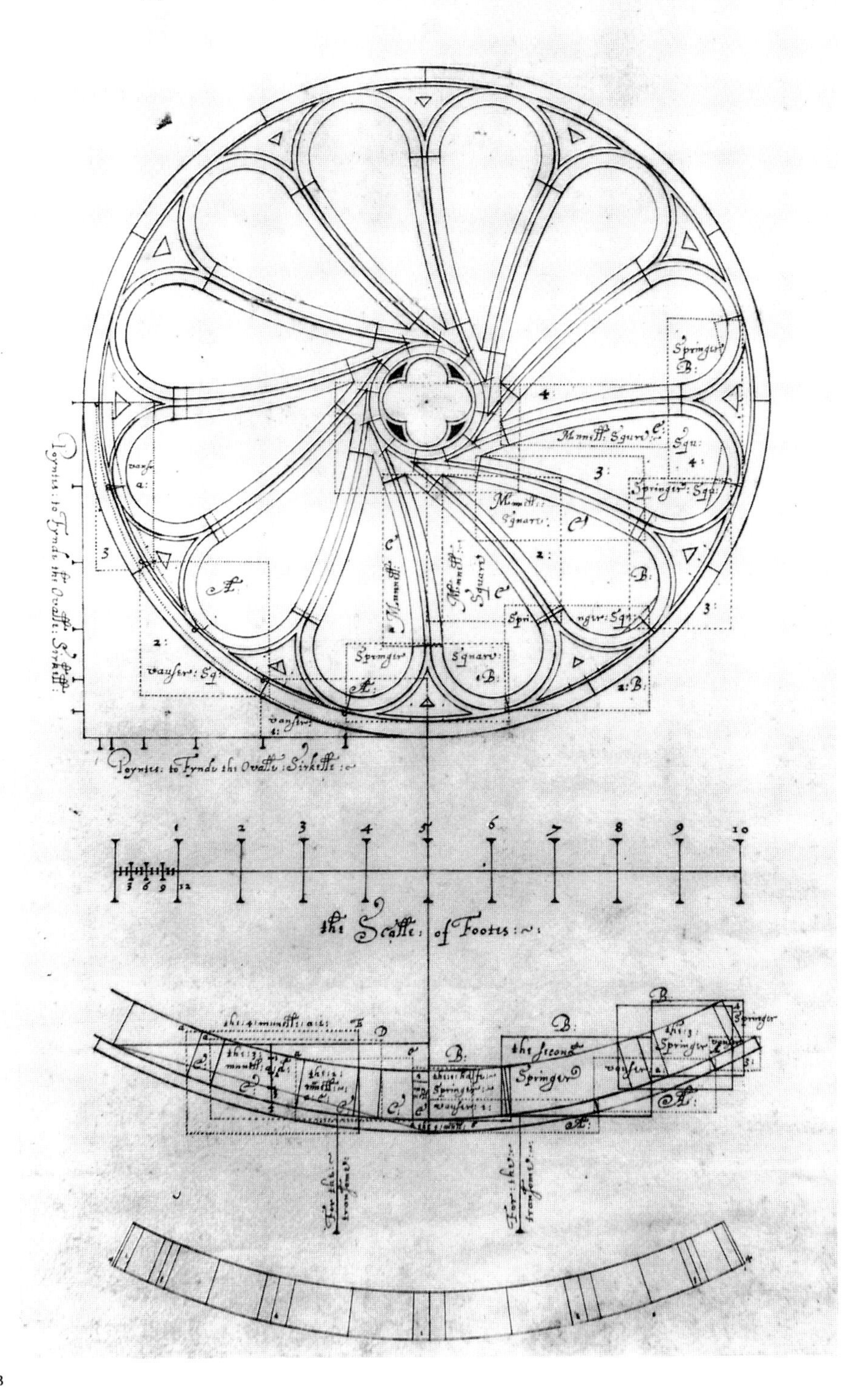
A Draughte For the Platte of a rounde windowe Standinge in A Rounde walle Anno 1599
Poyntes to Fynde the Ovalle Sirkelle
the Scalle of Footes

2B

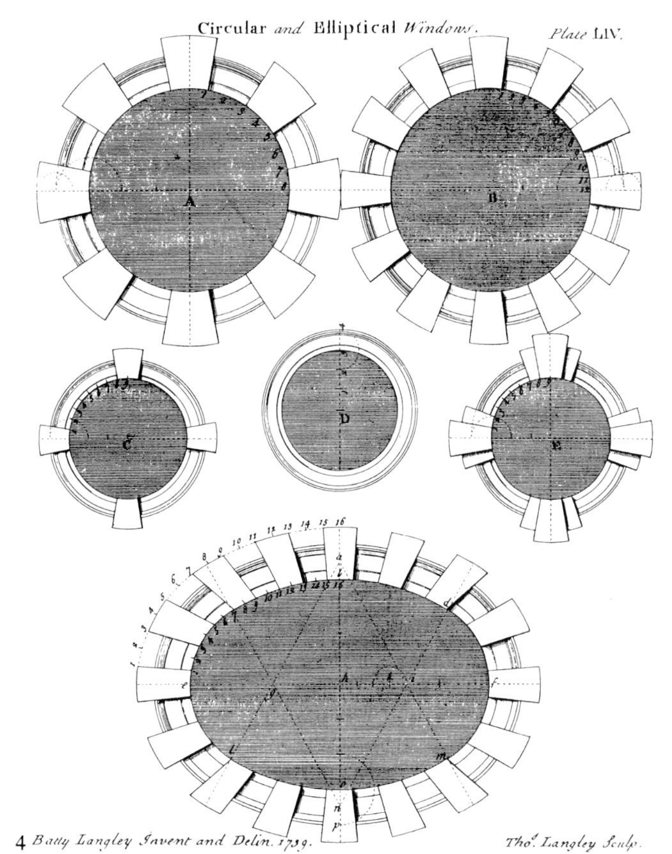

4

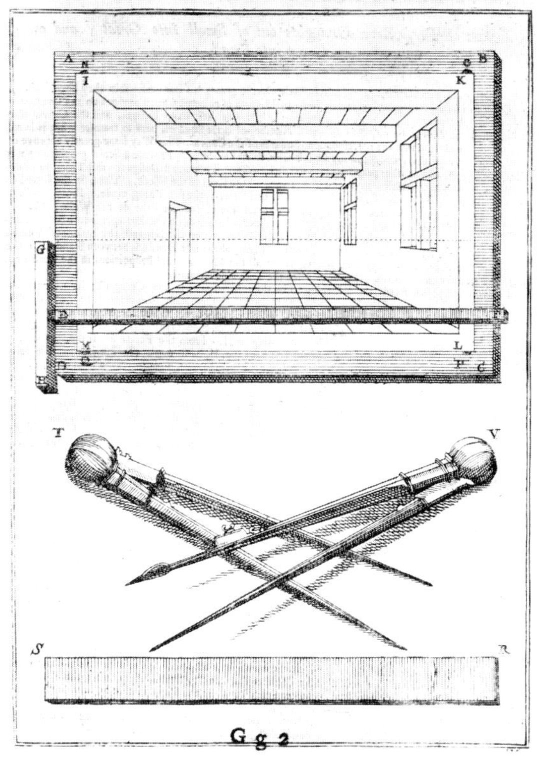

5

the utmost importance when complex drawings were to be engraved for printing: the extensive illustrations [126] provided to accompany Diderot and d'Alembert's *Encyclopédie*, from 1751 to 1782, show what could be achieved. These explored to the full the engraver's techniques for producing clear images in plan, elevation and both oblique and true perspective projection. The vocabulary demonstrated here and elsewhere, of contrasting line thickness and the use of shading by hatching, influenced the more ambitious technical draughtsmen. Innovative engineers such as James Watt and Richard Trevithick produced informative technical drawings and evolved additional drawing conventions to overcome the problems of representing complex three-dimensional machinery on paper. For all these types of drawing reliable geometrical drawing instruments were essential [7].

Important advances in the field of technical illustration were made in England in the late eighteenth and early nineteenth centuries, as can be seen in the plates prepared for encyclopaedias by such skilled contributors as Peter Nicholson and John Farey. These men continued the tradition of the earlier French encyclopaedias by depicting complex subjects in perspective [126].

The introduction in the early nineteenth century of reliable drawing-boards and truly aligned tee-squares (use of which became widespread after 1850), coincided with the enormous growth in the size and number of drawing offices associated with simple technical drawing. The preparation of specialist detailed Ordnance Survey drawings, drawings in connection

[4] Plate from Batty Langley's *Treasury of Designs* (London, 1740) which gives the method for setting out circular and elliptical windows. *British Architectural Library*.

[5] Compasses with an ink point, dividers and a rule together with a drawing board and tee-square set up for a central perspective. Based on a plate from Jean Dubreuil's *La perspective practique* ... (Paris, 1643).

[6] Plate from Jan Vredeman de Vries' *Perspective* (Leyden, 1604) which demonstrates the use of fine hatching in an example of central perspective.

6

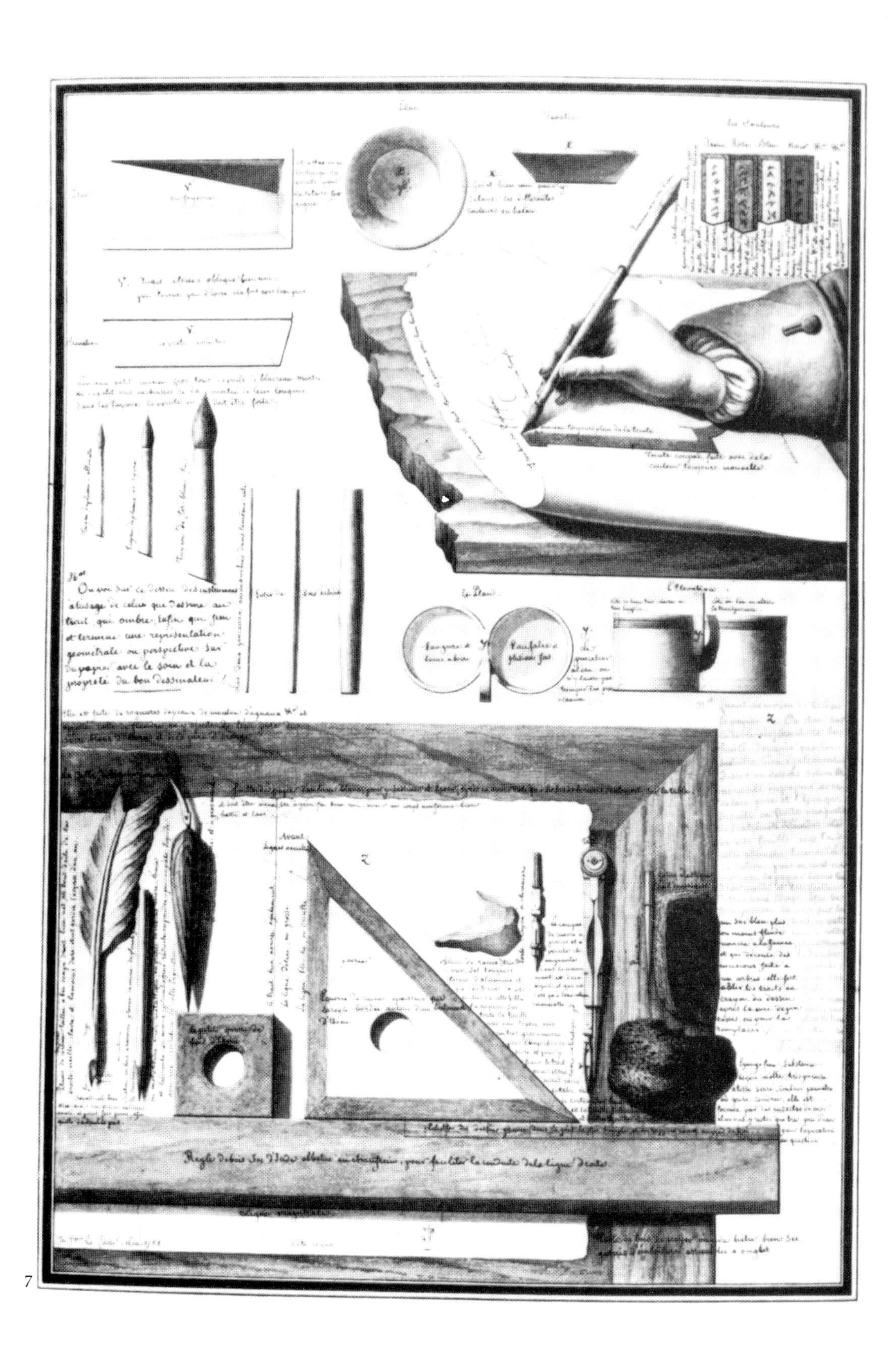
Les Couleurs
On voit sur ce Dessin des ustensiles à l'usage de celui que dessine au trait qui ombre, lafin qui finit et termine une représentation géométrale ou perspective sur du papier avec le soin et la propreté du bon Dessinateur
Le Plan
L'Elevation
Avant

7

with the construction of the railways and mechanical production drawings for the engineering industry now called for the use of machine-divided linear and circular scales, isographs and triangles as well as improved devices for drawing geometric and free curves accurately. The introduction of economic printing processes and inexpensive paper brought an increase in the number of cheap educational handbooks and manuals advocating a variety of techniques, styles and conventions for technical drawings for both architecture and engineering. The best of these methods were to become established practice by 1900 and, following attempts to issue standard information drawings during the First World War, led eventually to the creation of the first legislated standards for engineering drawing which were introduced as a British Standard in 1927.

During the period 1850–1900 a wide range of specialist ruling pens and compasses was manufactured to satisfy the needs of cartographers and engineering draughtsmen. In addition to such simple aids as railway and French curves there were improved elliptical trammels and ellipsographs and more complex devices for other conic sections. These drawing instruments continued to be made as standard items until the decline in their use during the 1960s.

The above chronicles the main advances in technical drawing during the past five hundred years, but the rate of progress varied in the different trades or professions involved directly in the preparation of technical drawings. In the sixteenth century the most complicated drawings were those prepared for fortifications, buildings and ship-building. (The latter required full-size setting-out drawings as templates for the complicated shapes of each piece of timber used.) Preparation of the earliest engineers' drawings was based on conventions originally established for buildings and it was not until the nineteenth century that detailed drawings of mechanical parts took into account a system of minimum tolerance. With the introduction of standardization and interchangeable parts, mechanical engineering now required the greatest degree of accuracy. Over the past one hundred years the major demand for drawing instruments and such items as proportional compasses, and more recently, for drawing machines, has been from the engineering professions. The same need for accuracy in repetitive drawing has made computer-aided draughting systems (CAD) more relevant to these professions and in particular to those involved in the most advanced branches of aeronautics, electronics and graphical communication. Cartography has also required a high standard of accuracy and cartographers and land-surveyors have also now seen the relevance of CAD for their work in recording information or plotting complicated sites or buildings.

[7] Plate illustrating drawing aids in use by the French architect Jean-Jacques Lequeu. A triangle and tee-square and a pair of ink compasses and a pencil insert are shown on the drawing board. From Lequeu's *Nouvelle Méthode appliquée aux principes élémentaires du dessin* (Paris, 1782).

[8] Portrait of an English architect, an elevation of a Palladian house behind him. Signed 'E. Coffin', inscribed 'Exeter Sept. 26 1786'. Size 245 × 205 mm.

8

By contrast architects' and civil engineers' drawings have varied in quality and accuracy throughout the past four hundred years and have always been dependent on the attitude and skill of the individual. In these professions the benefits of standard drawing conventions for layout, such as the use of consistent line thickness and clear annotation, both considered usual in mechanical engineering drawings, have not been generally accepted. Architectural drawings are more diverse in character, and it still requires a considerable change in approach by many architects before they begin to consider computer draughting.

As a reaction to the advanced new techniques there has also been a marked return in the architectural

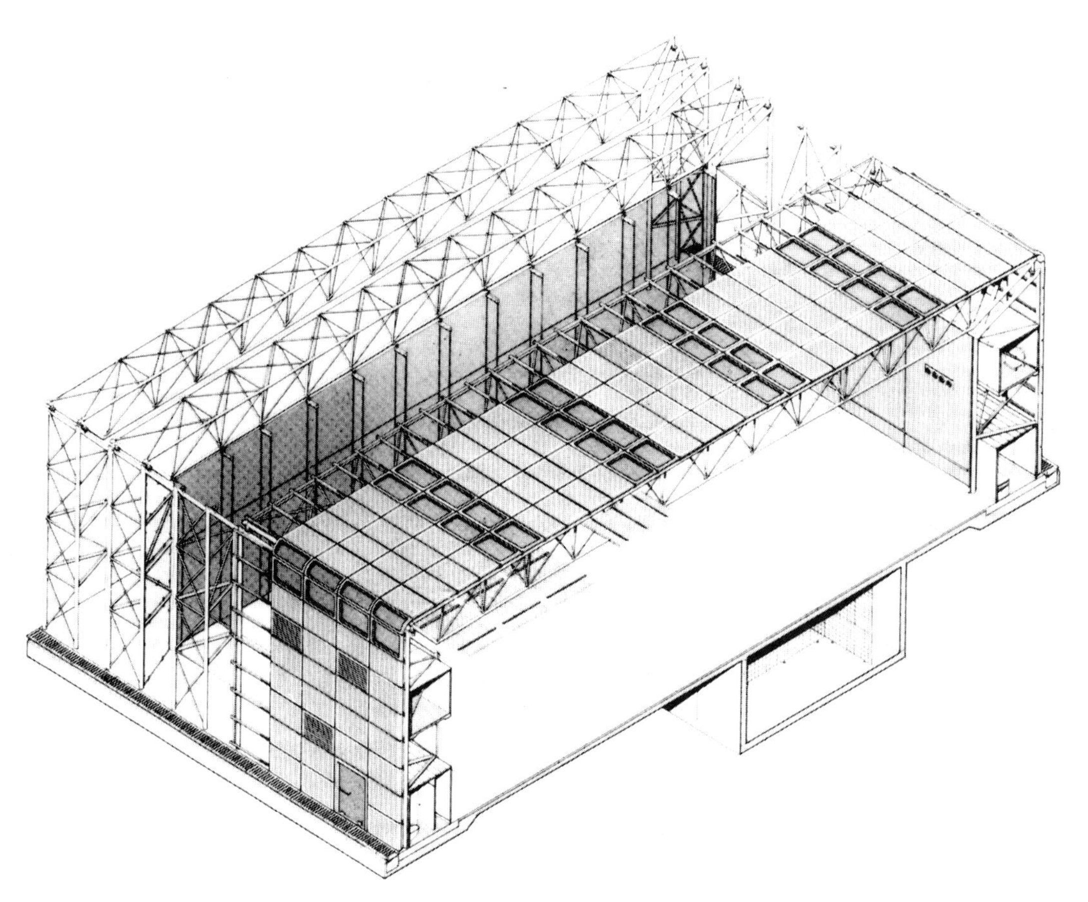

[9] Design for the Sainsbury Centre for Visual Arts, University of East Anglia, Norwich. Isometric section showing structure and cladding. Rotring ink pen on polyester film (1974–78). Norman Foster Architect.

and graphics professions to the appreciation of fine drawings prepared by hand. To make such drawings today a technical pen used with traditional drawing instruments is still considered desirable, and the quality of the resulting drawing depends purely on the skill and the intuition of the individual draughtsman's eye and hand: much the same situation as five hundred years ago [9].

1

History of Drawing Instruments and their Makers

Early civilizations to the Renaissance

There is sufficient evidence from the layout and construction of major surviving buildings to establish that, in the ancient civilizations of Egypt, Babylon and Greece, use was made of some form of geometrical instruments. Drawings or diagrams for a few of these buildings have been found inscribed on clay tablets or on stone or marble panels. A scale rule and scribing instrument together with a plan of a ziggurat or temple-tower were depicted in Babylon about 2150 BC. In Greek temples, from the development of geometry which culminated in the work of Euclid *c.*300 BC, one can deduce that geometrical instruments such as compasses, scale rules, and set squares would have been employed by builders to achieve the refined mathematical proportions of the architectural orders then in use. Recent archaeological discoveries by Lothar Haselberger have revealed evidence of detailed drawings of the Temple of Apollo at Didyma near Miletus, begun after 334 BC. Full-size and scaled drawings on the walls of the temple itself appear as thin lines and curves incised into the wall surface by means of a fine metal gouging instrument guided by a long straight edge, or by dividers for the curved lines.

The Romans used knowledge of geometry to great effect in their engineering, in their formal town-planning and in their further, highly decorated, elaboration of the Greek orders. No drawing instruments recognizable as such remain from pre-Roman times, but there are numerous versions of dividers, set squares, scale rules and callipers dating from the Roman period. Most of these instruments belong to the category of craftsmen's tools rather than drawing instruments, as do later instruments, dating well into the Middle Ages. The most complete surviving set of Classical instruments is a bronze set found in Pompeii, the Roman city which was destroyed during the volcanic eruption of AD 79 [10]. These instruments can be seen as the prototypes of many still in use today. Many examples of Roman styli, used for scoring, and a few ruling pens (some of them clearly intended for use with ink) can be found in museums with Roman collections (see Chapter 3). During a significant period of the Byzantine Empire and the ascendancy of Islamic civilization (AD 330–600) several mathematical instruments such as geared clocks and astrolabes were developed. In Western Europe, although Roman organizational and technical skills were lost, some geometrical instruments were in continuous use in the monasteries, which were the repositories of such texts as survived from the Classical period. The use of small compasses for drawings and manuscripts and larger simple versions of dividers and compasses for craftsmen continued. Throughout the Middle Ages wing-dividers and wing-compasses were developed, as metal workers' skills improved, to provide masons and carpenters with essential tools for use in the 'trasynghous' or drawing office, to prepare setting-out drawings for the individual elements which made up their buildings. Indeed, a pair of compasses became the symbol for the Guild of Masons and was later adopted by the Freemasons. There are many examples of these medieval craftsmen's forged iron dividers in museums; few were made as drawing instruments, since they were not provided with a drawing point.

Ultimately, the goldsmiths became the élite amongst the metal-workers, and they provided several important contributors to the Renaissance. One of the most remarkable was Filippo Brunelleschi who became an architect in Florence early in the fifteenth century. He combined his interest in mathematics and his role as a building engineer with reviving Roman architectural forms accurately, a task which involved geometric drawing. This marks the beginning of the practice of preparing designs and drawings to scale prior to the work being carried out. For the first time drawing instruments – dividers, compasses, the scale rule, the set square or the straight edge, and the stock set at right angles to the blade – were as important as the tools from which they were derived.

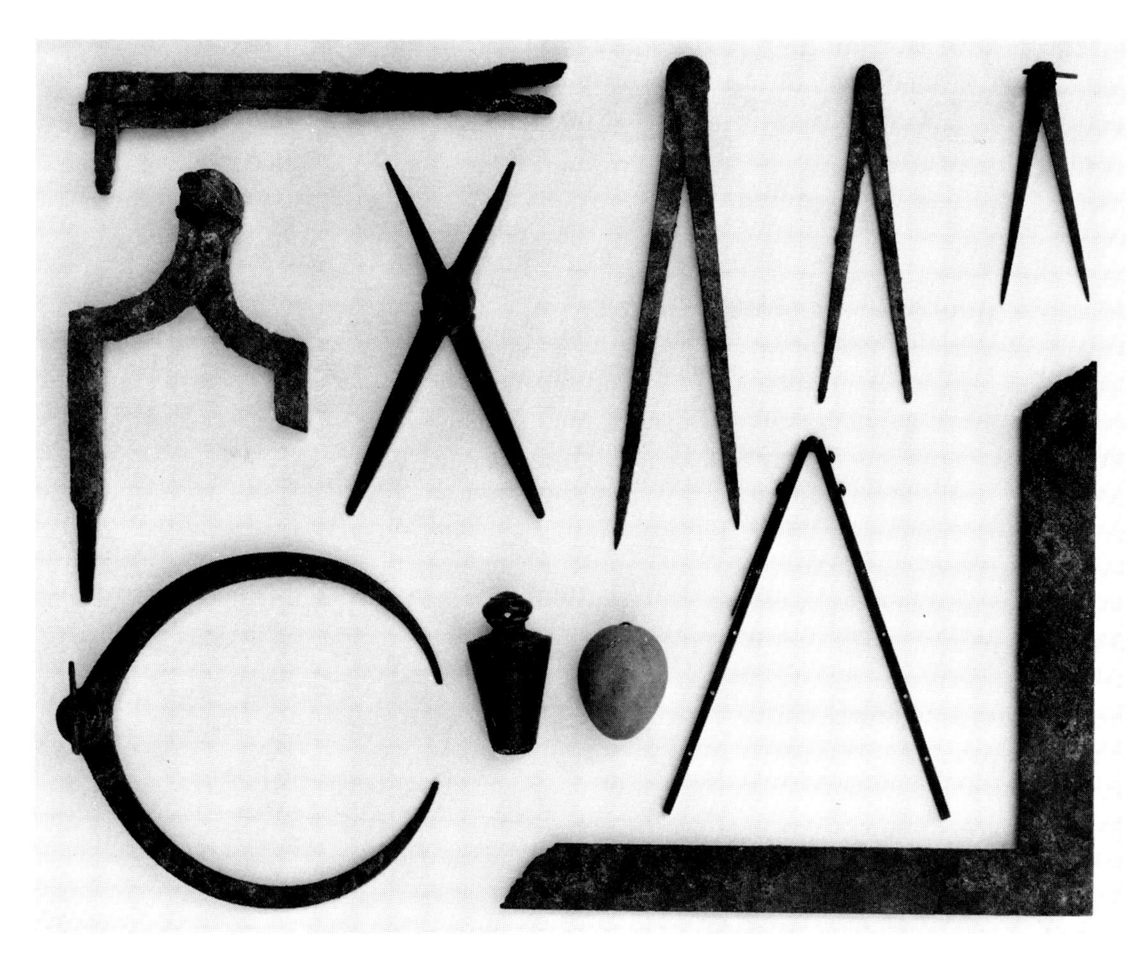

[10] Replica set of Roman bronze instruments *c.*AD79, found in Pompeii. *Science Museum, London.*

The Renaissance and the era of exploration, 1400–1600

The Renaissance, which took the form of the rediscovery of Graeco-Roman arts and sciences in Italy, gave a great stimulus to expanding the knowledge of the universe. This resulted in the development of mathematics and systems of measurement by pioneers engaged in astronomy, navigation, military engineering and land-surveying. Investigation in these subjects was accompanied by the introduction of geometrical perspective in the field of art. For the first time, new instruments – some of them very elaborate – were developed specifically for geometrical and mathematical purposes. Drawing instruments have always formed a small section of this group of instruments, defined, since the sixteenth century, as mathematical instruments.

The revival of the Classical Vitruvian precepts for proportions (see Chapter 2) coincided with the general adoption by architects of orthogonal drawing, for which drawing instruments were necessary. The basic pattern for the most common drawing instruments remained unchanged from the earliest examples, but the materials from which they were made benefited from the development of metals used and the techniques of manufacture for such disparate skills as armour- and clock-making. In addition, after 1450 the gradual introduction of printing in such European cities as Augsburg, Nuremberg and Ulm encouraged the skills of cartographers and engravers, who also required drawing instruments for the preparation and reproduction of drawings and the copying of maps.

As early as 1450 the German cities of Nuremberg and Augsburg were pre-eminent as centres for instrument making, and they continued to be so throughout the sixteenth century. This was due to their location on the main trade route from south to north Europe and the availability of local minerals such as copper and tin. Both cities developed highly skilled metal workshops with an early reputation for fine clock-making. In Nuremberg the workshops were unusually free of a restrictive guild system; the city was later to be renowned for its compass-smiths [11]. The Thirty Years' War (1618–48) between the Catholic southern and the Protestant northern German states led to a decline in the output of instruments in both Nuremberg and Augsburg.

By the late sixteenth century specialist instrument makers were becoming more numerous in certain European centres: Cassel, Dresden, Nuremberg, Augsburg, Milan, Paris and London. The guilds to which they belonged varied from city to city: in Paris they were members of the Cutlers & Metal-Founders whereas in Milan it was the Armourer's Guild. Throughout the period 1400–1600 instrument makers were often attached to courts where the ruler was particularly interested in, and gave support to, scientific investigation. The first European observatory was built at Cassel in 1560 by the Landgrave of Hesse, Wilhelm IV, who was himself an astronomer. Among several instrument makers and mathematicians working there was Jost Bürgi (1552–1632), a Protestant of Swiss origin who joined the court in 1579. Bürgi is of interest because of his design for a variable proportional compass published *c.*1588 and a delicate perspective apparatus designed in 1604. Bürgi was attached to the court at Cassel until his death but he also travelled regularly to the court of the Emperor Rudolph II in Prague, where he worked intermittently from 1604 to 1631 with the Imperial astronomer, Kepler. The most important of the other well-known instrument makers employed by the Emperor in Prague was Erasmus Habermel (1538–1606). Many of Habermel's scientific and drawing instruments appear to have been intended as presentation pieces for patrons interested in science. Heinrich Stolle was another German maker working in Prague at this time. He is known to have made a silver octagonal compendium *c.*1610 which contained several drawing instruments.

In Augsburg one outstanding maker, Christoph Schissler (1530–1609), maintained a large number of specialists in his workshop producing both mathematical and astronomical instruments, many of which are typical of the finest work produced for individual patrons. His son, Hans Christoph Schissler, augmented the family reputation, working in Augsburg until 1591 and then in Prague where he became clockmaker to the Emperor. Another contemporary German maker was Christoph Trechsler (1546–1624), who worked at the Saxon court in Dresden. There are several drawing instruments amongst his fine surviving instruments now in museum collections, some of them signed with the unique 'C+T+D+E+M' (Christopher Trechsler der Elter Mechanicus [158]). His son of the same name was also a maker of repute.

[11] A compass-smith offering his wares for sale from his Nuremberg workshop. Wood-cut by Jost Amman (1568).

In Italy, during the sixteenth century, skilled metal-workers were also producing complex geometrical instruments, many finely engraved. Until 1500 the Sforza and d'Este families, of Milan and Ferrara, acted as their patrons; later several worked under the patronage of the Medici in Florence, and some remarkable examples of their work can be seen in the Museo di Storia della Scienza there. One well-known maker was Baldassare Lanci (*c.*1571), who was military engineer to Cosimo de'Medici, and the designer of a triangulation compass for surveying and an elaborate

[12] Portrait of the astronomer Nicolas Kratzer by Hans Holbein, 1528. Kratzer later worked for Henry VIII at Hampton Court *c.*1536. *Musée du Louvre, Paris.*

combined perspective and triangulation device. (It was quite usual to combine several purposes in one instrument at this time.)

Compared with Italy and central Europe England was rather backward: mathematics made little headway under Henry VIII. One of his ministers, Sir Thomas More, invited the German mathematician and astronomer Nicolas Kratzer (1497–1543) to Hampton Court [12]. Kratzer is thought to have introduced more detailed knowledge of instrument making into England and is known to have asked Albrecht Dürer for his help in obtaining instruments such as triangulation devices for carrying out land-surveys. During the reign of Elizabeth I (1558–1603) the practice of accurate land-surveying was established; this became important following the breaking up of many estates after the dissolution of the monastries in 1539, with the consequent increase in land values. Leonard Digges set out the principles of this new science in his work *A Geometrical Practice named Pantometria*, which his son, Thomas Digges, had printed in 1571 by Thomas Gemini (1510–72), a refugee Huguenot printer from Liège who was also a map-engraver and instrument maker.

The first native London instrument maker, Augustin Ryther (fl.1576–95), was also an engraver, as was his pupil Charles Whitwell (1560–1616), who combined instrument making with map-engraving. The most important Elizabethan instrument maker was Humphrey Cole (1560–91), who was a die-sinker to the Mint, an expert engraver and a member of the Goldsmiths' Company. By 1600 London instruments could be distinguished from those made in Europe by their design and engraved inscriptions. Their makers had acquired the technical skills necessary to make complex mathematical instruments; only a few connected with drawing survive.

Similar developments occurred in France at this time, where instrument making was concentrated in Paris and restricted to particular guilds. Philippe Danfrie (1525–1606) is well known for his *trigonomètre*, which he evolved in 1597 as a triangulation instrument. It could, like that of Jost Bürgi, be mounted on a tripod for surveying use. The first published work to include designs for drawing instruments was prepared by Jacques Besson and first issued after his death in Lyons in 1569 (see Chapter 2).

By the end of the sixteenth century mathematical instrument makers had evolved in several European cities from a lineage of skilled metal-workers: blacksmiths, locksmiths and gunsmiths on the one hand, and clock-makers, engravers and jewellers on the other. These makers achieved the technical virtuosity needed to construct the precision hinges required for folding rules and sectors, the mitre hinges required for folding squares and the long joints with octagonal heads for dividers and compasses. A variety of compasses was now made to serve the needs of draughtsmen, navigators, cartographers and metal-workers. Some were provided with either a wing or arc stay or a threaded rod to fix the adjustment of the opening of the legs. Drawing pens also became more complex, with a ring provided to adjust the opening between twin blades; sometimes the reverse ends had holders with tighteners to contain charcoal or crayon. Measuring rules were divided to the locally agreed scales. Beam compasses – important tools for engravers – were also made in a variety of sizes. In addition to all these drawing instruments there were various versions of fixed proportional compasses, the first variable proportional compasses used for copying and sectors used for calculations.

The Age of Reason, 1600–1700

Throughout Europe during the seventeenth century there was a steady increase in the number of individual workshops with skilled instrument makers who included mathematical instruments in their output. A slowly growing clientele emerged for technical drawing instruments: land surveyors, architects, navigators and military engineers. In England scientists with a university education, now free from the restraints of the court patronage still common in Europe, were directly involved in the design and commissioning of instruments: Robert Hooke, for example, and Sir Christopher Wren (who both also worked as architects and surveyors). Sir Roger North, a distinguished lawyer and historian, was an example of those who took a serious interest in the art of building; he acquired a comprehensive set of mathematical instruments [150]. The establishment of the Royal Society in 1660 promoted the exchange of ideas and prominent instrument makers were included as members much earlier than in the equivalent body in France, the Académie des Sciences.

There are several examples of drawing instruments which date to the early years of the seventeenth century, especially small Italian cases, but many more of great interest were made in the last quarter. By 1650, in addition to improved versions of compasses and ruling pens, triangular compasses were introduced, and the first small bow compasses occur in some sets. 'Elliptical compasses' were mentioned by Hooke in his diary for 1674; they can be found in the form of elliptical trammels (see Chapter 5) in some Italian sets of instruments by 1700. Proportional compasses, both fixed and variable, were now regularly included, and the sector was made in several patterns for use as a calculating instrument, based on the properties of the sides of triangles. The English mathematician Edmund Gunter (1581–1628) designed a sector which was suitable for navigational purposes; others by European makers were for the measuring of angles by geometers or surveying by gunners. Such sectors also served for calculating ratio and proportion when used by architects. After 1650 the pantograph was in general use and provided a mechanical solution to the problems of copying, reducing and enlarging drawings, maps and charts. The fascination for inventing aids to perspective drawing continued, and Sir Christopher Wren tackled the problem himself in 1669 (see Chapter 10 on perspective aids).

Most drawing instruments were made of brass or silver, with 'steel' for the core of the hinge joints, the triangular points of compasses and the blades of ruling pens. The more efficient pens now consisted of twin blades or 'chops' adjusted by a wing-screw, and wheel or dotting pen inserts were increasingly provided in cases usually made to fit the large pair of compasses.

There was an increase in the number of instrument makers in London in the seventeenth century. Most were still situated in the City of London although the move westwards had begun, and Elias Allen was in the Strand by 1616. In order to set up in business independently, membership of one of the City companies was required. This could not usually be obtained before the completion of a full apprenticeship of approximately seven years. There were many well-known makers who became freemen of the Clockmakers, the Goldsmiths, the Broderers and the Merchant Tailors, and recent evidence shows that from 1650 onwards an increasing number of mathematical instrument makers became members of the Grocers' Company. From Joyce Brown's detailed study *Mathematical Instrument Makers in the Grocers' Company*, it can be seen that several of the more renowned makers were members, often with a lineage which can be traced through the apprenticeship system. Some families continued membership of this company well into the nineteenth century. The Grocers' Company was concerned with weights and measures and the purity of certain commodities, which may account for the early connection with mathematical instrument makers. Another source for information on London instrument makers in the mid seventeenth century is the diarist Samuel Pepys. He records his regular visits to various instrument makers in search of the latest devices available for his work with the Navy and for his personal use. He mentions John Spong and 'Greatorex'. The latter was probably Ralph Greatorex (1625–1712), an apprentice of Elias Allen, who later became Royal Instrument Maker to William III. Elias Allen was the foremost English maker in the early part of the century and he made Gunter's version of the sector in 1623. Walter Hayes (1651–92) was of equal importance in the latter part of the century. The work of Thomas Tuttell (fl.1695–1702) also belongs to this period. Tuttell was a most talented English maker with a remarkable output of finely engraved instruments of high quality achieved during a short working life. (He died young, drowning in the Thames.) A pocket set of his drawing instruments exemplifies the advances made in instrument making in England by 1700 [169].

Although the court of Louis XIV was based in Versailles, Paris continued as the centre of instrument making in France. Many makers worked in the area around the Quai de l'Horloge together with other craftsmen. They were all members of the Founders' Guild after the mid seventeenth century when membership of this guild became compulsory. Before this some makers belonged to the Cutlers' Guild. The conservatism and restrictive practices of these guilds may have inhibited innovation but it did not prevent talented mathematical instrument makers from producing precision items. Early in the century, Alleaume, who was one of those entitled to use the inscription '*Ingénieur du Roi*' on his instruments, made sectors; and *c*.1612 Daniel Chorez, a well-known maker of telescopes, made sectors to D. Henrion's design. Pierre Sevin (fl.1665–85) is known to have made a number of mathematical instruments including, *c*.1665, several *Graphomètres* (semi-circular instruments divided into degrees with reading arms and sights, used for surveying in both France and Germany until *c*.1800). The Chapotots – father Louis (fl.1670–86), and son – included mathematical and some fine drawing instruments amongst the output of their workshop, from 1670 to 1720.

The two French makers of this period most widely known by collectors are Butterfield and Bion. Michael Butterfield (1635–1724) was an Englishman working in Paris from around 1677 who became *Ingénieur du Roi*. He published various works but is better known for his instruments, including the sun-dial named after him, and such drawing instruments as folding squares, protractors, scale rules signed 'Butterfield à Paris' and pocket cases. Other instruments appeared after his death signed 'au Butterfield à Paris'. This form of inscription was used by an eighteenth-century shop of that name which paid tribute to Butterfield's reputation. Nicolas Bion (1652–1733) also became

Ingénieur du Roi. Numerous examples of his drawing instruments [168] still exist, but his main reputation now rests on his published works, the most important in connection with drawing instruments being *Traité de la construction et les principaux usages des instruments de mathématiques*, first published in 1709 (see Chapter 2).

In Italy the mathematician and astronomer, Galileo Galilei (1564–1642), contributed to the design of several scientific instruments. His sector, primarily designed as a calculating instrument, was also of importance for drawing in connection with its use for proportion. A fine example exists made by Marcantonio Mazzoleni, who made several of Galileo's instruments in his Padua workshop. In the late seventeenth century the Lusuergs, father and son, were two of the most important Italian instrument makers. Jacobus Lusuerg worked at the court in Modena until 1674 when he moved to Rome with his son Domenicus. The latter appears to have started working in Rome, judging from instruments by him which are signed '*Romae*' with dates between 1695 and 1719. There are examples of the Lusuergs' work on display in several museum collections, and cases of mathematical and surveying instruments demonstrate their great skill as metal-workers and engravers [VI]. Several surviving examples of small sets of drawing instruments by unknown Italian makers and lesser known Italian makers also date to this period [160 and XVI].

The Age of Enlightenment, 1700–1800

During the eighteenth century instrument makers specializing in mathematical instruments found demand increasing from both the expanding professional classes, comprising architects, surveyors, naval, military and civil engineers and wealthy educated collectors. Makers therefore supplied a wide range of practical drawing instruments for daily use and more elaborate items found in larger instrument cases or individually cased. However, drawing instruments (almost always 'bespoke) still formed only a minor part of the instrument maker's workshop output as can be seen from price lists and trade cards.

The tradition of making special instruments, including drawing instruments, for royal or aristocratic collections continued. Important collections include those of the Landgrave of Hesse in Cassel, the Elector of Saxony in Dresden with its renowned Mathematisch-Physikalischer Salon, the Duc d'Orléans and Bonnier de la Mosson in France, the latter with a notable personal collection of scientific instruments. The Duc de Chaulnes (1724–69) was himself involved in designing a dividing machine in 1768. In England a remarkable collection was formed by Dr Demainbray for the Prince of Wales, later George III, which contained several interesting drawing instruments, some of which are described in Chapter 3. In addition, there were collections for research and education such as those formed at the monastery of Kremsmunster in Austria and the University Cabinet in Utrecht.

[13] Eighteenth-century engraving showing a building under construction and the architect discussing some detail with his client. The accompanying verse is taken from Pope's Epistle to Lord Burlington, 1731. *Mansell Collection.*

The supremacy of London as the centre of instrument making was established by the middle of the eighteenth century. In London the freedom from restrictive guild practices allowed greater innovation than elsewhere and this, combined with the excep-

14

[14] Illustration of a late-18th-century scientific instrument maker's workshop from *Encyclopédie méthodique* (1784 edn). This shows a bench with a lathe, a workbench for the assembly of instruments and a marble-topped table for finishing surfaces, with the forge and bellows to the right. *British Architectural Library.*

[15] Early-19th-century German compass-smith's workshop: copperplate engraving from Johann Peter Voit's work *Comprehensive description of useful arts* ... Nuremberg (1804). *Deutsches Museum, Munich.*

tional talent of many of the individual makers, resulted in rapid improvement in both design and workmanship. The workshops established earlier in the centre of the City of London were joined by new ones, concentrated mainly in the west in Fleet Street and later in the City of Westminster, with several in the Strand and at Charing Cross. The high reputation of the London makers in the latter part of the century resulted in an increased demand for their drawing instruments, including items for export to both Europe and the American colonies. Several London makers now combined publishing treatises with their workshop practice (see Chapter 2) and issued trade cards as advertisements and, in some instances, catalogues with price lists.

John Rowley (fl.1698–1728), who was a contemporary of Thomas Tuttell, became a member of the Broderers' Company and had his workshop in Fleet Street. He is of interest for several individual drawing instruments as well as for a giant pocket case now in the Whipple Museum of the History of Science in Cambridge. His apprentice Benjamin Scott (fl.1712–51), a member of the Grocers' Company, had the distinction of making instruments for the Czars. Scott went to Russia in 1733 and died there. Rowley had earlier supplied instruments which were given to Peter the Great by George I, and another London maker, George Hearne (fl.1725–41), supplied telescopes to St Petersburg. Another English maker, Francis Morgan, worked in St Petersburg from 1773 to 1803 and made drawing instruments for a flat pocket, or wallet case.

Richard Glynne (fl.1705–30), also had a workshop in Fleet Street and was, like Tuttell, a member of the Clockmasters' Company. He is an early-eighteenth-century English maker notable for his varied sets of drawing instruments [170]. Thomas Wright (fl.1707–48), who worked for and succeeded John Rowley, is renowned for his orreries but also made drawing instrument cases [X]. Rowley's workshop was taken over from Wright by Benjamin Cole Senior (b.1695), followed by his son of the same name (w.1704–1766), and it became the address of John (w.1764–1788) and Edward Troughton (w.1804–1826) from 1788 onwards until William Simms joined the firm in 1826.

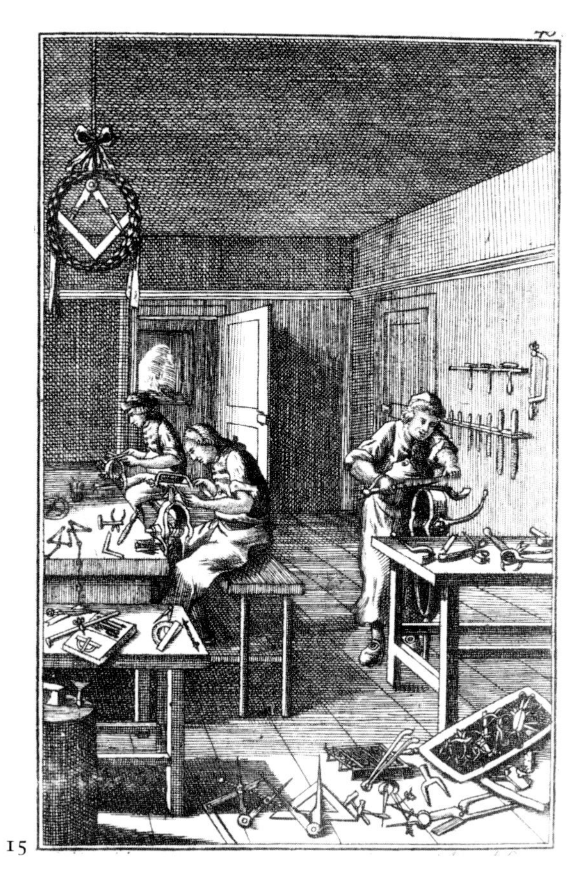

15

Thomas Heath (fl.1720–72) was another important instrument maker of the period. Apprenticed to Benjamin Scott, he entered the Grocers' Company and set up in business at 'the Hercules & Globe in the Strand' where he continued working until his death. There are examples of his drawing instruments – parallel rules, protractors, pantographs and pocket cases [171] among others – in several of the major public collections in England. Heath was joined by his son-in-law, Tycho Wing, in 1751.

George Adams the Elder (1709–73), who was born in London and whose workshops became one of the most well known in London due in part to royal patronage, completed his apprenticeship to Thomas Heath in 1733. Adams and his family also became members of the Grocers' Company. Adams was a brilliant technician and innovator, with a wide reputation for his presentation pieces. He was also the author of several publications (see Chapter 2). His workshop was active from 1735 and was continued first by his son George Adams the Younger (1750–95) and finally by his younger son Dudley, who ran the business until 1820. The stock-in-trade and copyright of George Adams the Younger's books were sold on the latter's death to W. & S. Jones, who continued in business on their own account until the middle of the nineteenth century. Drawing instruments formed only a small part of the wide selection of items recorded in the Adams's workshop price lists. There are several examples of the Adams's drawing instrument cases and individual instruments in museum collections, and items with the Adams signature appear regularly in the sale-rooms.

The Adams workshop is of particular interest since it adopted organized production methods before the end of the century, apparently one of the first workshops to do so. There is no direct evidence of when 'batch production' was first established; how the labour was organized is still conjectural, but some pieces would probably have been assembled after individual parts had been prepared by specialists. Such large workshops were the forerunners of what was to become normal practice for producing 'off-the-peg' instruments in the early nineteenth century. The increased use of mechanical aids such as lathes was gradual, and templates would still have been used for the division of protractors and scales [14 and 15].

Benjamin Martin (1704–82) is an example of a different type of London instrument maker – one without a trade apprenticeship. He was self-educated and had established his retail shop at 171 Fleet St by 1755. Martin lectured on scientific matters, published over thirty small works and achieved some success as an entrepreneur until his financial difficulties shortly before his death. Several examples of the pocket cases he supplied survive together with his improved pantograph [XI].

A major London maker also notable for his drawing instruments was Edward Nairne (fl.1741–1806), whose address was 'At the Golden Spectacles Royal Exchange', in the City of London. Nairne specialized in electrical apparatus but he also made other instruments including mathematical instruments. He was joined by Thomas Blunt (fl.1760–1822) and from 1770 their work was marked 'Nairne & Blunt, 22 Cornhill, opp. Royal Exchange'.

Mention must also be made of Jesse Ramsden (1735–1800), who ran a large workshop employing a considerable number of workers and may, like Adams, have been among the first to adopt organized production methods. Considered by his contemporaries to be the foremost maker of the late eighteenth century, his reputation for accuracy, if not speed of execution, brought him international acclaim. A superb technician and innovator, he became a Fellow of the Royal Society in 1786 and was accepted as an equal amongst academic colleagues (a situation which was unthinkable in France at this time, where skilled makers such as Lenoir and Fortin were only accredited with official status after the Revolution) [161B].

In France established makers such as Bion, Chapotot and Sevin, who had commenced their workshops in the late seventeenth century, were joined by Jacques Lemaire (fl.1720–40) and his son Pierre Lemaire (fl.1735–60). All of these makers included drawing instruments in their output. One of the better known French workshops was that of Langlois, which existed in Paris from 1730 to 1780, first under its founder, Claude Langlois, from 1730 to 1756. Claude Langlois made a considerably improved design for the pantograph in 1743 and a range of high quality mathematical instruments, standard measures and drawing instruments. On his death the workshop was taken over by his nephew, Canivet (fl.1751–74), who also made pantographs, drawing instruments and standard measures. Around 1774 Lennel (who made a fine set of drawing instruments for the Duc d'Orléans) took over the firm, which he ran until his death when it was taken over by his widow. Many Parisian makers were still located in the then traditional area for instrument making around Quai de l'Horloge, Bion amongst them. The exception was Langlois, whose address was 'à Paris aux Galleries du Louvre'. Claude Langlois, with others who were designated as 'engineer to the Academy of Sciences', was awarded free lodging together with a retail outlet in the Louvre.

An instrument maker emerged in South Germany who can be compared with George Adams the Elder or Ramsden. This was Georg Friedrich Brander (1713–83), who was born in Regensburg and studied in Nuremberg under the mathematician Johann Gabriel Doppelmayr (who had translated Bion's works into German). Brander moved to Augsburg in 1734 where he worked and eventually died. He is best known for his scientific instruments. Few drawing instruments by him are recorded, but his work on comparative scales and the improvement of fine divisions to the Nonius scale by the use of a diamond for etching onto glass was of considerable importance for mathematical instruments. Brander also issued engraved plates together with descriptions of his many instruments.

By the end of the eighteenth century the progress made in achieving greater accuracy in mathematical instruments [14] by Short, Bird and Ramsden in England, Brander in Germany and Lenoir and Fortin in France, resulted in the improved instruments for both linear and circular measurement required by mechanical engineers and land-surveyors in the early nineteenth century. There was also an increased interest during the next fifty years in designing various complex instruments for drawing ellipses and other conic sections together with simpler instruments as aids to drawing architectural perspectives and for copying drawings accurately.

Early industrialization, 1800–1900

The most significant change during the nineteenth century was that new firms were established in Britain and Europe specializing in the manufacture of drawing instruments. Before this drawing instruments had formed only a small part of a wide range of mathematical instruments.

In Britain and in Europe, too, a new material was in common use by 1850 for the main range of metal drawing instruments, which was to replace silver or brass for quality instruments. In Britain this was to be known as 'German silver', also sometimes called 'electrum'. This was due to its resemblance to the metal of that name; which was white gold and had been used in the Classical period of Antiquity. In Germany this new material was known as 'Argentan' or sometimes 'Neusilber'. Both German silver and electrum consisted of a similar alloy of zinc, copper and nickel which provided a durable non-corrosive metal more suitable for high-quality drawing instruments than either sterling silver or brass. Elliott & Sons is known to have used this alloy by 1835 and Watkins & Hill, instrument makers of Charing Cross, refer to it in 1832 as a new white-metal not liable to tarnish and very suitable for damp and warm climates.

Between 1800 and 1900 there was a considerable increase in the range of drawing instruments produced in London, in small workshops producing by hand and a few larger workshops which gradually adopted the use of some machines and batch production for 'off-the-peg' instruments. During this period sets of spring bows, various patterns of folding and pocket compasses, compact beam compass fittings and individually cased proportional dividers, all capable of greater precision, were introduced. These, together with circle-dividing instruments such as protractors with hinged folding arms and pricking points and a full range of specialist ruling pens, became available as standard items. Some of the larger firms in existence in 1800 such as Wm. Elliott (from 1830 Elliott & Sons and later Elliott Bros), Troughton (from 1826 trading as Troughton & Simms) and Wm. Cary were in business to the end of the century. These firms, together with W. & S. Jones and a smaller firm, R. B. Bate (later to become Potter of Poultry), also made specialist drawing apparatus, for instance improved pantographs, ellipsographs and, from 1825 onwards, eidographs.

There were now several firms of consequence in the provinces, where before there had only been individual makers or outlets for London makers. In Oxford, Edinburgh and Bristol there had been individual instrument makers as early as 1700, and during the eighteenth century new workshops were opened by makers who had served their apprenticeship in London, and outlets for London makers existed in Bath, Birmingham, Bristol, Dublin, Glasgow and Plymouth. (It can be noted that most of these were ports.) Now more small workshops and retail outlets were established, in such provincial cities as Liverpool where A. Abraham opened his workshop. After 1850 new small firms were established in the main centres of metal-working industries like Sheffield and Birmingham. Some of these firms provided the cheaper ranges of drawing instruments required by students and technical draughtsmen.

In central Europe an important expansion of drawing instrument making occurred with the emergence of several new firms early in the nineteenth century. Until this time, as in all the main traditional European centres of instrument making, master craftsmen had made drawing instruments by hand and mainly to individual order (that is, 'bespoke'). Already by 1801 Ludwig Esser, an Alsatian, had begun to organize the making of drawing instruments on a larger scale in the small town of Aarau in Switzerland. His apprentice Jacob Kern (1790–1867) studied with the renowned instrument maker Frauenhofer in Munich, then returned to Aarau to found his own firm in 1819. The firm of Kern produced a wide range of drawing instruments throughout the nineteenth century and still continues to manufacture high quality drawing instruments, precision surveying instruments and binoculars [56A].

In southern Germany, Thomas Haff, a skilled clockmaker, expanded his workshop in the Bavarian village of Pfronten after having repaired surveying instruments brought to him by some of Napoleon's engineers. Haff's three sons were trained as toolmakers and also received a mathematical and technical education in Munich. In 1835 the firm of Gebrüder Haff was founded by the sons for the manufacture of drawing instruments, and later it produced a version of the planimeter, an instrument designed for measuring the area of small irregular shapes, which had been perfected by the Swiss mathematician Jacob Amsler in 1854. The original Haff workshops were organized within a rural seasonal economy, and the employees combined their skilled metal-working in the Haff workshop with maintaining their smallholdings. The hand lathes were adapted to water power and a new workshop was built in 1860. This was subsequently enlarged to provide for mass production of standard items, but the final assembly and finishing of the drawing instruments was still carried out by hand, as it is today. Haff continues to be a major manufacturer of quality drawing instruments.

A similar firm was founded in 1841 outside the neighbouring town of Nesselwang by Clemens Riefler (1820–76), following his apprenticeship with Ertel in Munich. Riefler's firm eventually combined the manufacture of drawing instruments with other precision instruments such as chronometers, and later specialized in electric clocks. By 1877 the founder's son, Sigmund Riefler (1847–1912), had patented a design for cylindrical pattern compasses, known as 'the round system', which were light and easy to handle. This was the first design which could be made by machine production and where the inserts fitted securely without screws: a pattern which has continued to be made, with some modifications, until today.

After the unification of Germany under Bismarck, Berlin, as the capital of Prussia, developed a growing naval and military establishment. This led to an increase in the demand for precision drawing instruments and new firms were founded in Berlin after 1870. There was also an increase in the number of firms in the old centres of instrument making such as Nuremberg [15], for instance the firm of Ecobra which continued in business until 1987. These firms met needs of those engaged in technical drawing in industry.

Another German maker of note was E. O. Richter (*c.*1841–1907) who, after training as a clock-maker, founded his own firm in Chemnitz, Saxony in 1877 for the manufacture of drawing instruments. In 1892 he patented his 'flat system' pattern compasses, which had considerable effect on those produced by other firms after the patent ran out in 1905. Richter also designed specialist instruments for drawing, including a universal dotting device and new improved ruling pens; his firm produced ranges both in brass and nickel silver. Richter, like Haff and Riefler, established a regular export trade for drawing instruments to the United States, a trade which has continued, with interruptions for both world wars, until today. E. O. Richter ceased trading in 1945 but the firm continues in East Germany as VEB Kombinat in Karl-Marx-Stadt (formerly Chemnitz).

The supply of mathematical and drawing instruments to North America started with those taken by the original settlers, whether French, Dutch or English. By the eighteenth century the American colonies were obtaining their drawing instruments by direct order from London makers or through agents who were established in the main ports such as Boston and New York. Skilled metal-workers with workshops serving these ports would have been responsible for repairing the imported instruments, but the shortage of fine ores and tools and lathes made the manufacture of quality instruments impossible there. The shortage of high quality raw materials continued after the War of Independence (1775–83) with the restriction of trade during the Napoleonic Wars. Following this imports of instruments from Europe recommenced.

As the West was opened up there was a rapidly growing demand for mathematical instruments by land-surveyors and by the railway engineers who followed in their wake. There was a steady increase in the number of skilled immigrants after the political upheavals in Europe of 1848, including specialist instrument makers. One was Theo Alteneder, who had been apprenticed to Riefler in Germany and founded his own firm in Philadelphia in 1850. He was later joined by his sons and produced a wide range of drawing instruments, judging by his catalogues. In 1871 his compasses were provided with a patented Alteneder joint. In New York William Keuffel and Hermann Esser set up their business in 1867 supplying drawing materials and imported drawing instruments direct to customers' offices. Later on they produced their own vulcanite French curves and triangles, and in 1876 they began to manufacture surveying instruments for which there was a great demand. Once established their business expanded; by the end of the century several branches had been opened: Chicago in 1891, St Louis in 1894, and San Francisco in 1900. This firm remains a major supplier of drawing accessories and materials and the main importer of Haff instruments into the United States.

In Britain a similar type of specialist drawing instrument maker had emerged by the middle of the century to meet the demands of the rapidly expanding technical professions: civil, railway, military and mechanical engineers, who were all involved in the preparation of technical drawings, as well as architects and surveyors. W. F. Stanley (1829–1909) set up in business in 1853 at Great Turnstile, Holborn in London, with the aim of providing improved drawing instruments to compete with the lighter instruments being produced in central Europe; the latter had begun to rival the traditional instruments made by established London instrument makers. Stanley began by making timber drawing aids such as architectural drawing curves and triangles or set squares, all in pearwood or mahogany, which until then had been imported from France and Italy. He also developed his improved tee-square and rigid drawing board, the former achieving instant success through the promotion it received in *The Builder* magazine. When Stanley finally entered the field of metal drawing instruments he was, like George Adams the Elder (the maker he most respected), a maker, a user and an innovator [16]. His firm soon manufactured a wide range of instruments which were technically efficient yet simple for the draughtsman to use. He published his treatise on drawing instruments in 1866, which ran into numerous editions. Like Haff, Riefler and Richter, Stanley sought to improve and simplify many drawing aids, but his firm was probably the first to expand to supply a full range of surveying instruments and drawing office equipment, which he was selling by 1888. Subsequently drawing materials and plan-printing equipment were included in Stanley's catalogues, and by 1900 the firm had become a major supplier at home and abroad.

Shortly before W. F. Stanley set up in business one of his apprentices, W. H. Harling, began to make drawing instruments and in 1851 founded his firm in Finsbury Pavement, Moorgate in the City of London. The firm continued in business there until 1961 when it became part of Blundell Harling of Weymouth. One of Harling's apprentices was A. G. Thornton, who founded his own firm in St Mary Street, Manchester

16

[16] W. F. Stanley's trade label, typical of the late 19th century, as issued with instruments in wooden cases such as pantographs, circle dividers etc.

[17] Typical late 19th-century English drawing instruments of nickel silver fitted to a removable tray. The assorted specialist ruling pens all have ivory handles. *RIBA Collection, London.*

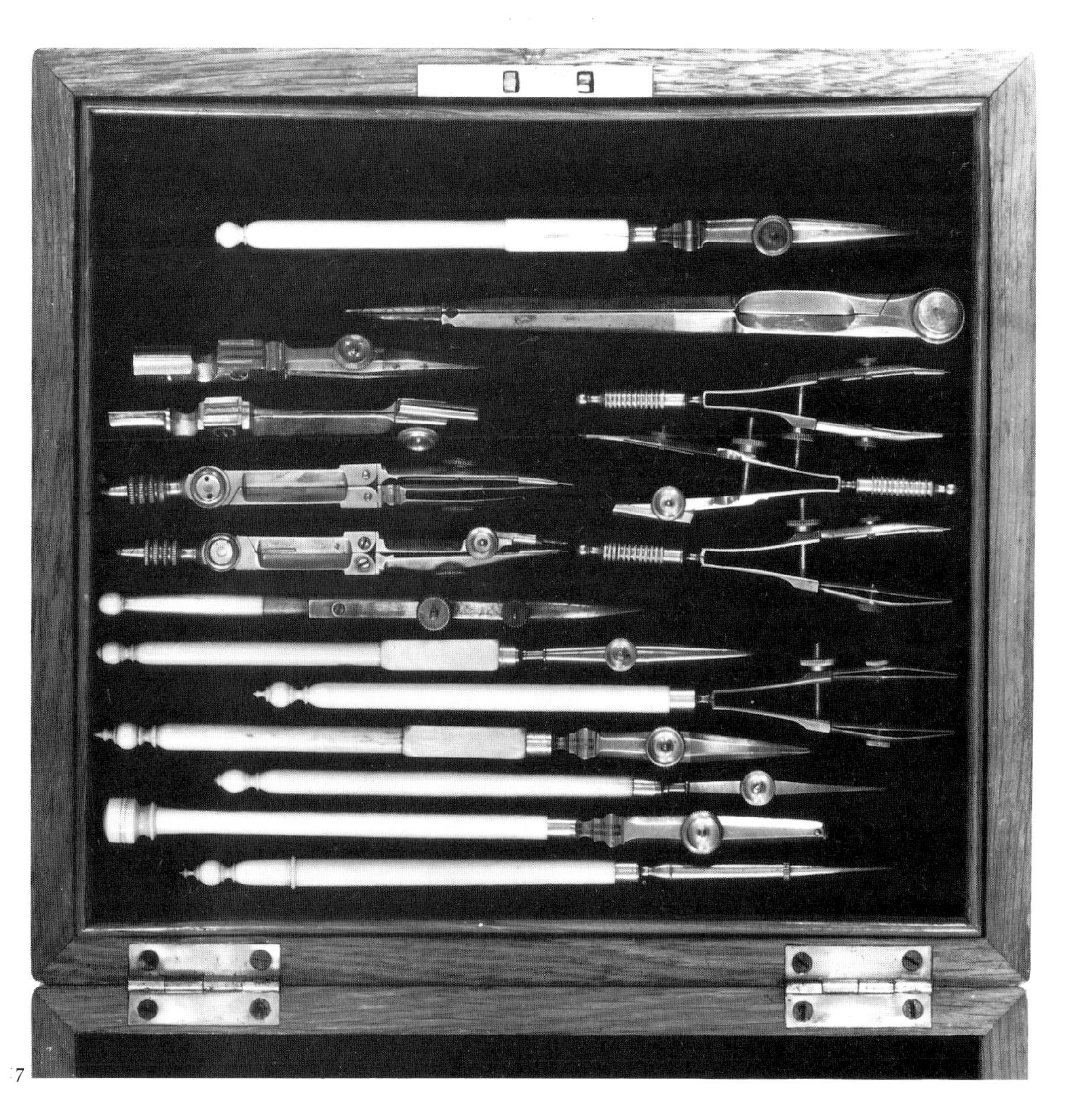

7

in 1880. This firm continues in business as British Thornton and now specializes in computer-aided drawing equipment. John Halden & Co, who had their works at Stockport, were also established in Manchester around 1880 and continued in business as major suppliers of drawing office equipment and drawing instruments until 1950. (In their heyday, in the thirties, Halden of Manchester had branches in London, Birmingham, Newcastle, Leeds and Glasgow.)

The supplying of drawing instruments in the largest industrial cities in Britain at this period underwent significant changes. By 1800 some retail outlets which sold drawing instruments bought in some of their stock and did not necessarily produce the full range of items which they sold. This is an area which still requires careful research and documentation; what is clear is that the name on a case, on a box or even on an instrument does not always signify its maker. Drawing instruments manufactured by, say, Stanley, Harling or Thornton were often boxed and marketed by factors or suppliers such as the art material firms of Reeves, Rowney and Winsor & Newton and outfitters to the services such as the Army & Navy Stores etc. It is also clear that, in order to fulfil the numerous orders for specialist equipment required by the East India Office and other Government departments many of the major manufacturers of drawing instruments sub-contracted the supply of items [17].

Around 1900, starting in London, a new type of firm was established, which sold a wide variety of drawing office materials and sometimes offered plan printing (blue-print and later black line print) services. By this time the major offices in London were centred around Victoria Street, because it was close to the Houses of Parliament – a necessary convenience during the years of constant activity on the many railway bills. Many of the best-known suppliers of drawing equipment had their shops there. J. Halden's London branch was there, for instance, together with Miss A. West of Broadway Chambers (later A. W. West & Sons) from 1888, and Norton & Gregory, established in 1898.

Twentieth-century manufacturers

During the first four decades of this century the market for drawing instruments continued to expand. On the whole this new demand was for medium quality instruments to supply the increasing numbers of technical draughtsmen in the industrialized countries of the world. British instruments were supplied to the Empire and later the Commonwealth, and European instruments went to North and South America. In Britain most of the quality instruments were still made by the principal makers already named: Stanley, Harling, and Thornton. Their products were made available nationwide through the growing numbers of retail outlets in major cities and towns. By 1924 W. F. Stanley advertised several ranges in their catalogue [18]: top-quality hand-made electrum, machine-made traditional patterns in electrum or brass; and their government 'flat-pattern' in brass which had been introduced during the First World War. Their chief competitors were offering a similarly wide range. There were also smaller workshops which produced hand-made drawing instruments for other specialist retailers, such as J. H. Steward Ltd of the Strand in London who supplied to the Army. Many of these workshops were situated in traditional metal-working districts of London like Shoreditch or in the Midlands near Birmingham. Machine-made instruments, such as student and school geometry sets, were also produced in these areas.

During the Second World War the firm of Lee-Guiness was set up in Northern Ireland specifically to supply quality drawing instruments made in nickel silver. The pattern for these instruments was a pirated version of the Riefler design available before the war, which proved very popular with British architects from 1943 to 1955. After 1950 W. F. Stanley introduced a range of stainless steel drawing instruments for use where corrosion was a problem.

In Germany during the period 1920–40 Richter of Chemnitz offered a wide range of drawing instruments and together with other firms with established reputations such as Haff of Pfronten, Riefler of Nesselwang and Ecobra and Olympia of Nuremberg, supplied both the home and export markets. All these firms now produced the lighter 'flat system' and Riefler improved their 'round system'.

Most British firms ceased manufacturing quality drawing instruments during the 1960s. Like others involved in manufacturing highly specialized metal goods such as ironmongery and cutlery, they were slow to realize that changes were necessary to sustain interest in their products. At the same time there was a dramatic reduction in the demand for drawing instruments – it was, in fact, the end of an era. In the 1920s and 1930s large drawing offices in Europe and the United States had began using various forms of drawing machines, a growing number of which entered British engineering offices during the Second World War. The constant need for compasses and their accessories was also removed when draughtsmen began using plastic templates for drawing simple circles.

The supply of quality drawing instruments for this reduced demand was taken over by some of the well-known European firms such as Haff, Riefler and Kern, who now exported to Britain and the rest of the world. New designs for a whole range of instruments were introduced from 1950 onwards, several patterns being made in nickel-plated brass or chrome-plated brass. (The latter was sometimes provided with a matt finish to prevent glare and finger marks.) Haff introduced a quick-set compass in 1950, and Riefler and other firms followed. From the 1960s onwards these compasses were provided with an attachment – at first rather crude – to take the new technical pens instead of the usual ruling pen ink insert. This was probably the most significant change in drawing technique since the invention of the ink- and crayon-holder inserts for compasses, *c.*1550. It made continuous drawing possible without constant refilling of the ruling pen

[I] Wing-compasses in gilt-brass with steel points, signed 'C + T + M' (Christoph Trechsler Mechanicus of Dresden) and dated '1604'. One of the points is detachable so that a drawing pen, now missing, can be substituted. Unusually the decorative pattern is acid-etched. The slotted arc, allowing the legs to be located accurately, is a replacement. Height 6 in (152 mm). *Museum of the History of Science, Oxford.*

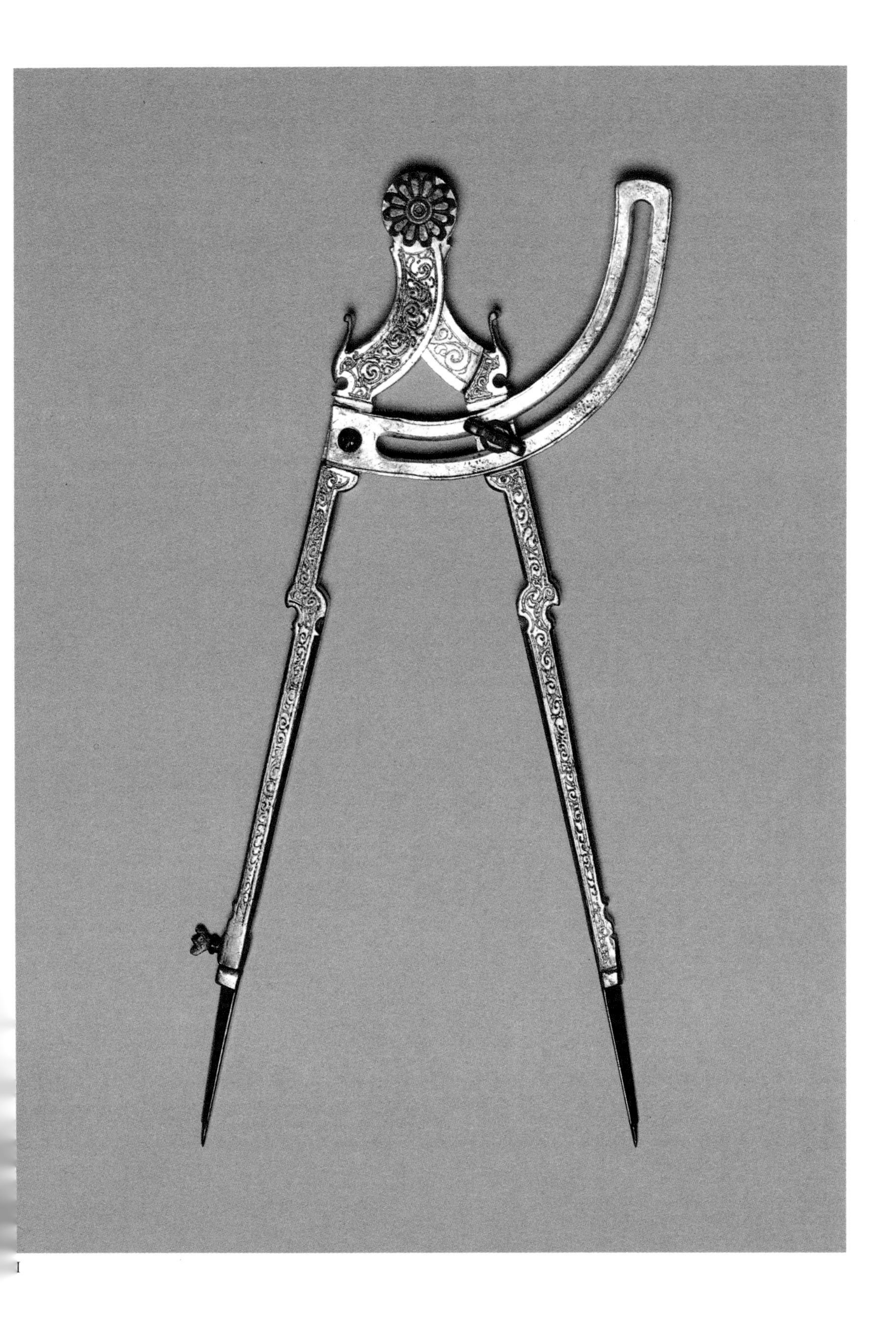

I

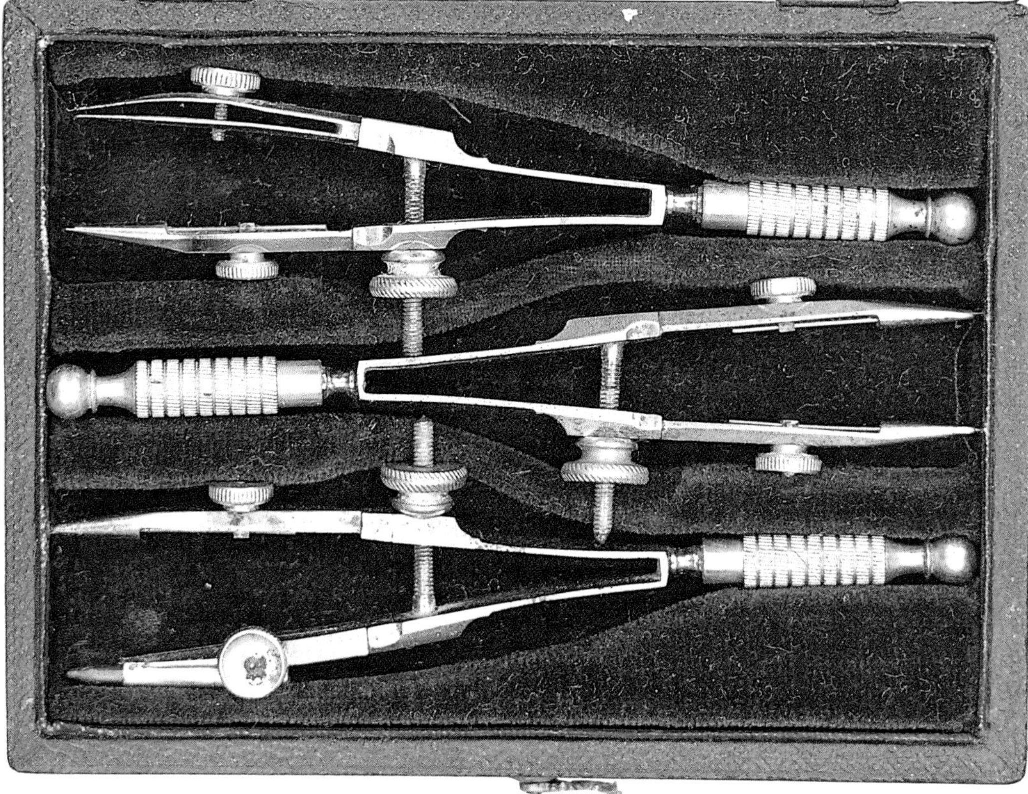

II

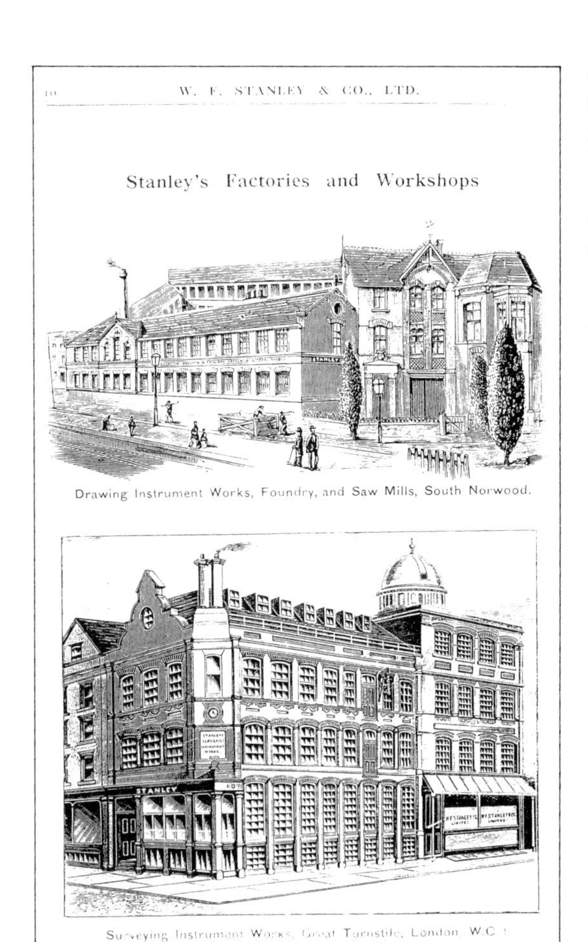

[18] (*Above*) W. F. Stanley's Drawing Instrument Works, Foundry and Saw Mills at South Norwood. (*Below*) The Surveying Instrument Works and the Shop at Great Turnstile, Holborn, London WC1.

[II] Set of spring bows of electrum in maroon leather covered case with lining stamped STANLEY, GT TURNSTILE, HOLBORN W.C. Note the finely knurled handles to the dividers, pencil and ink compasses. Case $3 \times 2\frac{1}{2} \times \frac{1}{2}$ in ($76 \times 64 \times 13$ mm). Late 19th century. (Shown enlarged.) *Andrew Alpern Collection, New York.*

and gave regular line thickness which matched the straight lines. When used with a precision compass it gave greater accuracy.

During the 1970s the long-established pencil manufacturing firms of Staedtler and Faber-Castell, both of Nuremberg, began to market a new range of compasses and accessories in less expensive materials, using machine-made dye-cast limbs electro-plated in nickel on brass with moulded nylon joints. Rotring of Hamburg-Altona, specialists in technical pens since 1953, have produced a range of drawing instruments since the 1960s, but the precision versions have been made for them by either Haff or Riefler who, together with Kern, still supply such items as beam compasses, specialist ruling pens and proportional compasses.

The full impact of the introduction of computer-aided drawing systems since the mid-1960s did not begin to affect the majority of draughtsmen for some twenty years. Progress in the use of this facility was made first in the larger engineering drawing offices and a few architectural practices, particularly those producing specialized information drawings. These systems are now used by graphic designers and other draughtsmen involved in new technology industries like commercial and television graphics.

Until the mid-1980s the principal drawing instrument for CAD systems was the pen. This might be a technical pen using special free-flowing ink, a fibre-tip pen using special coloured ink or a ball-tip pen using special ink-pastes. All the inks used have to be suitable for the plotters, which operate at very high speeds (see Chapter 3). In 1982 Staedtler began production of a special range of pen heads suitable for use in the vertical drum plotters which formed the draughting element of the early CAD systems. Additional pen heads were designed for reliable high-speed performance with the more recent drum- and flat-bed plotters and various papers. Some of these are variations on the fibre-tip and ball-tip pens introduced by the Japanese in the 1960s.

The recent CAD systems are rapidly being superseded through the advances of microchip technology, now applied to computer-aided draughting. The laser plotters introduced in 1983 operate by electronic circuits and produce an image of minuscule dots so that the drawing point, using either ink or pencil, is rendered redundant. It is the start of a new era in the production of drawings. As a consequence large sets of drawing instruments are rarely in demand. The more traditional users of drawing instruments – those draughtsmen who specialize in technical or geometrical drawing – have been joined by graphic designers, who have multiplied during the past ten years. For them small sets of compasses, with their extension fittings and an adaptor to take a technical pen, are now sold in practical transparent acrylic cases or are included in cases containing a range of technical pens. The instruments they use – the ruling pen and pair of compasses – have, despite improvements, survived almost unchanged since antiquity: a tribute to the continuity of functional design [35, 42 and 57].

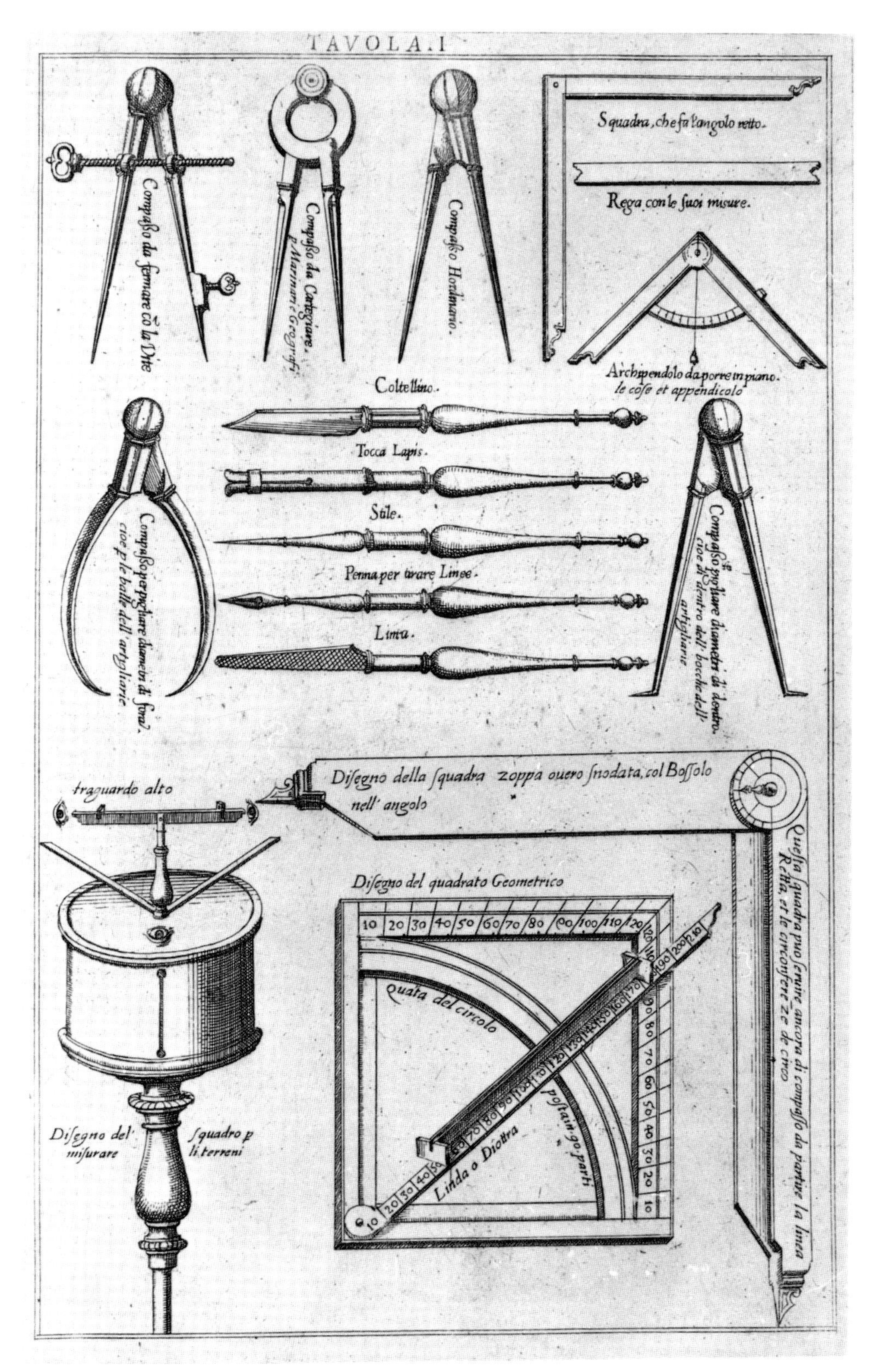
TAVOLA . I
Squadra, che fa l'angolo retto.
Rega con le suoi misure.
Archipendolo da porre in piano le cose et appendicolo
Coltellino.
Tocca Lapis.
Stile.
Penna per tirare Linee.
Lima.
Compasso da fermare cō la Vite
Compasso da Cartegiare p' Marinari Geografi
Compasso Hordinario.
Disegno della squadra zoppa ouero snodata, col Bossolo nell' angolo
traguardo alto
Disegno del quadrato Geometrico
Quata del circolo
Linda o Diottra
Disegno del misurare
squadro p li terreni

19

2

Literary Evidence

The most interesting sources of information on the development of geometrical drawing and the history of drawing instruments are early works and treatises on these and related subjects. They are to be found in specialist libraries, with several now published in facsimile editions.

The earliest is the only surviving treatise on the practice of Roman architecture and building, Vitruvius's *De architectura*, a technical handbook which dates to about 27 BC. It deals with such subjects as town-planning, water supply, machines, sundials, water clocks and decoration as well as building design. Vitruvius mentions the use of compasses and a scale rule in relation to drawing the ground plan of a building and the necessity for rules governing the proportion of the elements which make up the Classical orders. His book remained a standard work until the fifth century when Byzantine styles and techniques of building were introduced in Eastern Europe. The text survived in manuscript form in Western Europe throughout the Middle Ages in several monastic libraries and was copied and distributed. One copy reached the court of Charlemagne early in the ninth century, via the Benedictines of Jarrow in Northumberland. A second copy lay in the library of the monastery of St Gallen in Switzerland through much of the medieval period, remarkable for having a plan drawn on vellum for rebuilding the monastery, which dates to the eighth century. There was, therefore, some continuity in the use of the knowledge acquired during the Greek and Roman civilizations. In addition, the practical skills based on Greek geometry were handed down throughout the medieval period within the exclusive Guild of Masons.

In the Renaissance there was a renewed interest in Roman architecture, and in 1452 Leone Battista Alberti prepared his treatise *De re aedificatoria*, which was based on the principles set out in Vitruvius's work but reinterpreted to suit his own times. Alberti's Latin text was printed in Florence in 1485 and Vitruvius's original text was first published in Rome soon after, probably in the following year. Both these works provided inspiration throughout the next three centuries for many subsequent treatises prepared by architects. Plates to accompany Alberti's work were issued in 1546 with an Italian text. They formed the basis of many later works which set out the geometrical method of drawing Classical architecture, but strangely enough neither Alberti nor those architects who followed and also published treatises – notably Serlio, Vignola, Palladio and Scamozzi – included details of the drawing instruments required for this discipline. By 1600, however, drawing instruments were incorporated into the frontispieces of architectural treatises as symbolic tools of geometric drawing.

The first designs for individual drawing instruments appear to be those found in the sketch-books of Leonardo da Vinci of *c.*1500. In these he drew his ideas for particular instruments – such as beam compasses, ruling pens and proportional compasses – but it is doubtful if any were actually made. His contemporary Albrecht Dürer showed drawing instruments in some engravings executed between 1500 and 1525; these included a semi-elliptical trammel, his perspective devices, and a large pair of compasses in his plate entitled 'Melancholia'.

Early technical treatises on mathematical instruments

The earliest published work illustrating both engineering machinery and mathematical instruments appears to be that of a Frenchman, Jacques Besson (fl. 1550–70). First published in Orleans in Latin in the

[19] Engraved plate dated 1599 from Giovanni Pomodoro's *Geometria prattica* (1722 edn), showing a selection of mathematical instruments including a military sighting device. *Museo di Storia della Scienza, Florence.*

year 1569, after Besson's death, it was entitled *Theatrum instrumentorum* and reissued in French in Lyons in 1579 as *Théatre des instrumens mathématiques et mécaniques*. It included sixty plates engraved for Besson by Jacques Androuet du Cerceau, a brilliant architectural draughtsman, showing all kinds of mechanical devices along with a few drawing instruments – rulers, compasses and protractors – and several complex designs for inventions which were probably never made. There is a compass for drawing spirals which is of interest and a version of variable proportional compasses with grooved rods for legs.

The earliest book to include a plate devoted to a full range of geometrical drawing and surveying instruments is an Italian work by Giovanni Pomodoro, *Geometria prattica*, first published in Rome in 1603 and reissued (again in Rome) as late as 1772 [19].

Galileo's work *Le operazioni del compasso geometrico e militare* was published in 1606. It followed the development of his design for a geometric and military compass between 1597 and 1599.

Pantographice, or *The Art of Delineating* by Christopher Scheiner was published in Rome by the Society of Jesus in 1621, some sixteen years after he had introduced his design for a pantograph, a parallelogram for copying [125].

In England during the latter part of the sixteenth and the early seventeenth centuries the introduction of new mathematical instruments was recorded in such published works as Thomas Hood's *The Making & Use of the Geometrical Instrument called a Sector* (1589) and Edmund Gunter's *Description & Use of the Sector* (1624). Leonard Digges' work *A Geometrical Practice named Pantometrica* (1571), completed and published by his son Thomas Digges, set out both the methods and the instruments needed for surveying.

In Germany during the seventeenth century cities with flourishing metal-workshops and new printing presses were responsible for several works that combined the subjects of geometry and drawing. An early example is Hans Lencker's *Perspectiva*, first published in Nuremberg in 1579, with a plate showing the geometrical use of dividers [20]. Joseph Furttenbach, who had earlier issued works on architecture and fortifications, published his *Mechanischer Reissladen* in Augsburg in 1644. This small volume included both theoretical and practical subjects covering the extent of mechanics at the time, and of the four pull-out plates two illustrate drawing and writing instruments. The plate illustrated here shows twenty-three math-

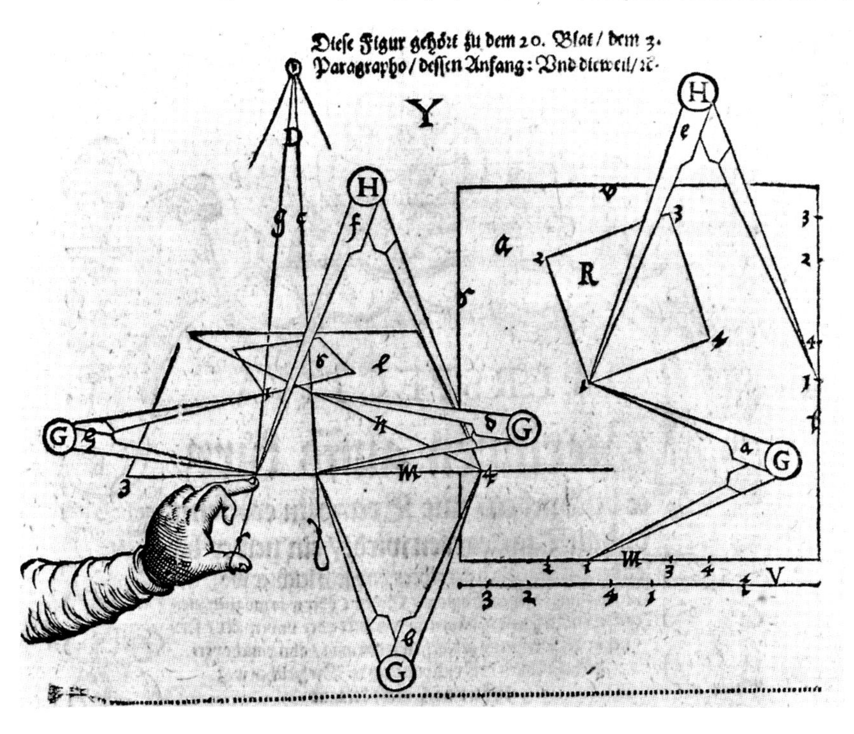

[20] Plate from Hans Lencker's *Perspectiva* (Ulm, 1617; first published in 1579), which shows the use of dividers when setting up a perspective.

ematical and surveying instruments [23]. Another German work from this period is by Daniel Schwenter, *Mathematische und philosophische Erquickungsstunden*, which was published in Nuremberg in 1653. This is a compendium of practical knowledge with numerous small rather simple illustrations within the text. The subjects dealt with are varied and include the then current obsessions with shadows, magic or optical deception, properties of mirrors and vision, water and fountains. There are several plates for setting-out sundials and one showing four varieties of compasses and callipers.

Eighteenth-century treatises on mathematical instruments

In the treatises prepared from 1700 onwards one finds a more accurate record of contemporary drawing instruments. The French instrument maker Nicolas Bion published his *Traité de la construction et des principaux usages des instrumens de mathématique* in 1709. It was reissued in 1712, first translated into German in 1717 and reached a fifth edition in French in 1752. In this case many of the drawing instruments illustrated can be taken as typical of the late seventeenth rather than the eighteenth century; they were already out of date or very traditional by the time the work was reissued. Of the twenty-five plates two – plates 8 and 9 – deal with the main groups of drawing instruments [21 and 22]. The book was aimed at a wide public: the users of mathematical instruments, the aristocratic collectors and the new professional classes. Members of this last group were now becoming collectors with a thirst for knowledge and an interest in mathematics, astronomy, surveying and simple mechanics.

Bion's work was first published in English in 1723, under the title *The Construction and Principal Uses of Mathematical Instruments*. The translator was Edmund Stone (1700–68), a young protégé of the Duke of Argyll. After a busy life connected with publishing and translating works on mathematical subjects, Stone was reluctantly persuaded to prepare a revised English edition of Bion in 1758. This included an important supplement which described and illustrated the major English contributions to mathematical instruments then known. To the drawing instruments taken from Bion's illustrations, Stone added a detailed drawing of proportional compasses together with a fine pair of turn-about compasses of much greater sophistication than the instruments shown by Bion.

[20A] Engraved plate by Thomas Tuttell for the revised edition of Joseph Moxon's *Mathematics made Easie* of 1701, published with a supplement entitled *Description and Explanation of Mathematical Instruments.*

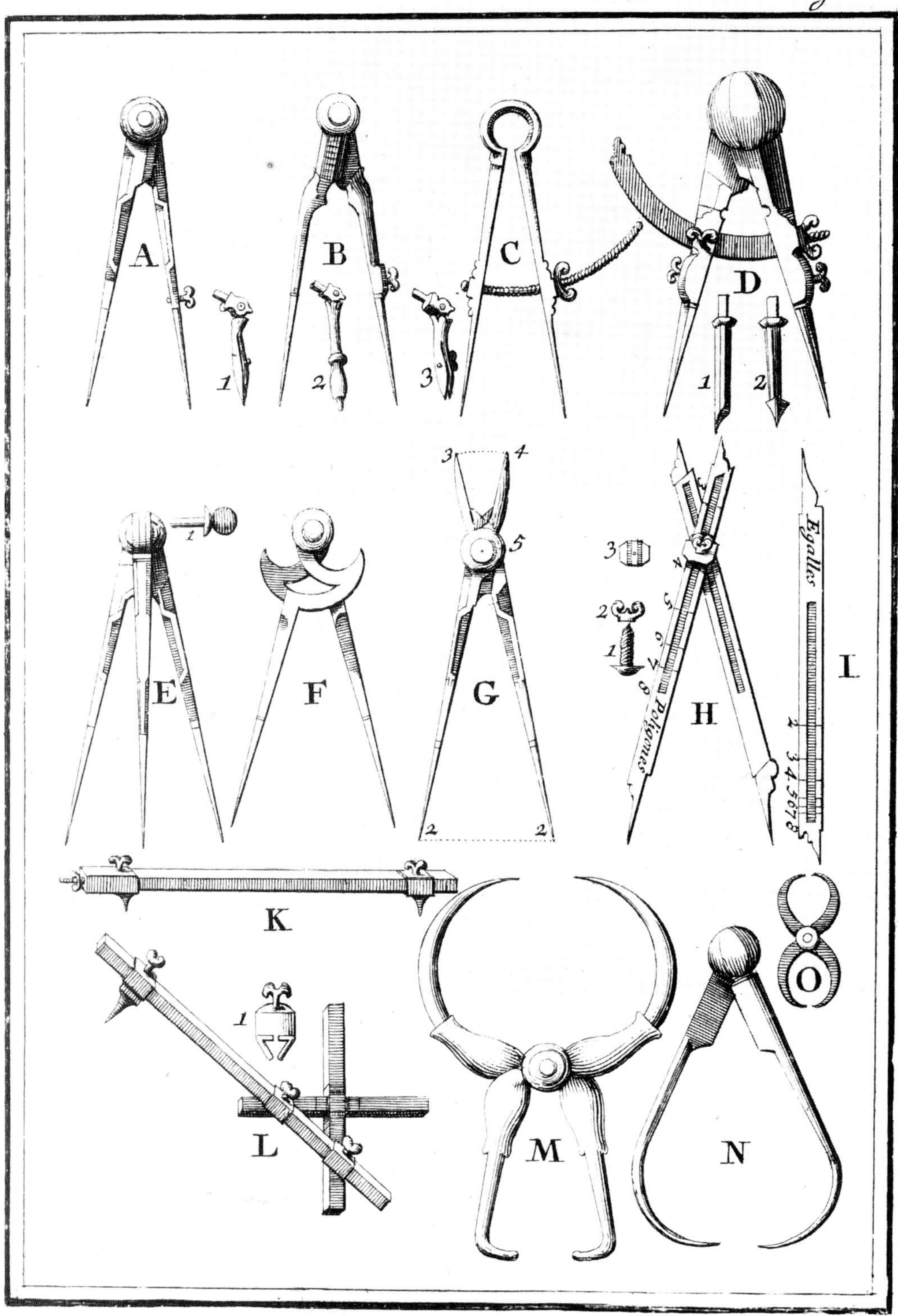
Planche Huitieme . Page 86.
A
B
C
D
E
F
G
H
I
K
L
M
N
O
Egalles
Polygones

21

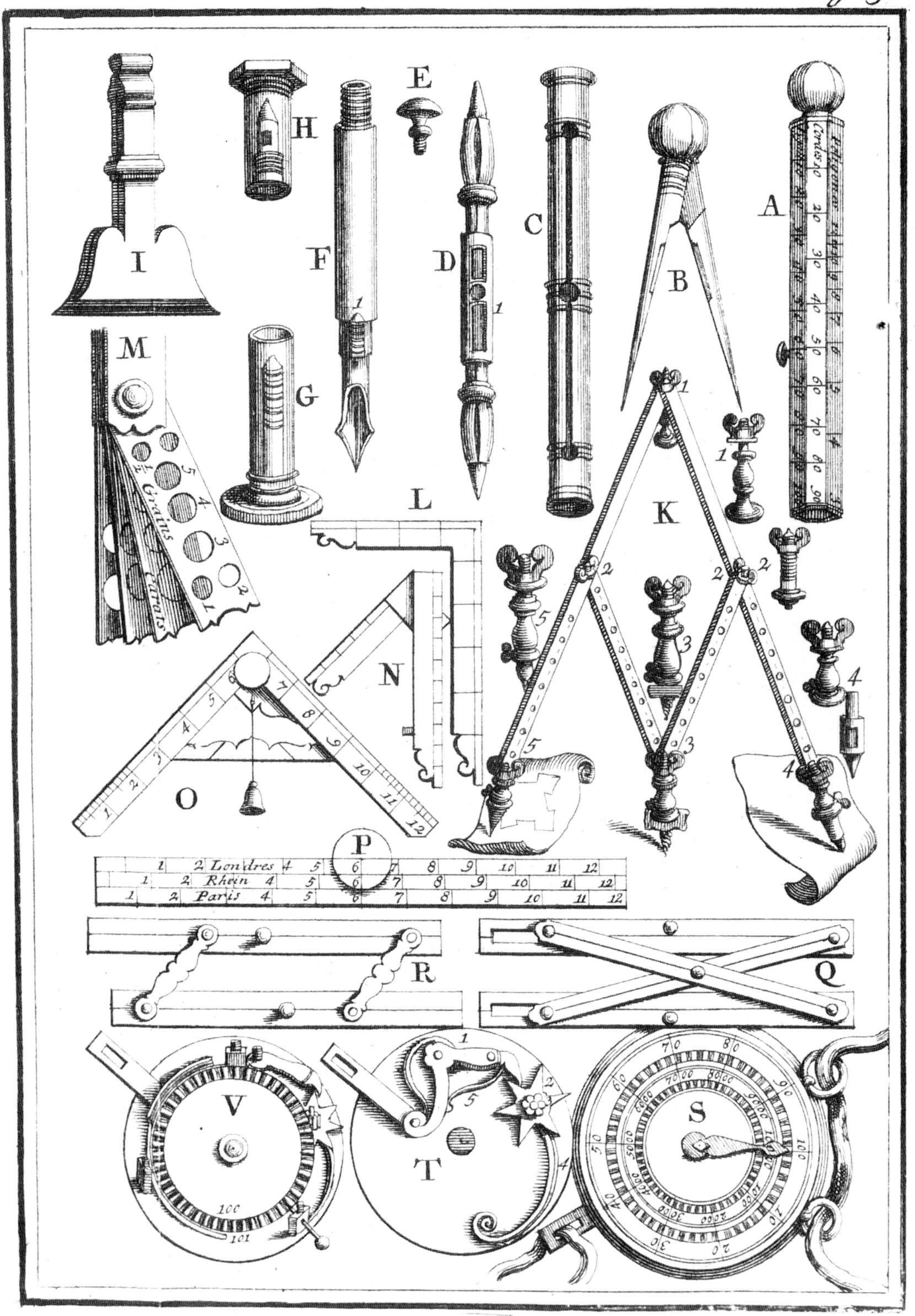
Planche Neuvieme.
Page 96.
A
B
C
D
E
F
G
H
I
K
L
M
N
O
P
Q
R
S
T
V
1 2 Londres 4 5 6 7 8 9 10 11 12
1 2 Rhein 4 5 6 7 8 9 10 11 12
1 2 Paris 4 5 6 7 8 9 10 11 12
Grains
Carats

22

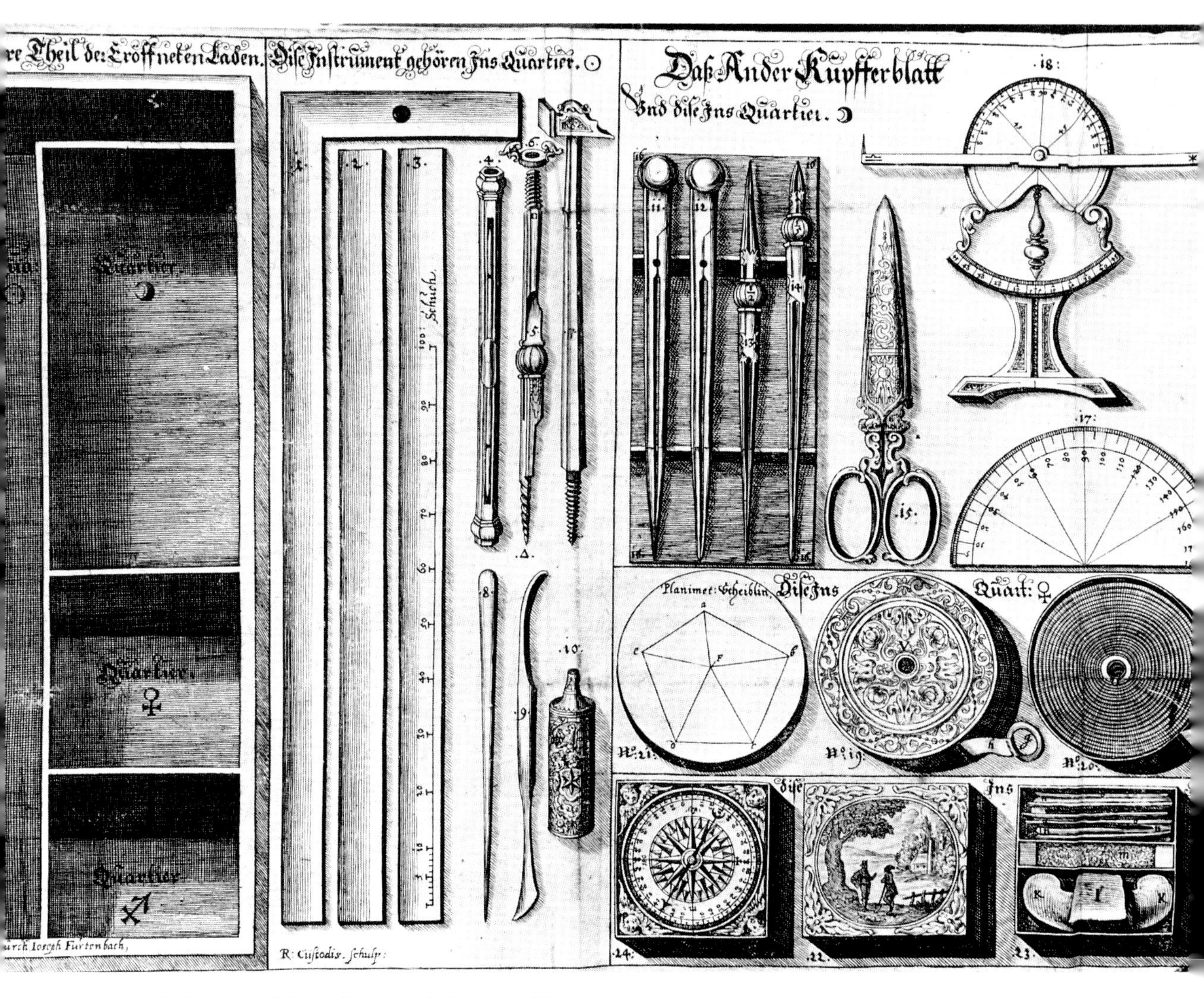

[23] Engraved Plate 2 from Joseph Furttenbach's *Mechanischer Reissladen* (Augsburg, 1644), which includes 23 instruments used for drawing and surveying. Note the plain dividers and the fixed proportional compasses.

PAGE 38
[21] Engraved Plate 8 featuring compasses from Nicolas Bion's *Traité de la construction et des principaux usages des instrumens de mathématique* (The Hague, 1723; first published in Paris in 1709). (A) hair compasses, (B) German compasses, (C) wing-divider, (D) wing-compass with metal cutting inserts, (E) 3-legged compass, (F) sea-chart compasses, (G) fixed proportional compasses, (H) variable proportional compasses, (K) beam compass, (L) elliptical compasses, (M) spherical compasses, (N) cylindrical compasses, (O) equal or symmetrical spherical compasses. *Science Museum Library, London.*

PAGE 39
[22] Engraved Plate 9 from Bion's treatise (The Hague, 1723; first published in Paris in 1709) which includes: (A) and (B) hexagonal scale-holder containing dividers; (C) and (D) double-ended crayon-holder; (E), (F) and (G) views of an early fountain pen; (I) Bion's paper clip; (K) simple pantograph; (L), (N) and (O) set squares (the last can be used as a level with a plumb-bob); (P) scale rule with three comparative graduations for London, Paris and the Rhineland; (Q) parallel rule with scissored links; (R) parallel rule with diagonal links; (S) pedometer; (T) and (V) two dials. *Science Museum Library, London.*

This English edition is in constant use by curators and collectors and is available in facsimile; the information it contains is still relevant.

Nicolas Bion's work was translated into German by the renowned Nuremberg mathematician and astronomer, Johann Gabriel Doppelmayr (1671–1750). It formed part of *Weitere Eröffnung der Neuen Mathematischen Werkschule*, which was published in Nuremberg in 1717 and reissued in 1726–28 and 1741. Doppelmayr added two interesting plates illustrating perspective apparatus, which included designs by Benjamin Bramer, J. F. Niceron and Sir Christopher Wren [see 139 and 140].

A notable German original treatise is that by Jacob Leupold, *Theatrum arithmetico geometricum*. First published in Leipzig in 1727, it formed part of a nine-volume work issued between 1724 and 1739 under the title *Theatrum mechanicum generale*. Leupold, originally a carpenter, became an expert on geometrical, mathematical and mechanical problems. His book covers much the same ground as the work of Bion and Stone but it does not include theodolites or nautical instruments. Most of the plates illustrate surveying instruments but several innovative designs for drawing instruments appear, including some which try to solve the practical problems of bisecting angles and drawing at a known angle (for which Leupold devised a hinged rule similar to a bevel or adjustable setsquare). There were also plates devoted to compasses, beam compasses, parallel rulers and a fine plate on ruling pens [38, 53].

The German architect Johann Friedrich Penther (1693–1749), a contemporary of Leopold, published his *Praxis geometriae* in Augsburg in 1732, and this was reissued regularly until the ninth edition in 1788. The plates cover geometry, astronomy, sundials and drawing and surveying instruments; the two devoted to drawing instruments give useful information on German eighteenth-century designs and patterns [25 and 26]. Penther also wrote books on architecture, construction, building materials, costs, etc., with an emphasis on practical matters.

Seventeenth- and eighteenth-century handbooks and patternbooks

In late-seventeenth-century England the need for simple information on mathematics, geometry and drawing suitable for both architects and craftsmen was met by handbooks and patternbooks. There were a number of good European examples to follow, many of them deriving from Serlio's architectural treatises, and they were often combined with design manuals: in German those by Nicholas Goldmann (1611–65), *c.*1660, transcribed from the original Dutch by the German architect Leonard Sturm (1669–1719); and in French by Pierre Le Muet (1591–1669), also an architect, between 1623 and 1664. Le Muet's *Manière de bastir* (1623) was translated into English *c.*1670 by an engraver and publisher, Robert Pricke.

The most interesting English handbooks in relation to instruments and tools are the works of Joseph Moxon (1627–91). A mathematician and hydrographer and later a member of the Royal Society, Moxon translated Vignola in 1659 and Dubrueil's *La perspective practique* in 1670. His original works, such as his *Mechanick Exercises* (first published in 1677) provided practical information. He describes several building trades, and plates showing all the craftsmen's tools necessary for these are included. Moxon's *Mathematical Dictionary*, first published in 1679, was reissued by his son James in 1701 together with a supplement entitled 'Description and Explanation of Mathematical Instruments, with copper cuts by Thomas Tuttell'. The latter consisted of an alphabetical list of one hundred mathematical instruments available, and sixty-one of which were included in a plate by Tuttell [20A]. This gives a clear indication of the range being made in London by 1700.

The eighteenth century was the heyday for practical manuals and patternbooks in England, some of which

OVERLEAF

[24] Engraved Plate I from the 1788 edn. of Johann Friedrich Penther's *Praxis geometriae* (first published in Augsburg in 1723), which shows (1) dividers; (2–5) large compasses with inserts for ink, pencil and wheel pen; (6) a pricker; (7) a spanner; (8) a ruling pen; (9) wheel pen insert; (10) both sides of diagonal scales; (11) a wood triangle.

[25] Engraved Plate II from Penther's *Praxis geometriae* (1788 edn.), which shows (1) an ebony parallel rule; (2) a semi-circular protractor; (3) a sector; and (4) triangular compasses.

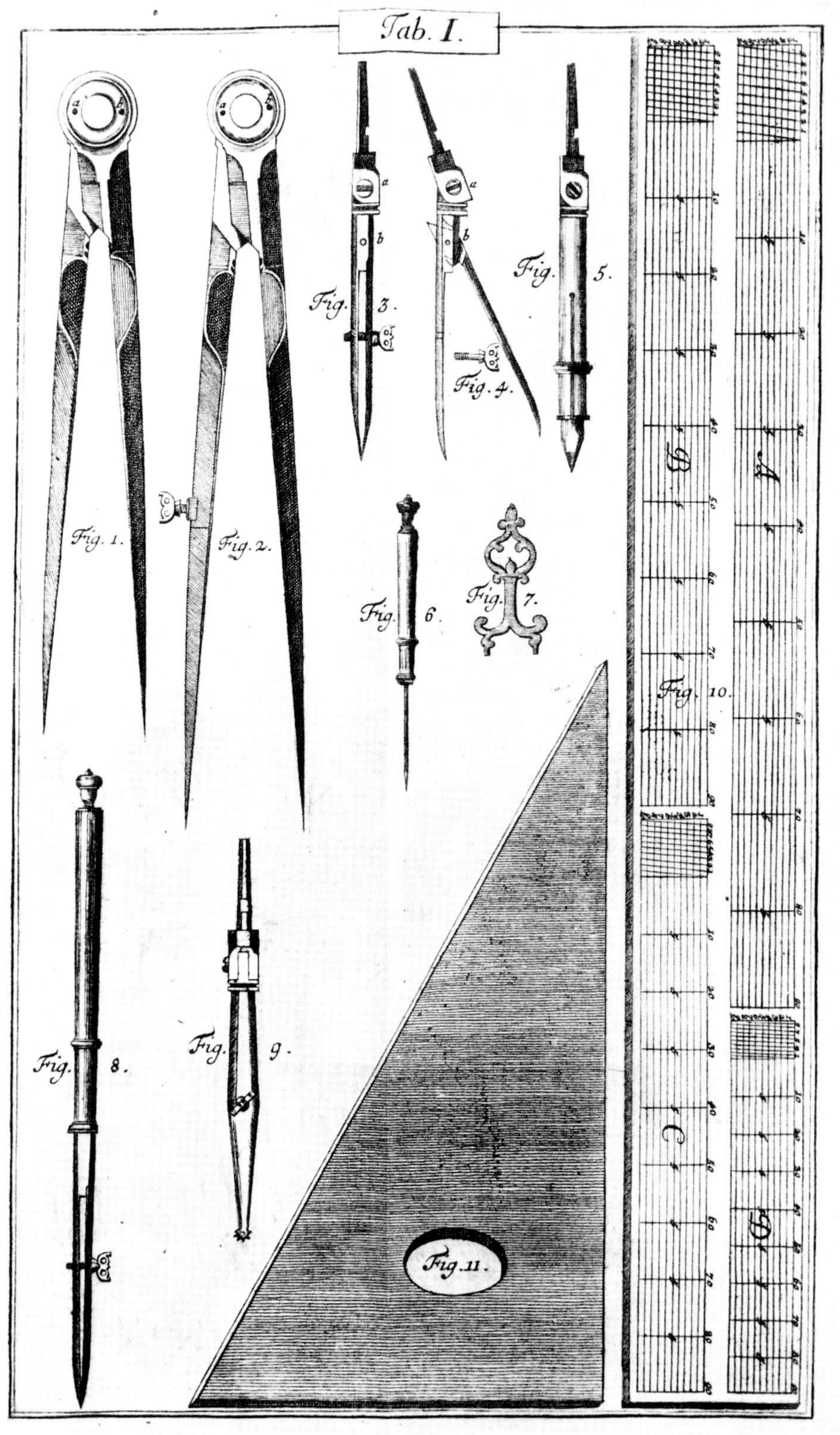
Tab. I.
Fig. 1.
Fig. 2.
Fig. 3.
Fig. 4.
Fig. 5.
Fig. 6.
Fig. 7.
Fig. 8.
Fig. 9.
Fig. 10.
Fig. 11.
A
B
C
D

24

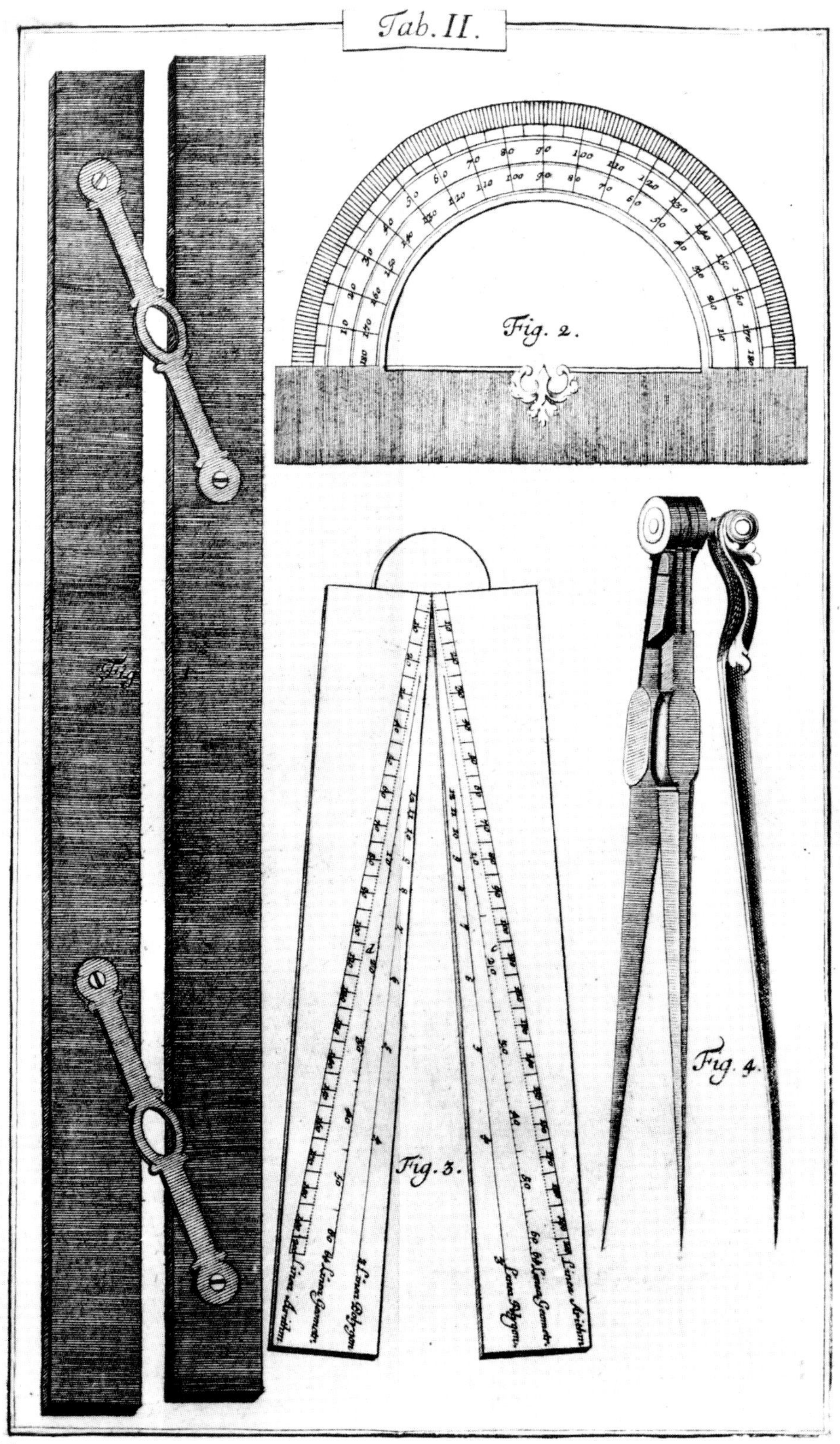

25

included illustrations of instruments to be used either for drawing or calculating proportions. William Halfpenny, a builder-architect, and William Salmon, a carpenter-joiner, both published works dealing with the architectural and technical background to building, which included the practice of geometrical drawing amongst its required skills.

In his early handbook *Magnum in Parvo or The Marrow of Architecture* (1725) William Halfpenny inluded his design for an architectonic arc, together with an explanation on its use, graduated with the proportions for the five orders of architecture. In the plate the instrument is inscribed 'Wm. Halfpenny Inv. Tho. Heath in the Strand Londini fecit'. This work was followed by William Salmon's *Palladio Londinensis or the London Art of Building* of 1734, which included an early illustration of a drawing board set-up together with paper, tee-square and detail of a parallel rule [107].

Probably the most comprehensive and widely known of these patternbooks is Batty Langley's *The City and Country Builder's & Workman's Treasury of Designs*, which was first published in 1740. It was issued in a facsimile edition in 1967. The boldly engraved plates [87] give the geometry for setting out the five orders of architecture as well as for constructing the carpentry for supporting vaulting and arches over niches and for complex roof trusses. This geometry entailed accurate drawings for which drawing instruments were absolutely necessary.

Another patternbook of interest is William Pain's *The Builder's Companion & Workman's General Assistant* of 1763. This includes the usual plates dealing with the five orders, but there is also a plate showing a folding rule graduated to enable the easy division of the diameter of a column in order to calculate all the elements which make up each order. The book also deals with the 'Gauging of Columns' or the setting out of the flutes on a column, all tapered to achieve the desired entasis. The instructions were intended to assist builders in dealing with the more complicated aspects of architectural features. It was the widespread use of the above patternbooks by both employers and their builders that produced the high standard of detailing and construction to be seen in Georgian buildings all over Britain.

Trade cards

Another source of information on drawing instruments is the trade literature issued by instrument makers. The cards often included small illustrations as well as descriptions of the items sold together with the name and address of the supplier; they sometimes included price lists. The earliest trade cards known in England date from *c.*1630. They became increasingly common over the next 150 years, and by the end of the eighteenth century it was standard practice for instrument makers to issue them with purchases or as advertisements. At this time many London makers exported their trade cards, and some highly decorative versions were printed with texts in French, German or Dutch [26]. By the early nineteenth century cards had become simpler and more dignified in design, usually with fine copper-plate lettering. Later in the century shadow lettering and bolder and more decorative type-faces were used while cheaper printing methods were introduced. A good selection of these trade cards appears in Gerard L'E. Turner's *Nineteenth-Century Scientific Instruments*, 1983.

Trade cards, together with the labels sometimes found inside instrument cases, can assist in dating an item, provided, of course, that the name and address can be checked against a known maker's dates and any change of address for their premises, etc.

London instrument makers' publications

Several London instrument makers combined publishing with running workshops or retail shops, and their books provide us with useful information. One of the earliest, of 1739, was William Webster's small handbook *Description & Use of a Complete Set or Case of Pocket Instruments, sold by J. Sisson Math. Instr. Maker corner of Beaufort Buildings in the Strand.* It originally formed an appendix to Webster's *A Compendious Course of Practical Mathematics*, in which the author styled himself as 'Writing master', stating in an announcement at the back, 'young Gentlemen are well boarded and expeditiously qualified for Business.' The four plates illustrate instruments made by Jonathan Sisson (fl.1736–88), one of which shows both faces of his sector together with protracting and plotting scales [110].

John Robertson's useful little book *A Treatise of such Mathematical Instruments as are usually put into a Portable Case* was first published in 1747 in association with the well-known instrument maker Thomas Heath. Robertson, a mathematician, covered such subjects as arithmetic, geometry, trigonometry, architecture, surveying and gunnery and gave detailed descriptions of all the drawing instruments that would have been available at the time. The high quality pull-out plate shows the drawing instruments clearly and to scale; detail of the proportional compasses should be compared with that of Edmund Stone. Robertson later became secretary and librarian to the Royal Society and published a revised edition in 1775 [27].

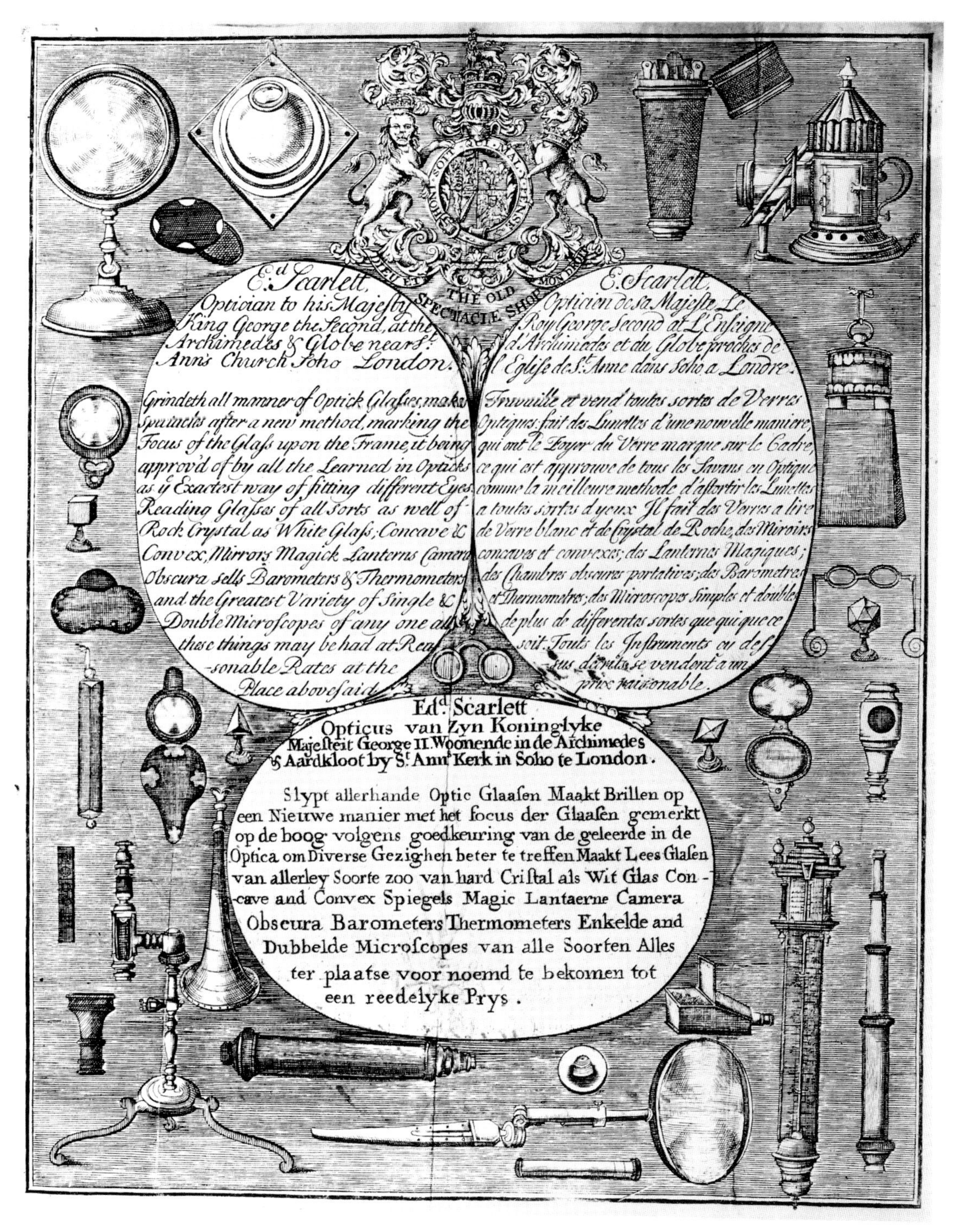

[26] Trade card for Edward Scarlett, optician to George II, which gives details of the items offered for sale in English, French and Dutch. Note the pocket case of drawing instruments covered in fishskin and mounted in silver to the right of the coat-of-arms.

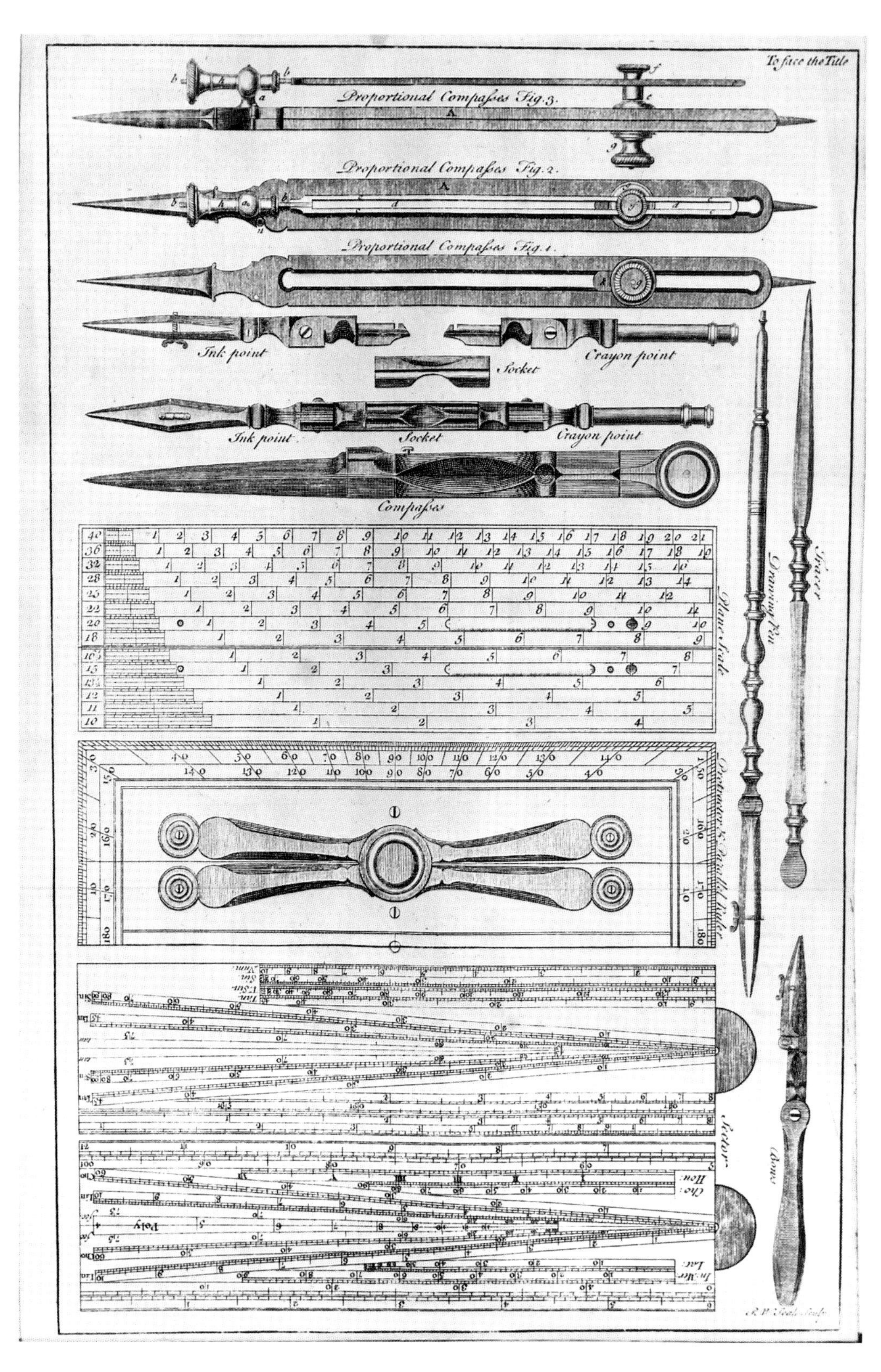

[27] Engraved plate from John Robertson's *A Treatise of Such Mathematical Instruments as are usually put into a Portable Case* (1757 edn; first published 1747).

Drawing instruments at this time also formed part of the formalized decorative frontispieces to books dealing with architecture or perspective as in the case of Isaac Ware's version of Sirigatti's *The Practice of Perspective* [28].

George Adams the Elder, Royal Instrument Maker to George III, was a practical and innovative technician but he had no formal education. Despite this he published several works including one which dealt with the subject of microscopes. This was his *Micrographia illustrata* of 1746. The work included a detailed description of all the instruments that he thought necessary for geometrical drawing together with a catalogue of over three hundred scientific instruments which could be obtained at his retail shop. (Not all the instruments were made in his workshop: the intention was to promote interest in a wide variety of items, and when he had a genuine enquiry he would set about making or obtaining the required item.) His son, George Adams the Younger (1750–95), with the benefits of an academic education unlike his father, also published several works on scientific subjects. His *Geometrical & Graphical Essays*, published in 1791, contains eight plates of drawing instruments. Some of the illustrated items would have been available from the Adams' workshop at the end of the century; others – particularly the more advanced perspective devices and the helicograph [29 and 89] – were designs which were available on order. On Adams's death the plates were sold by his widow to W. & S. Jones and these were revised and re-issued in 1797 and with further additions again in 1812 and 1823. They should be compared carefully with the originals, in particular the plate dealing with compasses [54].

Benjamin Martin also combined publishing educational tracts with his instrument-making business, and he printed instructions with some of his improved instruments such as his pantograph. His *Description & Use of a Case of Mathematical Instruments* was first published in 1771 and re-issued by P. & J. Dollond in 1790 and by John Bleuer in 1800. This small pamphlet has no illustrations, but it describes in detail Martin's recommendations for the principal instruments supplied in a pocket case, and he gives practical hints on their use:

of the DRAWING PEN and PENCIL

The Drawing Pen is only the Common Steel Pen at the end of a Brass Rod or Shaft of convenient length, to be held in the Hand for drawing all kinds of Black Lines by the Edge of a Rule. The Shaft or Handle has a Screw in the middle Part: and when unscrewed, there is a fine round Steel Pin, or Point, by which you make a nice Mark or Dot as you please, for terminating your Lines or Curious Draughts.

[28] Frontispiece which incorporates formalised decorative use of drawing instruments, from Sirigatti's *Practice of Perspective*; the English edition by Isaac Ware, London, 1755.

The Black-lead Pencil, if good is of frequent use for drawing straight Lines; and for supplying the place of the Drawing Pen, where Lines of Ink are not necessary. It is also substituted for the Common Pen in Writing, Figuring and because in all cases if what be drawn with it be not right, or does not please, it may be easily rubbed out with a Piece of Crumb-bread, and the whole new drawn.

Benjamin Martin

John Barrow's *Description of Pocket & Magazine Cases of Technical Drawing Instruments* was published in 1792 by the instrument makers J. & W. Watkins of Charing Cross, whose name is shown on the instruments illustrated in the finely engraved plate [30]. The design of pens and compasses is very similar to that in the Adams Plate I of 1791 [29].

The influence of George Adams the Younger appears in an interesting German work by Johann Gotthelf Studer: *Mathematical Instruments for Meas-*

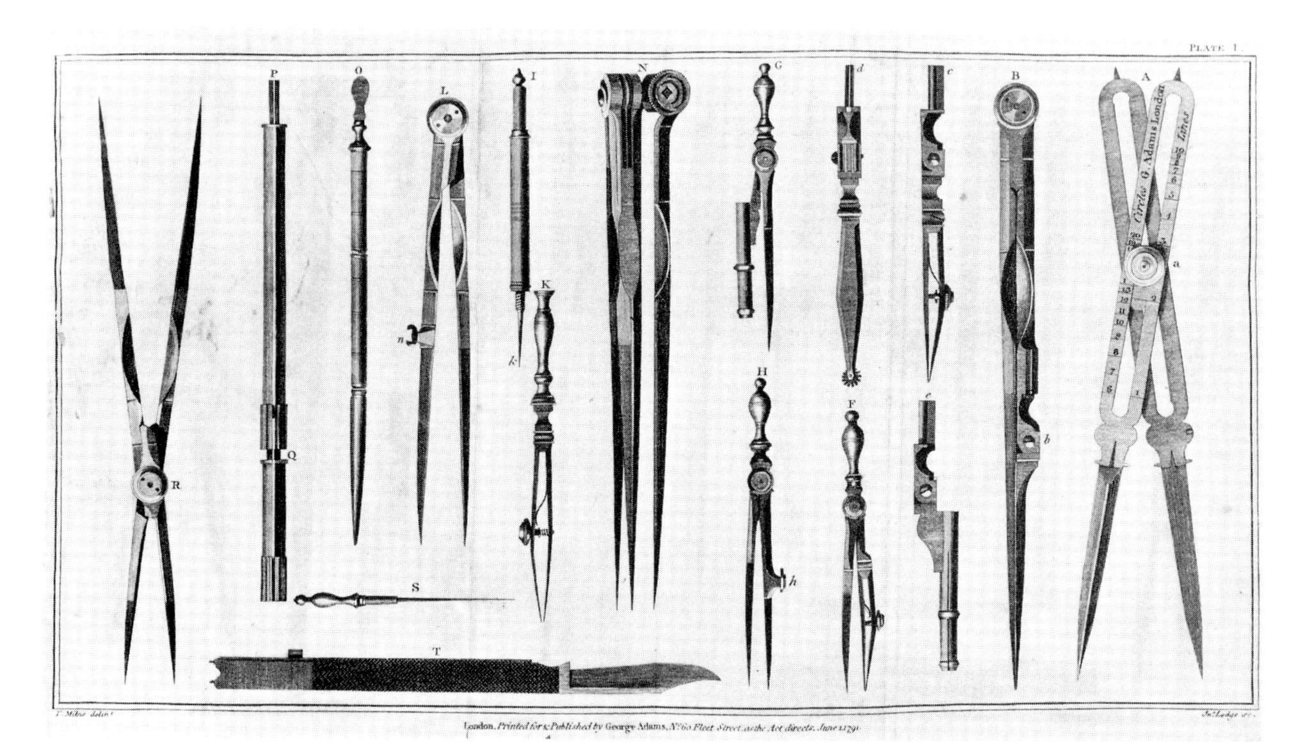

[29] Engraved plate from the 1791 edtion of George Adams the Younger's *Geometrical and Graphical Essays* which shows various patterns of compasses: (A) proportional compasses: (B) large compasses with (a) alternative inserts. (b) a point. (c) ink. (d) wheel pen. (e) pencil: (F) and (G) small bows for ink and pencil: (H) small dividers: (I) a pricker and (K) the drawing pen into which it is screwed: (L) dividers: (O) tracer/stylus: (P) and (Q) extension leg to compasses: (R) wholes and halves (fixed proportional compasses).

[III] Beam compass fittings of nickel silver for use with a hardwood beam with alternative ink and pencil drawing points. Milanese maker. *c.*1850. (Shown enlarged.) *Alessandro Ubertazzi Collection, Milan.*

[IV] Mahogany cased set of ten 12-inch engineers' drawing scales together with ten 2-inch off-sets, all of boxwood and signed STANLEY LONDON TRADE MARK. Case: $13\frac{1}{2} \times 3\frac{1}{4} \times 1\frac{3}{4}$ in (343 × 83 × 45 mm). *Andrew Alpern Collection, New York.*

uring & Drawing, published in Dresden in 1811. The author was an engineer attached to the court in Saxony. Before this Georg F. Brander, the most important German instrument maker of his time, published descriptions of thirty-one of his instruments with engraved plates; his development work on scales is only partly relevant to drawing instruments.

Encyclopaedias

Ephraim Chambers published the first edition of his *Cyclopaedia* in 1728. It included descriptions of several drawing instruments, although only parallel rules and proportional and elliptical compasses were illustrated. The revised edition, compiled by Dr Abraham Rees between 1779 and 1791, had a separate volume of plates which included finely engraved plates showing a wider selection of drawing instruments.

In France the first comprehensive encyclopaedia, which covered scientific and mechanical subjects, was prepared by Diderot and d'Alembert between 1751 and 1776. The volume on *Dessein* or drawing, issued in 1763, included only those instruments used for freehand drawing, but there were fine plates illustrating the perspective apparatus available and the use of the pantograph. This *Encyclopédie* was followed by the more comprehensive *Encyclopédie méthodique: Arts et métiers, mécaniques*, edited by Panckoucke, which appeared in sections between 1784 and 1797.

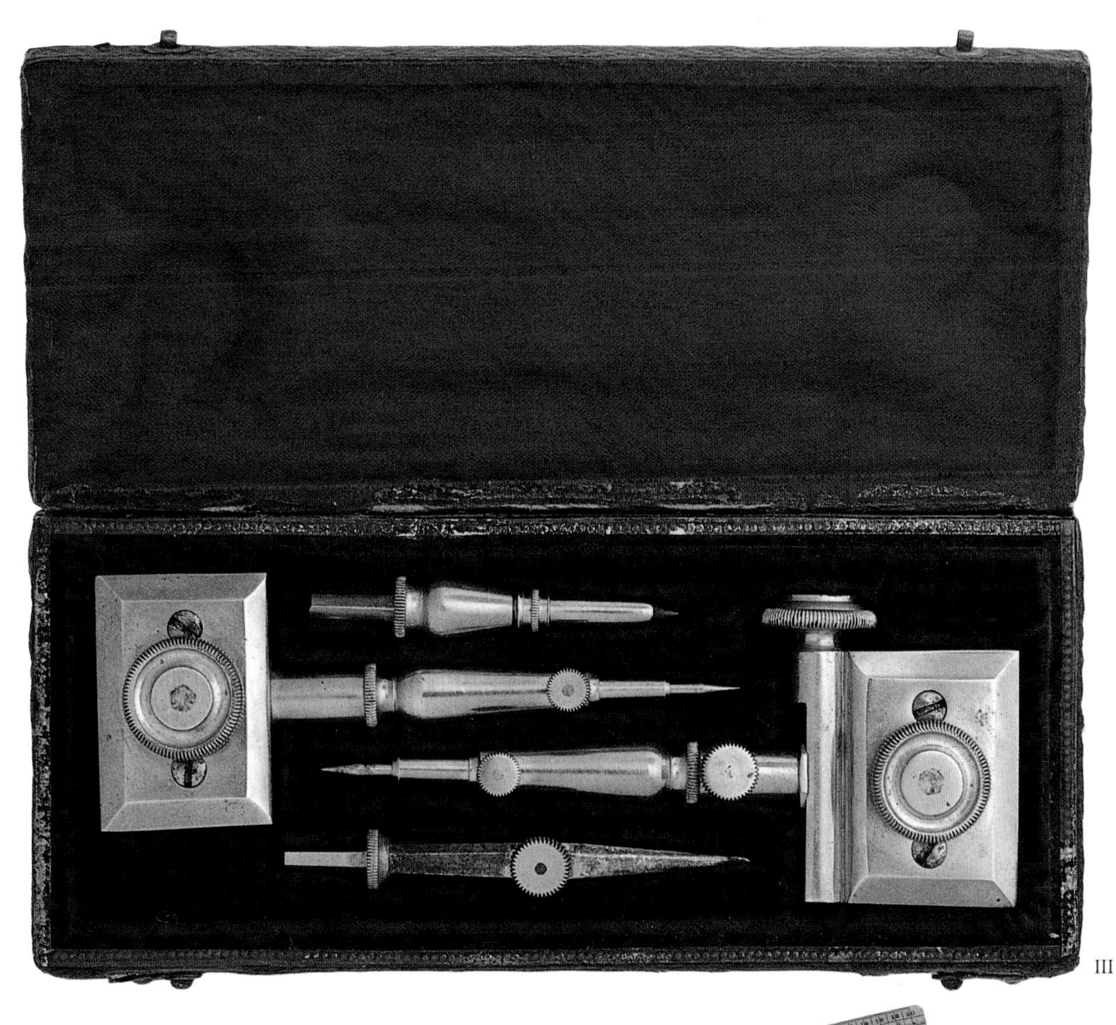

III

100
TRADE STANLEY MARK
LONDON
100
STANLEY
HOLBORN, LONDON
100
TRADE STANLEY MARK
LONDON
100
10
TRADE STANLEY MARK
LONDON
10

IV

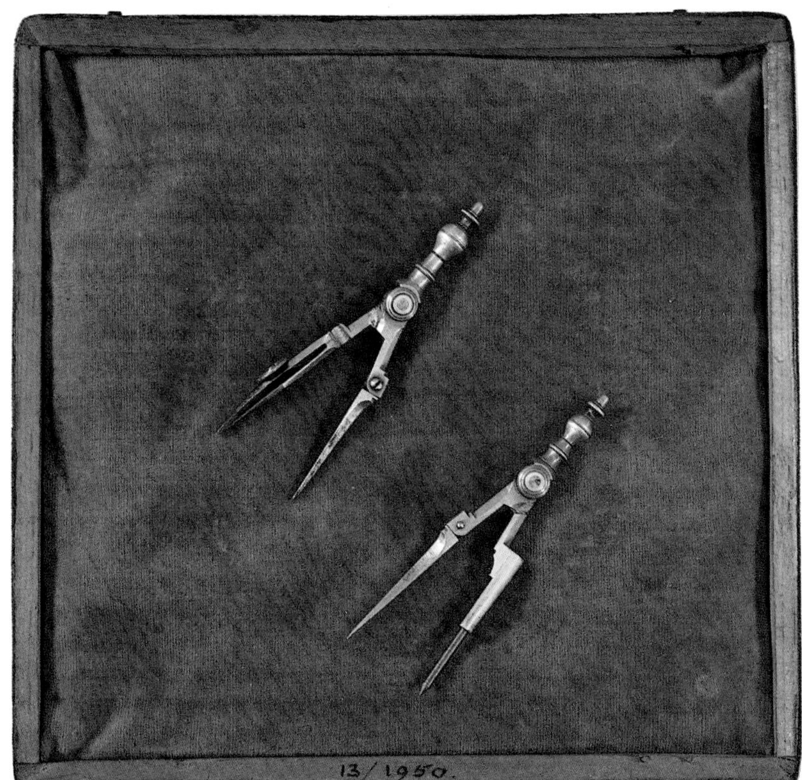

V

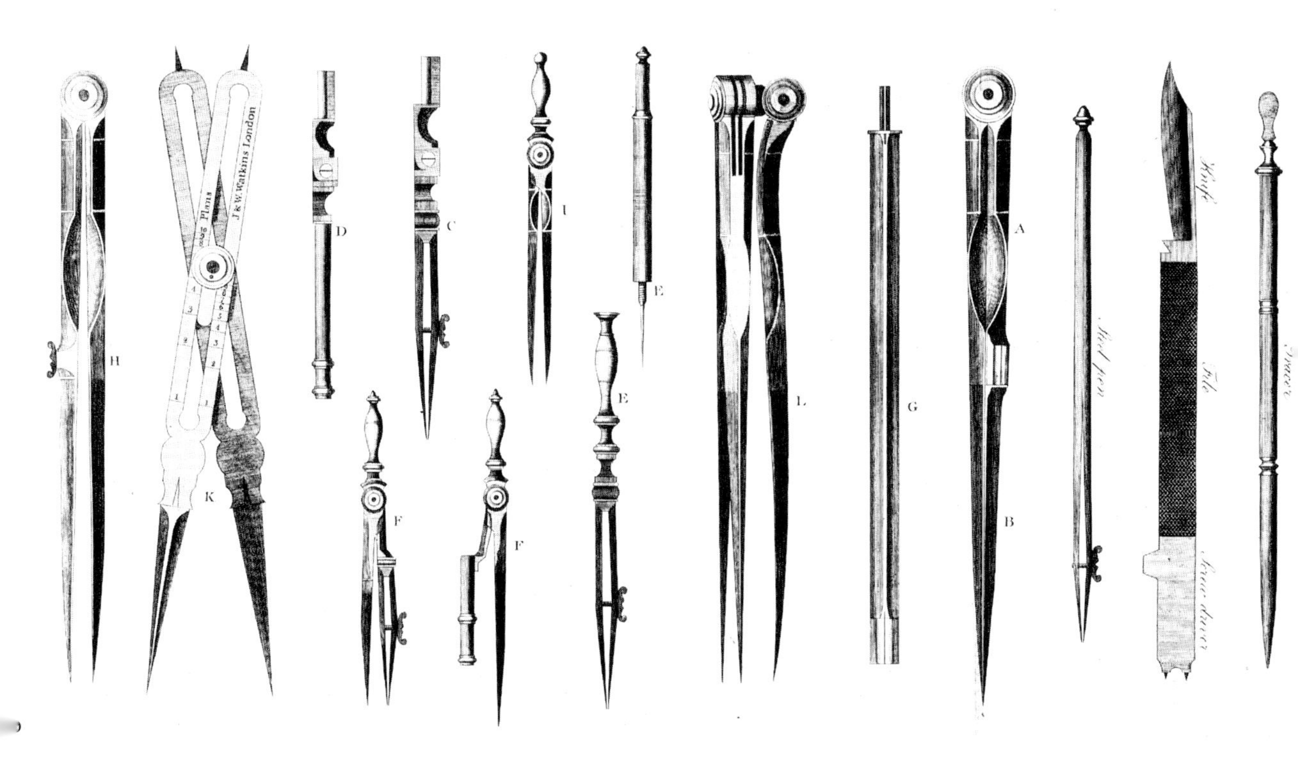

[V] Ellipsograph inscribed 'Farey London No 22' shown in its original fishskin covered case lined with velvet, complete with a pair of miniature bow compasses, one for pencil, one for ink. Case: 7 × 7 in (178 mm). English, *c.*1815. *RIBA Collection, London.*

[30] Engraved plate from John Barrow's *Description of Pocket and Magazine Cases of Technical Drawing Instruments* (1792).

The third volume included entries on both the manufacture of mathematical instruments, with a plate showing a workshop, and the tools and equipment used by eighteenth-century instrument makers. In addition there were detailed descriptions of the various instruments themselves, with plates illustrating them.

The best sources of information on early-nineteenth-century English drawing instruments are the various encyclopaedias of the period. Dr Rees's *New Cyclopaedia or Universal Dictionary of Arts & Sciences*, prepared between 1802 and 1819, set a standard: it eventually consisted of forty-five volumes, six of which were devoted to finely engraved plates. John Farey (1791–1851) was responsible for most of the drawings on mechanical subjects and also the plates on drawing instruments. The plates on geometry, architecture and perspective, scenography and shadow projection were prepared by Peter Nicholson. The high quality of the engravings owes a great deal to Wilson Lowry who prepared these plates [31].

The *Edinburgh Encyclopaedia* appeared in parts between 1808 and 1830 and was edited by Sir David Brewster (1781–1868), the Scottish scientist who invented the kaleidoscope in 1817. Brewster intended that these volumes should surpass those of Dr Rees. All contain excellent examples of the high quality achieved by Edinburgh engravers at this time. John Farey prepared new drawings for the plates dealing with drawing instruments, and he was also responsible for the text which accompanied them. Farey's plates illustrated the most recent patterns and included some new devices concerned with technical drawing. The set-up drawing-board, complete with tee-square, shown used with an adjustable bevel marks the beginning of nineteenth-century drawing office practice. Even the new brass drawing pins are shown in detail [32 and 33].

The last of the English encyclopaedias to include finely engraved plates is the *Encyclopaedia Metropolitana*, issued between 1817 and 1845. Some of the plates, though unsigned, appear to have been based on drawings by John Farey, especially those on drawing

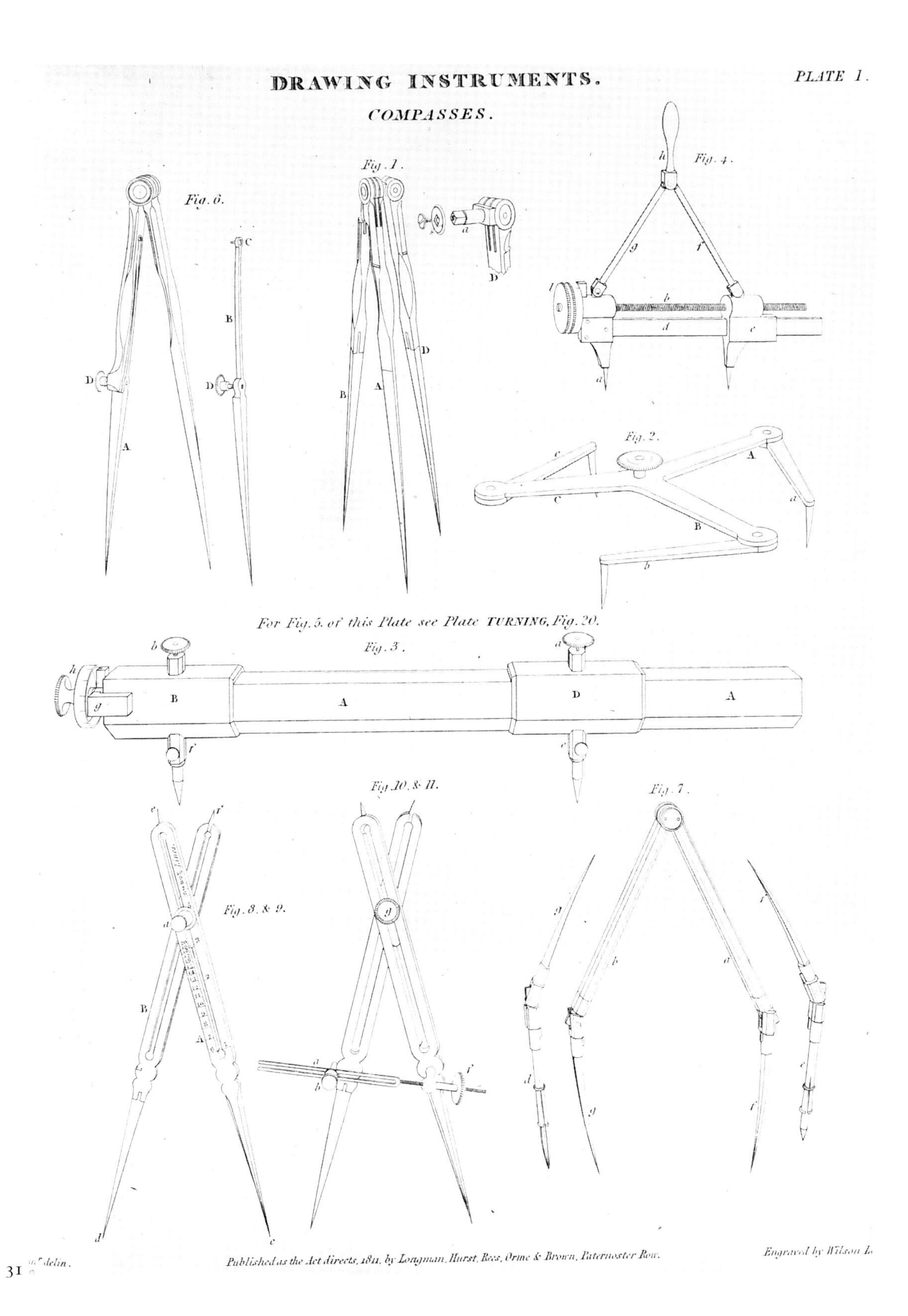
DRAWING INSTRUMENTS.
PLATE 1.
COMPASSES.
For Fig. 5. of this Plate see Plate TURNING, Fig. 20.
Published as the Act directs, 1811, by Longman, Hurst, Rees, Orme & Brown, Paternoster Row.

instruments. Farey is also known to have prepared plates on perspective apparatus for the sixth and seventh editions of the *Encyclopaedia Britannica*, published in Edinburgh in 1823 and 1842 respectively. These editions also include illustrations of drawing instruments.

Strangely enough, Joseph Gwilt's *Encyclopaedia of Architecture*, first published in 1841, contains systematic information for architects and builders, but no information at all on drawing instruments.

Mention must be made here of Peter Nicholson (1765–1844), already referred to in relation to the plates he prepared for encyclopaedias. Nicholson bridged the gap between the eighteenth- and nineteenth-century works on geometry, drawing and building techniques. One of his earliest works, *The Carpenter's and Joiner's Assistant*, first published in 1797, was in the tradition of the practical handbooks and derived from Joseph Moxon's work a century earlier. His *Five Orders of Architecture* of 1795 included instructions for students on the setting up of a conchoid in connection with the flutes of a Greek column. Originally apprenticed as a cabinet-maker in Scotland, he became an educator of both craftsmen and architects. He combined the skills of mathematician and expert architectural draughtsman and, with his knowledge of practical craftsmanship, rationalized the theory and practice of building and its individual skills. He spent the first years of the nineteenth century practising as an architect in Scotland but he later returned to publishing and contributed drawings for the plates in several of his own works as well as those mentioned previously. His *Architectural Dictionary* of 1819 included plates on drawing instruments, and his *Practical Builder & Workman's Companion* of 1823 contained plates which detailed the 'centrolinead', which he claimed as his invention in 1814. This instrument was designed to overcome the problems of drawing in perspective to remote vanishing points [144].

Nineteenth-century text-books

From the middle of the nineteenth century onwards the needs of the expanding engineering professions were met by small specialist text-books on mathematical instruments, which included drawing instruments. The first of these was by F. W. Simms, an engineer whose *Treatise on Principal Mathematical Instruments* was published in 1834. This was followed by J. F. Heather's *Mathematical Instruments* (first published in 1849; reissued in 1851); a sixteenth edition appeared in 1906. The first deals only with instruments used by a land-surveyor; the latter covers drawing instruments in the first ten pages, then concentrates on the mathematics and instruments required for surveying, optics and astronomy.

The main reference work for English instruments of this period, during which many drawing instruments became standardized and manufactured in larger quantities, is W. F. Stanley's treatise *Mathematical Drawing Instruments*, which was first published privately by the author in 1866, eleven years after he founded his own firm of instrument makers in 1853. This small book is by far the most comprehensive written at the time, with a practical appraisal of every drawing instrument then available, including those made by his firm. Each category of instrument is dealt with in detail, with a clear explanation of how it can be used. Stanley, like George Adams the Elder, was an innovative technician and often improved on previous designs. With other nineteenth-century makers like Haff, Riefler and later Richter, he was amongst those whose contribution to instrument making has benefited all technical draughtsmen. *Mathematical Drawing Instruments* was reissued in 1868 and regularly after that until 1888, with a final edition in

[31] Engraved Plate I dated 1811 by John Farey from Rees's *Cyclopaedia or Dictionary of Arts and Sciences* (1808–19). Note: (2) a new flat version of triangular compasses for taking distances of three widely spaced points, and (3) beam compass fittings. *Science Museum Library, London.*

OVERLEAF
[32] Engraved Plate CCXXXVII by John Farey from David Brewster's *Edinburgh Encyclopaedia* (1808–30). This plate illustrates more sophisticated patterns than [31]. Note (7) the folding pillar compasses, (8) the turn-about compasses, (12) a double bar parallel rule, (13) a beam compass and fittings, (14) Farey's device for striking curves of high radius, (15–17) a scale rule with offsets shown together with Farey's bevel, (19) a drawing board set up with Farey's tee-square and bevel shown with drawing pins holding down the drawing paper, (20–22) Farey's device for dividing circles, (23) Mr Donkin's steel pen, (24) a ruling pen with split handle for easy cleaning. *Science Museum Library, London.*

[33] Engraved Plate CCXXXVIII by John Farey from the *Edinburgh Encyclopaedia* (1808–30), which includes specialist drawing instruments: (1) elliptical trammel and drawing arm, (2–4) Farey's own ellipsograph in plan, section and detail, (5) and (6) Farey's perspective delineator, (7) Farey's Pentegraph with details, (11) and (12) Suardi's geometrical pen designed *c.* 1750, which produced a thousand varieties of ornamental figures in geometrical proportion. *Science Museum Library, London.*

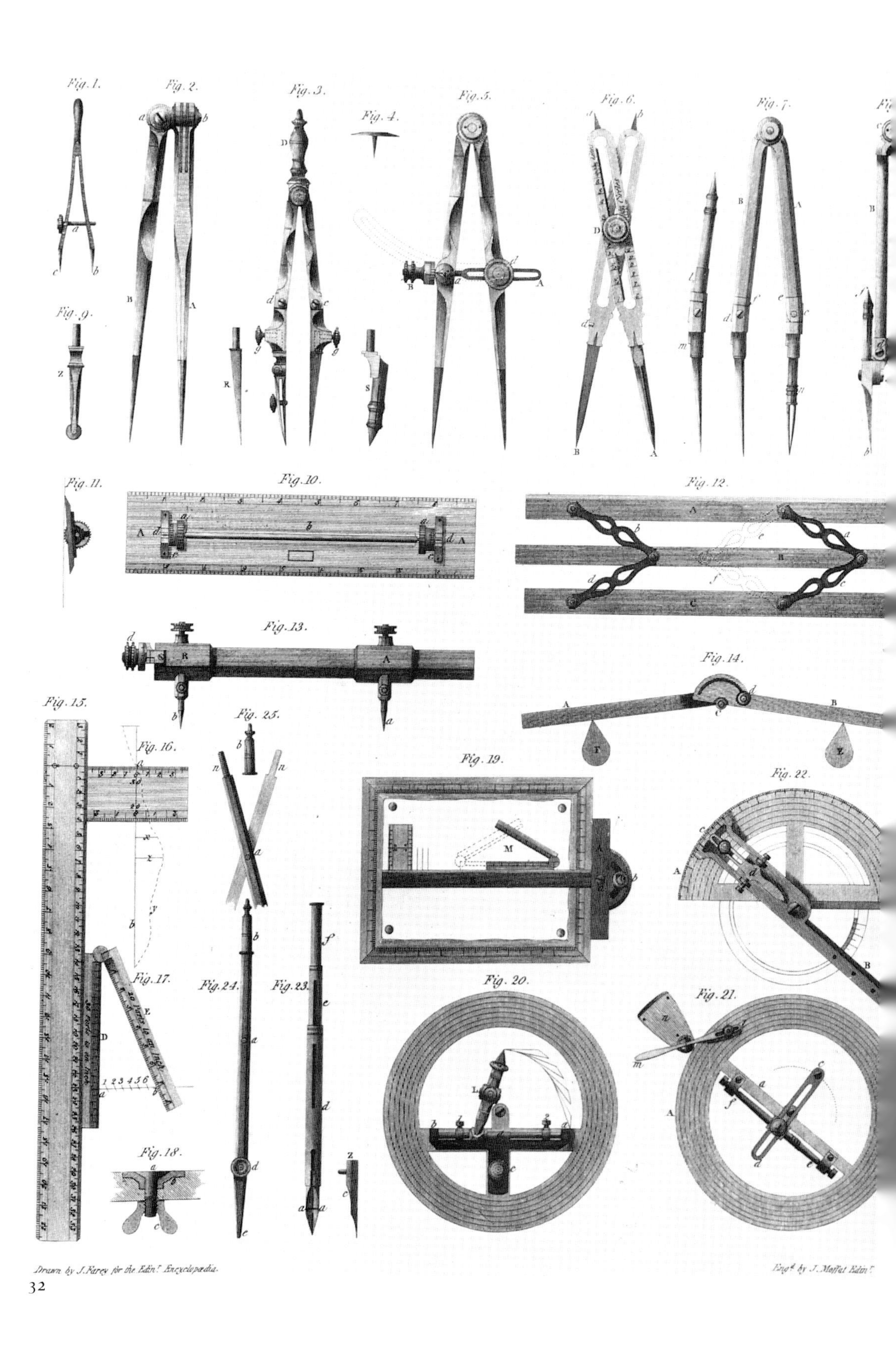
Fig. 1.
Fig. 2.
Fig. 3.
Fig. 4.
Fig. 5.
Fig. 6.
Fig. 7.
Fig. 9.
Fig. 10.
Fig. 11.
Fig. 12.
Fig. 13.
Fig. 14.
Fig. 15.
Fig. 16.
Fig. 17.
Fig. 18.
Fig. 19.
Fig. 20.
Fig. 21.
Fig. 22.
Fig. 23.
Fig. 24.
Fig. 25.
Drawn by J. Farey for the Edinr. Encyclopædia.
Engd. by J. Moffat Edinr.

32

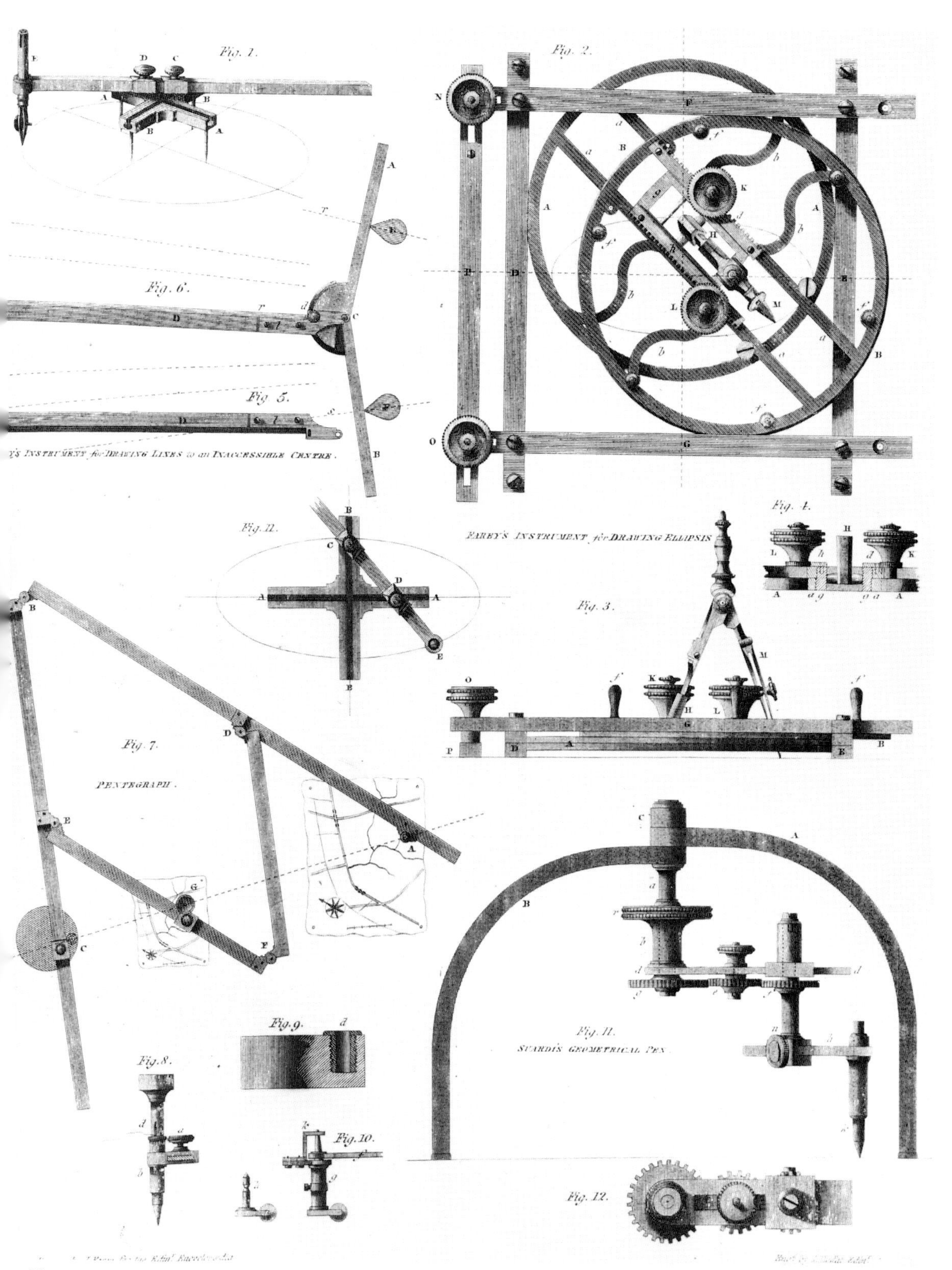
Fig. 1.
Fig. 2.
Fig. 6.
Fig. 5.
'S INSTRUMENT for DRAWING LINES to an INACCESSIBLE CENTRE.
Fig. 11.
FAREY'S INSTRUMENT for DRAWING ELLIPSIS
Fig. 4.
Fig. 3.
Fig. 7.
PENTEGRAPH.
Fig. 9.
Fig. 8.
Fig. 11.
SUARDI'S GEOMETRICAL PEN.
Fig. 10.
Fig. 12.
33

1925, when much of it was out of date. Strangely, the original clear explanatory illustrations which ran throughout the text were seldom revised.

Twentieth-century text-books

Books dealing specifically with drawing instruments are rare in the twentieth century. We have to rely on manufacturers' catalogues such as those issued regularly until 1960 by the firm of W. F. Stanley & Co. These together with smaller catalogues by such makers as W. H. Harling of Moorgate, J. Halden & Co and A. G. Thornton, both of Manchester, and J. H. Steward of the Strand are useful for verifying changes in patterns or designs and checking the range of items available at any given date. For researching European makers similar catalogues issued by Haff, Riefler and Richter exist for Germany, by Kern for Switzerland and by Baraban for France.

There is also an excellent German work which traces the history of technology from Antiquity and includes new information on the chronology for the introduction of the various instruments used for drawing. This is *Die Technik der Vorzeit* by F. M. Feldhaus, first published in Leipzig in 1914. At the end of his life Feldhaus expanded the subject of the history of technical drawing in *Geschichte des technischen Zeichnens* which was published in 1953 and issued as a commemorative volume by a German manufacturer of drawing machines, F. Kuhlmann. Another important reference for the history of technical drawing was issued as a series of articles by Alois Nedoluha under the title *Kulturgeschichte des technischen Zeichnens*. The articles appeared in the Austrian journal *Blätter für Technikgeschichte* between 1957 and 1959.

More recently two important English books have appeared: P. J. Booker's *A History of Engineering Drawing* (1963) and *The Art of the Engineer* (1981) by K. Baynes and F. Pugh. These provide information and examples essential to an understanding of changing techniques and approaches to technical drawing, most of which have involved the use of drawing instruments. However, neither of these modern works gives any history of drawing instruments.

There has also been an increasing number of well-illustrated books on scientific instruments published since 1960, which include a few drawing instruments. Henri Michel's work *Les instruments des sciences dans l'art et l'histoire* (1966) has been available in R. E. W. and F. R. Maddison's English translation as *Scientific Instruments in Art and History* since 1967. Michel was a Belgian, whose personal collection of early scientific instruments forms part of a gift made to the Museum of the History of Science in Oxford by S. A. Billmeir in 1957. There are some remarkable drawing instruments amongst the many fine items.

A vital reference work for anyone seriously interested in the history of European instrument making is *Les instruments scientifiques aux XVII et XVIII siècles* by Maurice Daumas, written when he was principal of the Conservatoire Nationale des Arts et Métiers in Paris and published in 1953. It was translated into English by Dr Mary Holbrook in 1972 under the title *Scientific Instruments of the Seventeenth and Eighteenth Centuries*.

Lastly, there is Dr Gerard L'E. Turner's *Nineteenth-Century Scientific Instruments*, published in 1983, which includes a chapter on drawing instruments; and Anthony Turner's *Early Scientific Instruments, 1500–1800*, published in 1987.

Types of Instrument

3

Straight Lines

Styli

The essence of all geometrical drawing is an even line. A stylus – a blunt pointed instrument of horn, ivory, hardwood or metal – was used from Antiquity until the sixteenth century, for scoring lines on waxed tablets or parchment. The Romans are known to have used lead discs for scoring their margins, and styli for writing and, with the aid of a ruler, drawing straight lines. There are many examples of these styli in museums with Roman collections.

During the Middle Ages lead styli were used for scoring parchment and vellum, and eventually also paper when it was introduced into Europe during the fourteenth century. In early technical and architectural drawings the lines were scored first with a stylus and then lined in ink freehand using a quill pen.

There are medieval pens extant for use with ink which have four tapered grooves or flutes [35], a design which continues to appear into the seventeenth century [159]. Another pattern, known as a 'goat's foot' pen, was made with a single groove to the underside; this can be found still in cases after 1700, in the Bion pocket case, for example [168].

Early ruling pens

The Romans are known to have used a form of drawing pen from the first century AD onwards [34]. Similar pens were introduced in the Renaissance for drawing lines in ink against a ruler. These – the earliest forms of ruling pen to be used with ink – came in several patterns: in some a piece of metal was bent over; in others there were two separate blades, and a heavy sliding ring with which to adjust the thickness of the line drawn [36]. Sepia and ferro-gallic inks were used with these until 1600. Carbon ink became more common after 1600 and was used until 1900; waterproof inks were developed from 1790 by adding shellac.

During the sixteenth and seventeenth centuries various ruling pens were developed from Renaissance patterns, usually with a pair of blades in the shape of a leaf or a spade, but without the earlier ring adjustment [37]. These pens relied on the inflexibility of the metal used to retain the opening to give a constant line thickness [38]. This became essential once drawings were prepared to scale and of paramount importance once the thickness of each line formed a part of the syntax of drawing. Examples of these ruling pens can be seen in early instrument cases of *c.*1600 by Christoph Schissler (1530–1609) and by both Jacobus and Domenicus Lusuerg in cases *c.*1680–1710, also by Nicolas Bion (1652–1723), Michael Butterfield (1635–1624) and Chapotot the Elder (fl.1670–86) between 1680 and 1720. Bion illustrates a pen with the reverse end arranged as a crayon-holder in his Plate 9 [22]. This also shows an ink insert for compass together with a dotting-wheel insert. The earliest specialist pens are those provided with this wheel device; a few date to before 1600 but it is not until 1700 that they were commonly included in instrument cases [39A and 39B].

Eighteenth- and nineteenth-century ruling pens

Fron 1700 onwards ruling pens were made with twin steel 'chops' or blades which were adjusted to give the desired line thickness by a small hand-cut wing or butterfly form screw. The ink was applied with a dropper or feed or by using a quill pen. The best quality pens were always made with one blade hinged so that the inside of the pen could be cleaned easily, and this practice continues for the best ruling pens today. Ruling pens, or 'drawing pens' as they were called in the eighteenth century, were made in several patterns and sizes to give a range of line thicknesses; the holders were usually of brass or silver [40]. It became common practice to incorporate a pricker or protracting pin into the turned handle. This was in general used for copying (see Chapter 8) but it could also be used to take dimensions off scales or to mark the starting point and the termination point of each line drawn. The

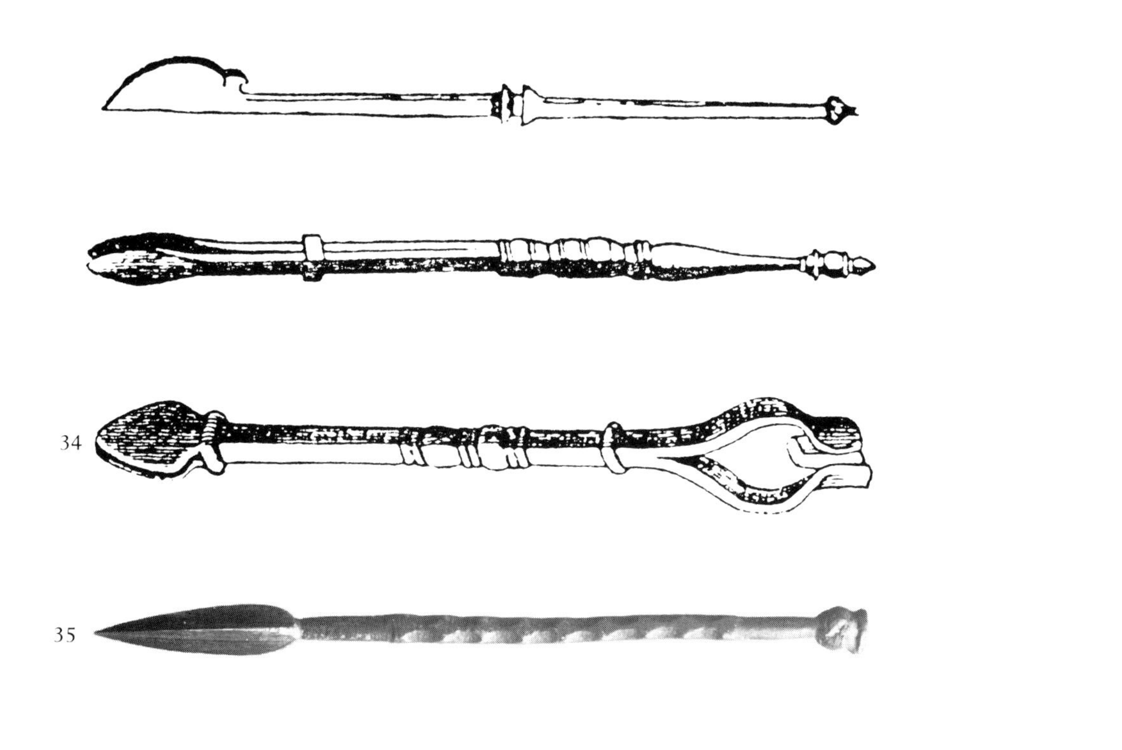

34

35

36

[34] Roman ruling pens. The simplest were made of lead bent over; others were of bronze with twin blades and a moveable ring to adjust the thickness of the lines drawn; some included a charcoal-stick holder at the other end. *Roman Collection, Museum, Bonn.*

[35] Medieval ruling pen of steel with four tapered grooves for ink; a decorated handle. English. Length 4 in (100 mm). 14th century. *Museum of London.*

[36] Ruling pen, known to be Dürer's, since it was found behind a skirting board in his house in Nuremberg; steel with a tapered handle and with twin blades adjusted by a heavy sliding ring to alter the thickness of lines drawn. *c.*1515. *Germanisches Nationalmuseum, Nuremberg.*

[37] Quill writing pen, various ruling pens and a penknife; some are steel, mostly brass-gilt. Designs show variations on those with folded blades, some twin leaf-shaped. German. 1580–1600. *Mathematisch-Physikalicher Salon, Zwinger, Dresden.*

[38] Five ruling pens: (II) with folded blade, (III) double-ended with hinged blade at one end, (IV) with crayon-holder at reverse end, (V) with pricker at reverse end, (VI) with tracer at reverse end, and hexagonal holder (I) for a pair of dividers, with sides engraved with scales. As shown in Plate XXIV from Jacob Leupold's *Theatrum arithmetico-geometricum*, of 1727 (1774 edn).

ruling pen could then be used to connect up the lines between the pricked holes. Some ruling pens were made with the reverse end arranged as a crayon-holder and these, together with double-ended ruling pens, appear to have been particularly popular in France [39A]. Ruling pens were further improved *c.*1800 with the introduction of fine milled thumb-screws, a point that can be useful when it comes to dating instrument cases.

Specialist drawing pens

By 1840 the range of specialist ruling pens had been extended to provide for specific needs of cartographers and railway and mechanical engineers. There were

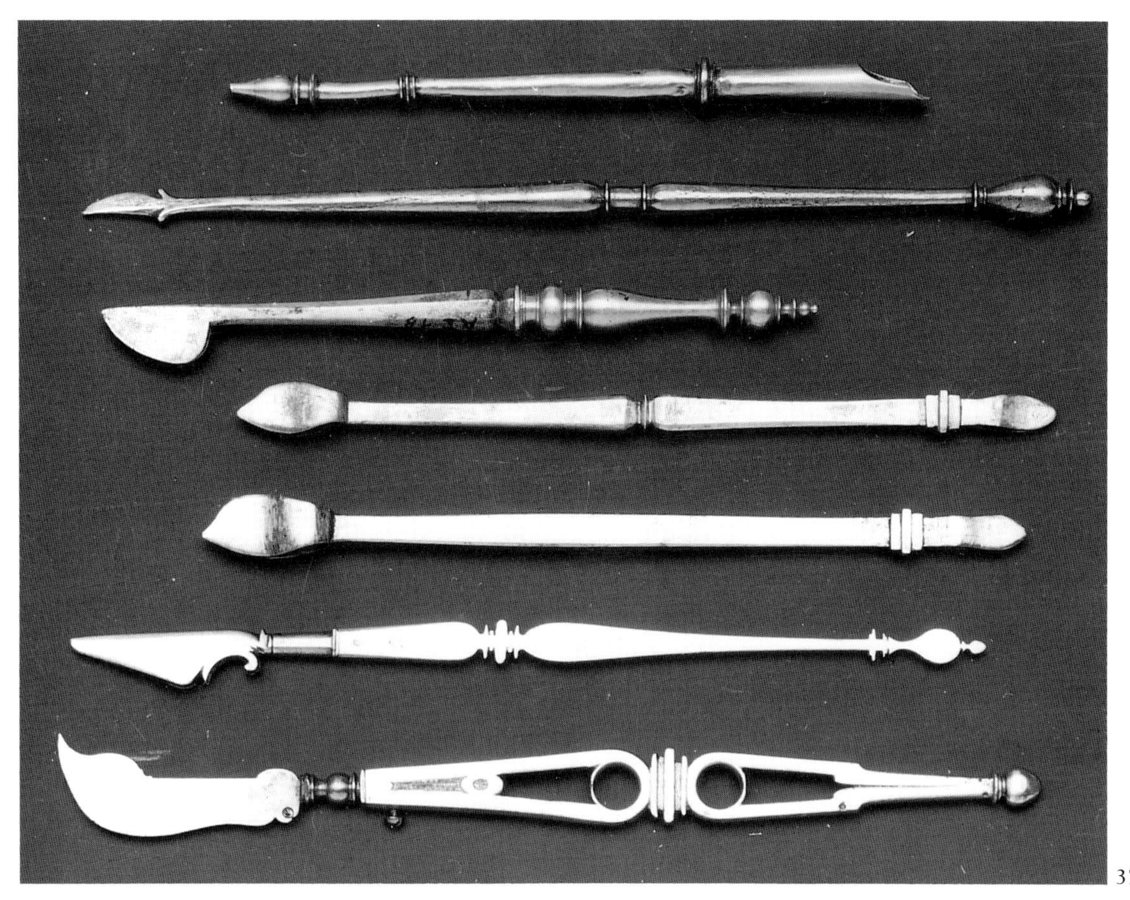

37

38

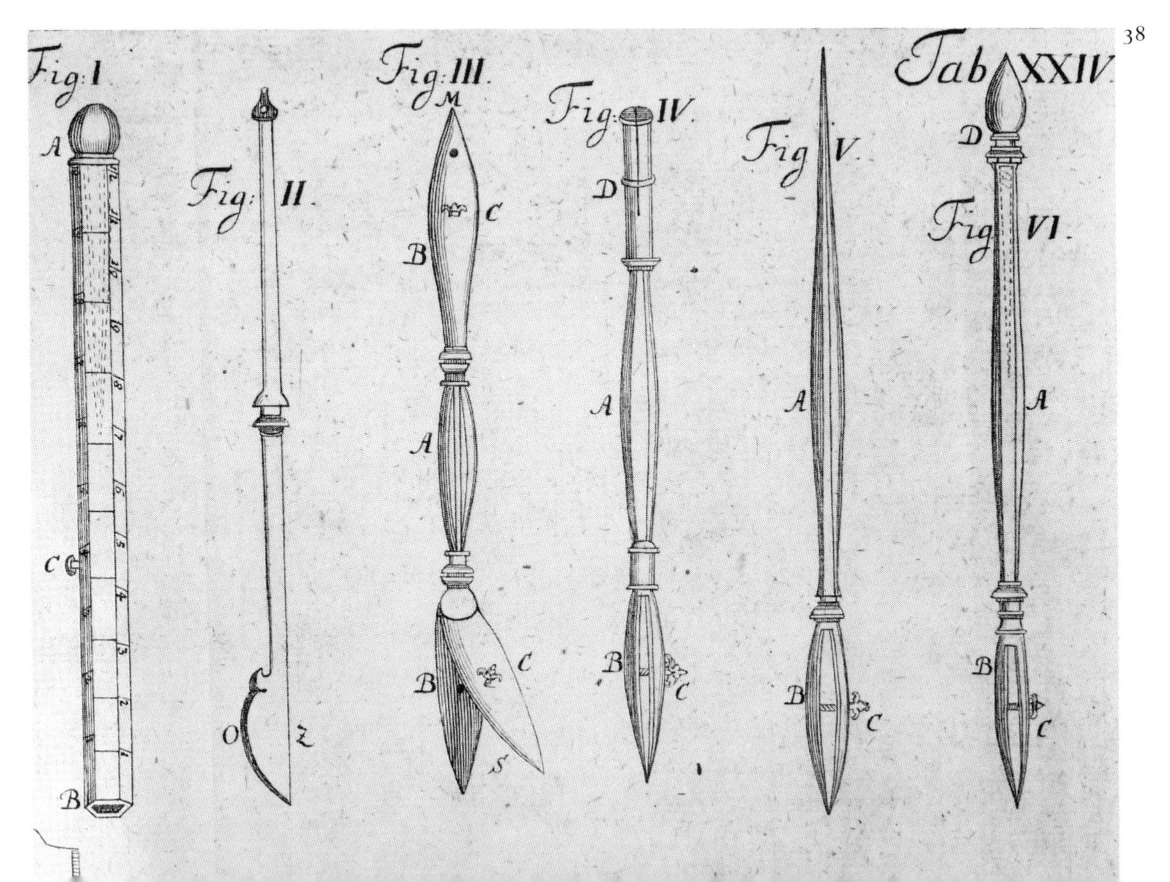

Fig:I
A
C
B
Fig: II.
O
Z
Fig:III.
M
C
B
A
B
C
S
Fig: IV.
D
A
B
C
Fig V.
A
B
C
Tab XXIV.
D
Fig VI.
A
B
C

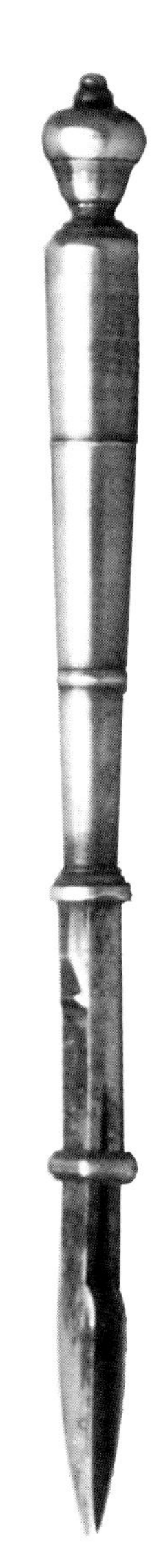

39A

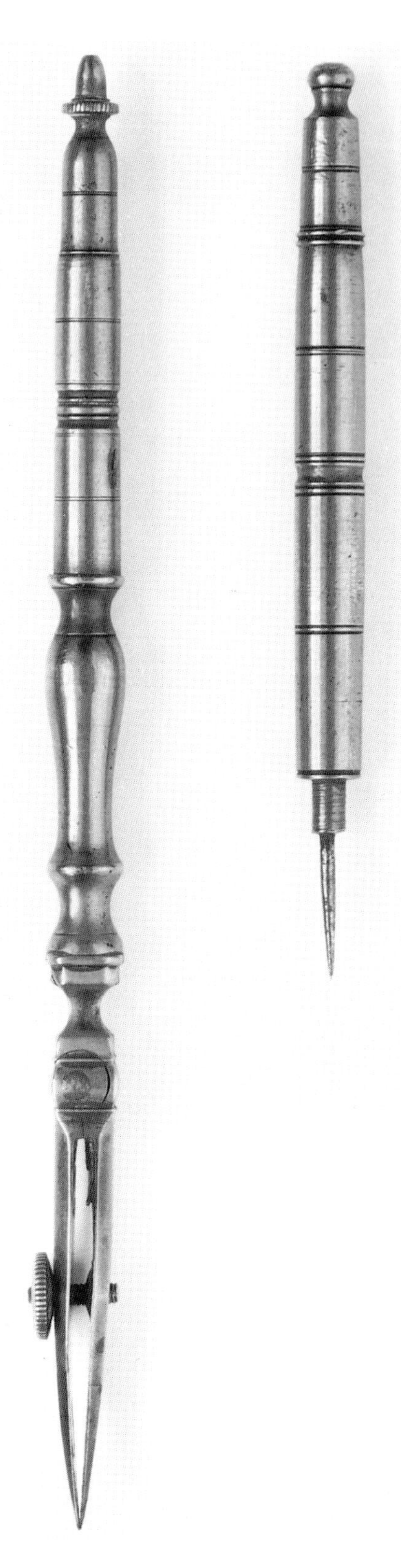

39B

[39A] Seventeenth-century German ruling pen with leaf-shaped steel blade and brass holder characteristic of period before 1730. *Museum fur Kunst und Gewerbe, Hamburg.*

[39B] Early-19th-century English brass ruling pen with finely turned handle and hinged steel blades which enable the pen to be cleaned easily. Length $4\frac{1}{2}$ in (115 mm). Separate pricker shown with cap removed.

[40] English ruling pens, those with hand-cut wing screws being 18th century. (*From top*) Ebony handle with brass mount and silver with turned handle, both with hinged blades; (*centre*) early-19th-century pen with plain ivory handle, turned finial, side inscribed ELLIOTT and a finely knurled thumb screw to adjust the blades; the two lowest in brass, with fixed blades and turned handles each containing a pricker or protracting pin. Length of each $5\frac{1}{2}$–6 in (140–150 mm). *Andrew Alpern Collection, New York.*

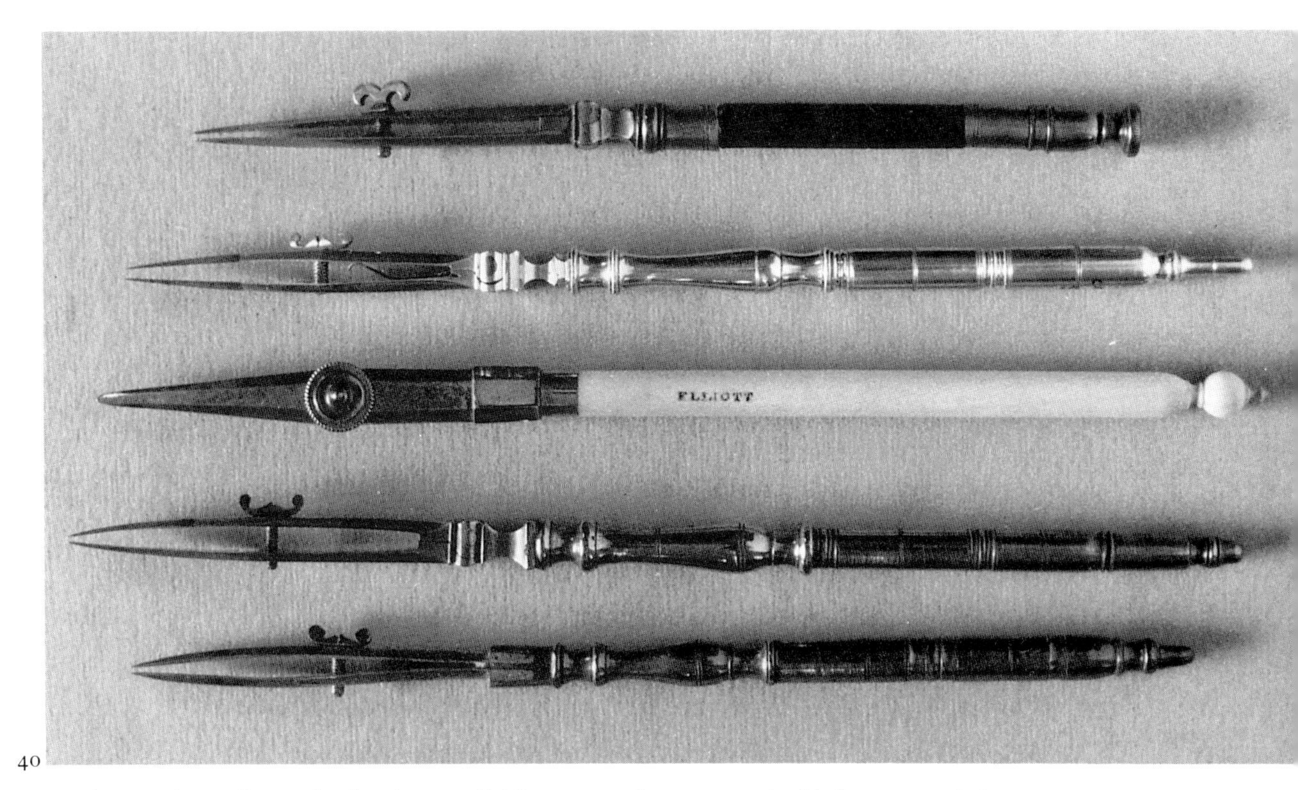

40

twin-line road or rail pens for drawing parallel lines, curved-blade pens for drawing against railway and other drawing curves, and thick and thin line or double thick line pens for drawing borders on formal drawings [41]. Dotting or wheel pens were also improved and provided with six to ten tiny alternative wheels to achieve the several combinations of dot-dash used by cartographers for maps, and by engineers and architects for delineating centre lines and objects hidden at a higher or lower level. These small wheels were stored either in the turned ivory head to the pen handle or in a separate ivory case. From 1860 to 1960 all the major drawing instrument manufacturers in Europe and Britain made these specialist pens. Widely used until the 1960s, they are still in demand by textile designers and the graphics profession, since they will easily take coloured inks and gouache colours. They are also used by print framers where the borders of mounts are executed by hand and the line thickness can be set by numbers inscribed on the fine screw. Today, Haff, Riefler and Kern, of the high quality European makers, produce a full range of specialist pens similar to the nineteenth-century patterns [42].

In the mid-nineteenth century ruling pens were made of steel with ivory or bone handles, often with turned finials of decorative design. Some had a square section next to the blades to provide better grip. By 1860 ivorene was used as a substitute for ivory, and plain handles of ebony – by 1900 ebonite – were also available. Similar patterns of ruling pens continued to be made, with gradual improvements in the steel used (eventually chrome-plated to avoid rusting) and handles that became simpler in design.

The problems of ruling pen maintenance deserve some mention for anyone who has not used a traditional ruling pen. The twin-blades require regular cleaning, using either a penknife or a razor-blade or fine emery paper to remove the dried ink. This is easier if one of the blades is hinged. The points to these blades become blunted when used constantly and have to be sharpened on either emery paper or on an oiled whetstone, a delicate operation if the pen is not to be irretrievably damaged. Before commencing work on an ink drawing, dozens of trial lines have to be drawn before the desired line thickness is achieved and then the pen has to be repeatedly refilled by means of a dropper or filler from a pot of waterproof Indian ink.

Technical pens

A form of fountain pen was illustrated by Daniel Schwenter in 1636, and in 1709 Bion included his version in his Plate 9. A Frenchman named Jolicar is described by F. M. Feldhaus as having invented a fountain-type

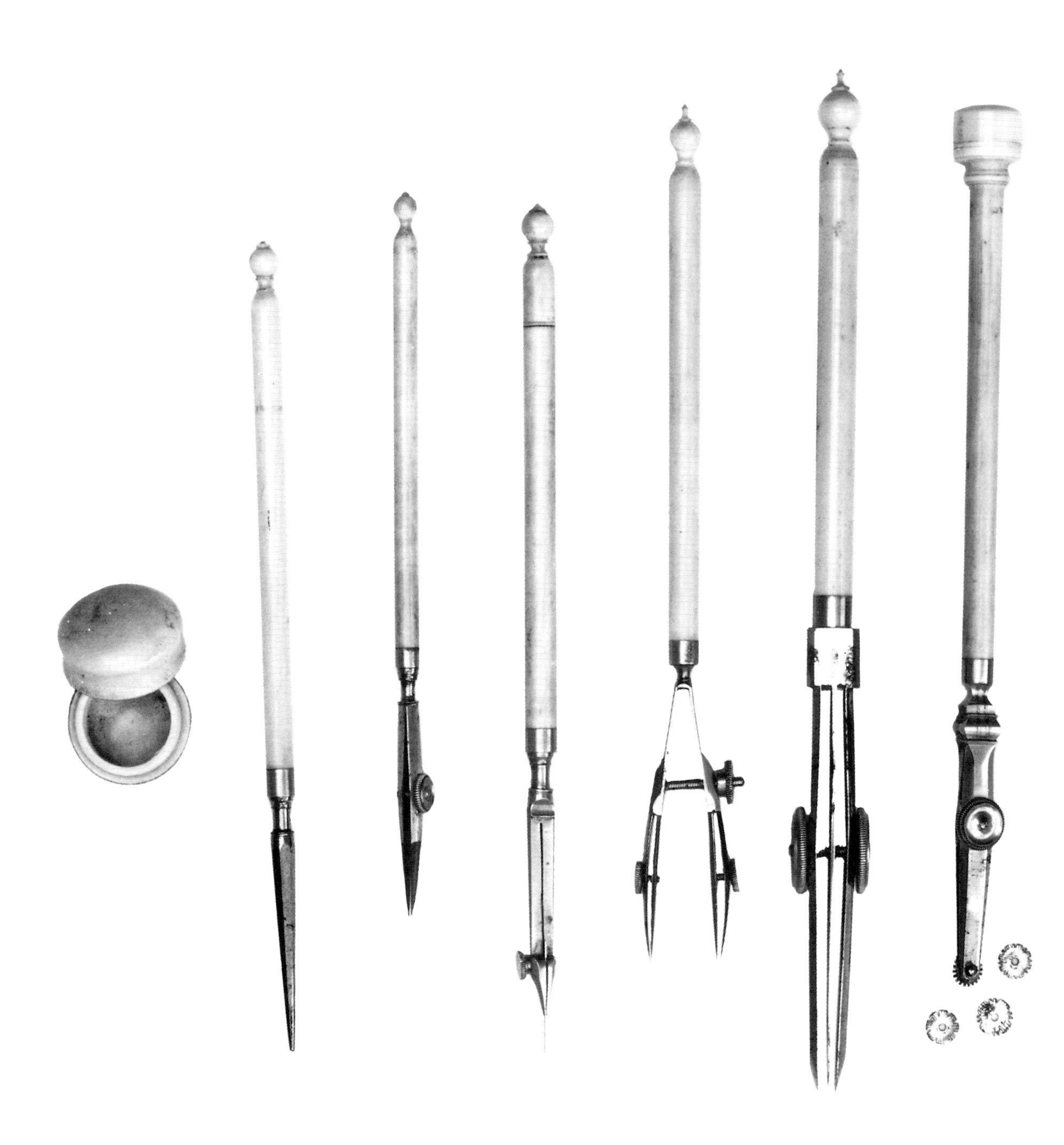

[41] Mid-19th century specialist drawing pens. (*Right to left*): Wheel-pen with spare wheels; thick border pen which draws twin lines; road or rail pen which draws parallel fine lines; a needle-point pricker; small fine-line ruling pen; electrum tracer; small pot, unscrewed which contained ox-gall (used to mix with drawing ink when used on greasy tracing paper). Length of each pen $5\frac{1}{2}$–6 in (140–150 mm). *RIBA Collection, London.*

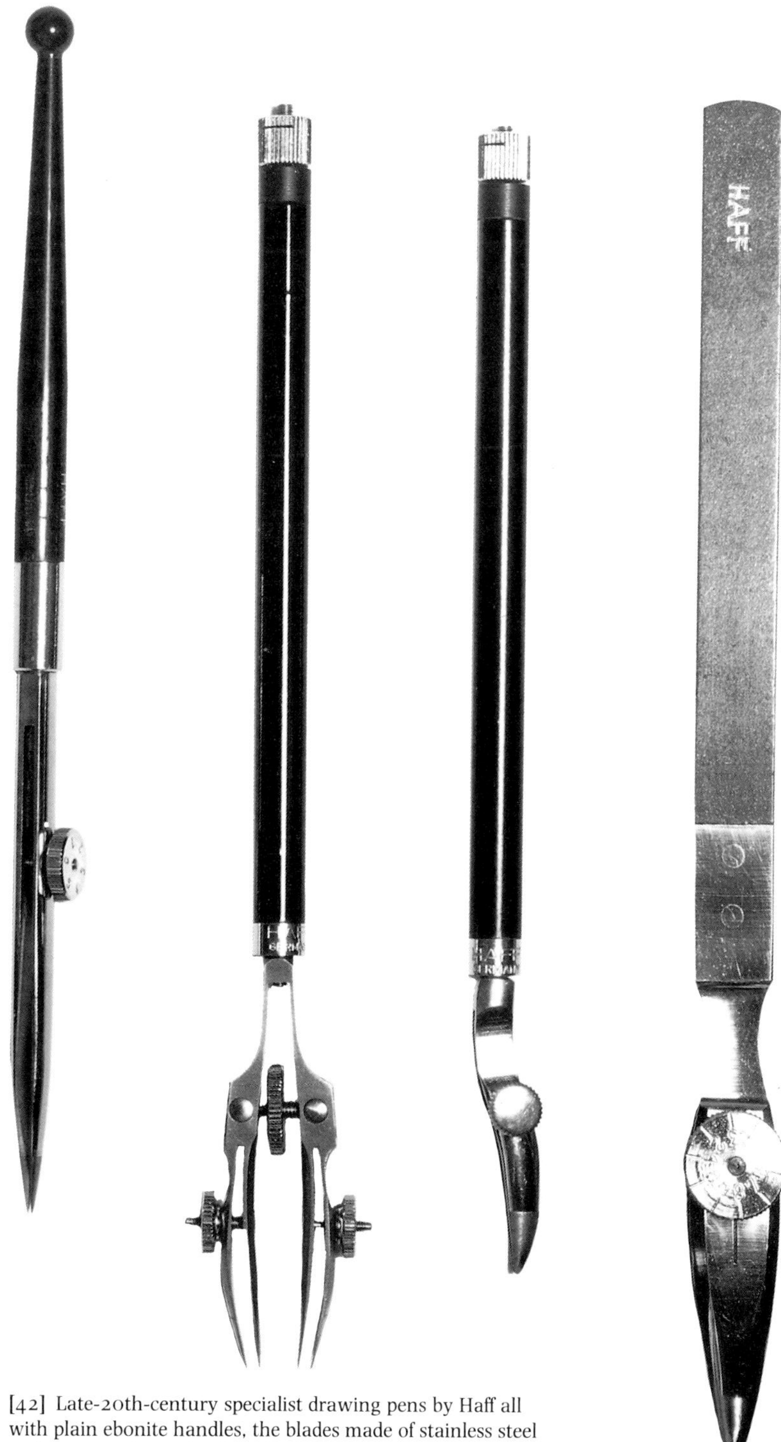

[42] Late-20th-century specialist drawing pens by Haff all with plain ebonite handles, the blades made of stainless steel with hardened tips. (*Right to left*): Broad pen with numbered settings on a thumb-screw from 0.25–1.20 mm thick; a curve line pen for lines 0.1–0.35 mm thick; a twin road or rail pen; a small fine-line pen for lines 0.2–0.8 mm thick. *c.*1980.

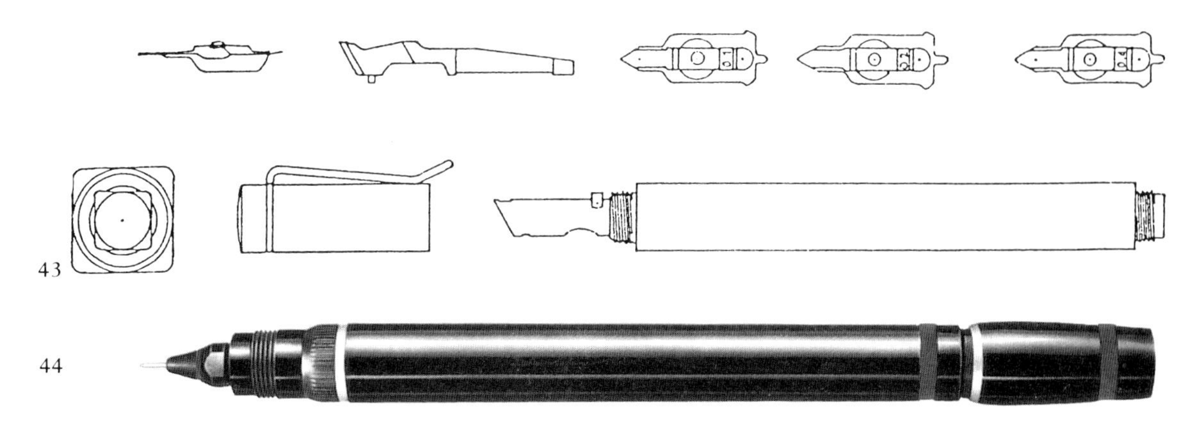

[43] The Graphos drawing pen, introduced in Germany in 1932. The first modern technical pen, it is capable of twelve different line thicknesses. Alternative size nibs with twin blades are clipped to a holder whose black plastic handle contains an ink reservoir and feed.

[44] The Rapidograph tubular-nib drawing pen, first introduced in 1952, the proto-type of several cylindrical-nib pens used with special free-flowing drawing inks. Various models were developed under the Rotring trademark. *Riepe Werke, West Germany.*

[VI] Presentation case of mathematical instruments by Domenicus Lusuerg containing an extensive range of over 30 items, which include a quadrant, a universal sundial, a set of Napier's rods in a case and a range of sectors. In addition to the main instruments intended for surveying and military purposes this set contains the following drawing instruments: (fitted to the lid) a pair of single-handed compasses; a ruling pen with a crayon-holder at the reverse end; a double-ended crayon-holder; a pair of medium size compasses with inserts for ink, crayon and wheel pen and a protractor; (in the case itself) a pair of dividers; a large pair of compasses with inserts; a pair of callipers; a medium pair of compasses with inserts for ink, crayon and wheel pen; a pair of spring bows with a wing-nut screw and an elliptical trammel which can be converted into a surveyor's cross, together with its drawing arm. Some items dated 1701 and signed 'Romae'. Case: 18 × 11¾ × 2¾ in (459 × 293 × 72 mm). *Science Museum, London.*

ruling pen around 1864. However, the technical pens or continuous ruling pens as we know them have only been in use since the 1930s. The original Graphos pen, invented by J. Kovac, was introduced in Germany as a manufactured product by Günther Wagner of Hanover and first appeared on sale in 1932. This pen is capable of a continuous line thickness in twelve variations. The handle contains an ink reservoir with a feed to the head of the pen to which different size nibs can be clipped; all are removable and easily cleaned. The Graphos pen is still used by many graphic artists and draughtsmen today since the fine lines produced are constant and in a wide range [43].

The Rapidograph, a tubular-nib drawing pen on the fountain-pen principle, known in German as *Tintenkuli*, was introduced by Wilhelm Riepe of Hamburg-Altona in 1952. It was soon improved to eliminate its plunger system and was marketed in nine different line thicknesses under the trade mark Rotring. The original pen used special inks with a tubular nib and was designed as a series of pens complete with nibs in a range of sizes [44]. The ink was transferred from a capsule reservoir by means of a thin metal wire through a plastic feed and the tubular metal tip onto the paper. The maintenance, or cleaning, of all these separate delicate parts has to be meticulous and is time-consuming. A traditional hinged ruling pen is easier to clean. By 1960 Rotring made separate ranges of pens for use with stencils and for free-hand calligraphy; in 1972 the 'micronorm' range was introduced to give metric line thickness essential for accuracy to retain relative scale when drawings are reduced by the micro-film process. The Isograph version of the technical pen, introduced by Rotring in 1977, was provided with a specially sealed cap to combat the problem of the drawing ink clogging and to obviate the constant shaking necessary to keep the ink flowing evenly. Special inks with non-clogging additive have become available from Staedtler and other firms since 1980.

Alternative versions of technical pens have appeared, made by the traditional German firms of pencil manufacturers – Staedtler with their Mars range in 1978 and Faber-Castell with their TG-1 system in 1982 [45] and by the Swiss instrument makers, Kern, with the Prontograph in 1979. All

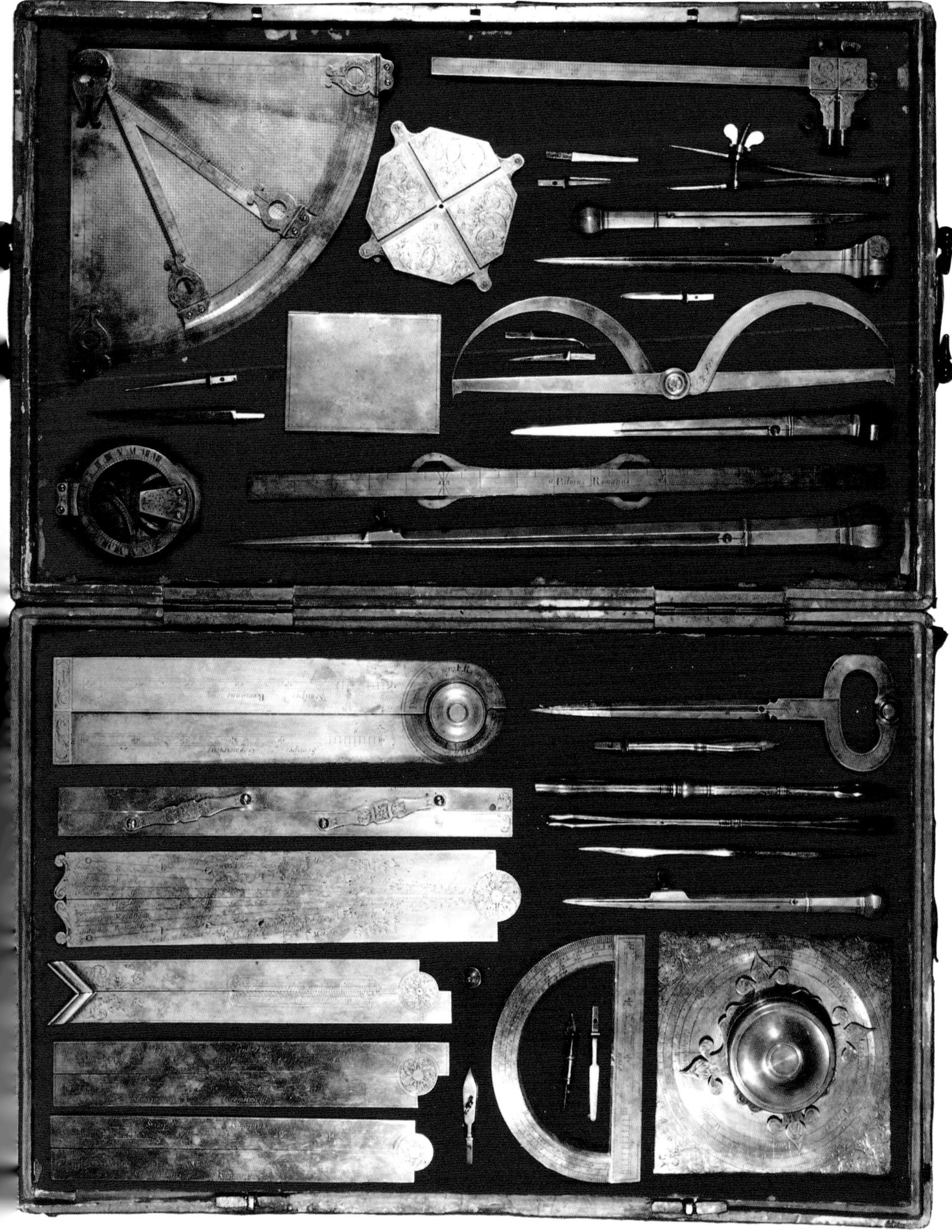

VI

100 90 80 70 60 50 40 30 20 10
Scalvino

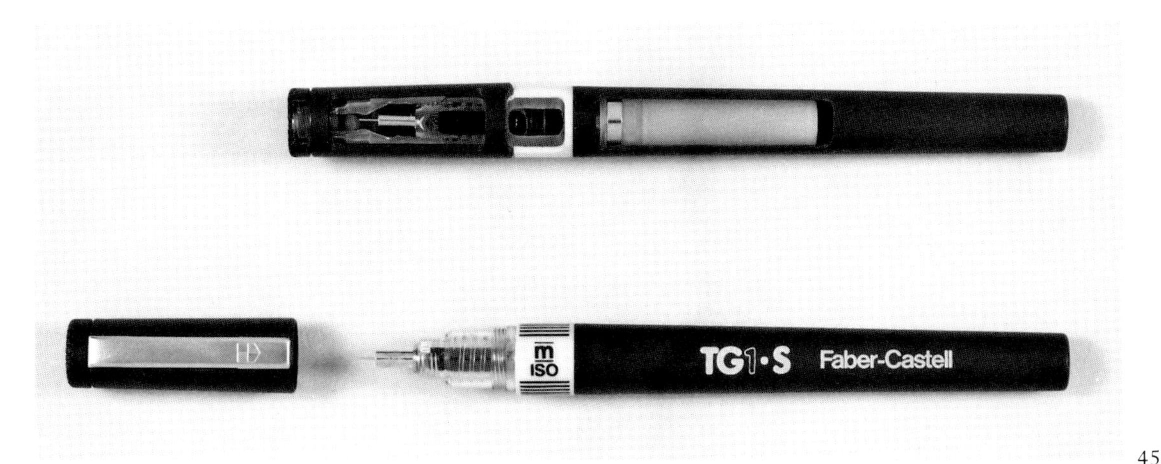

45

[VII] An Italian magazine case with a comprehensive set of brass instruments in a velvet lined tray, which includes 12 different inserts for the main pair of large compasses (see also [148]), an unusual pair of folding compasses and some Swiss pattern beam compass fittings. Among the instruments contained in the lid are a brass scale rule, two angles together with a brass sector and a protractor by 'Butterfield AParis', set squares and folding measure and an enamelled container. Made by Giovanni Cattaneo of the Brera Observatory, Milan, *c.*1850 for his brother the architect Luigi Cattaneo. *Alessandro Ubertazzi Collection, Milan.*

[45] TG-1 automatic technical drawing pen with tubular nib introduced by Faber-Castell in 1982. Its components are shown in a cut-away view: the helix, drawing cone, nib and cap. The latter has a humidifier unit built-in to prevent the ink clogging and two silicone balls which stop the moisture from coming into contact with the ink. Available with either a steel nib or jewel point, the latter for use with polyester drafting films.

claim the advantage of no clogging and are made in various sizes to give metric line thickness. Special tips made of tungsten carbide steel and ceramic are now made for some of these technical pens for use on the more abrasive surface of the new polyester drafting films which have been in use since 1980.

More recently special pens have been developed for use in the vertical computer-aided plotters which operate constantly at high speeds. Staedtler were the first to modify their technical pens, introducing the Mars Plot range in 1979, which uses a special quick-drying paste ink. These plotter pens are also provided with special tips to suit the various treated drawing papers suitable for use in the plotters.

Pencils

Graphite, a crystalline form of carbon, was discovered in Cumberland in the north west of England, and the first pits were in operation between 1540 and 1560. At the same time the Swiss naturalist Conrad Gesner illustrated a holder for a new writing substance in 1565 [46]. By 1610 graphite or blacklead, or 'plumbago' as it was first called, was being sold in London. The chief source was at the Borrowdale pits opened in 1664. In 1683 Sir John Pettus, Deputy Governor of Mines, described this graphite as being set into deal or cedar cases and sold as 'dry pencils' – until the seventeenth century, the word 'pencil' was used to denote a fine paint-brush, hence early encased graphite rods used for drawing were first described as 'dry pencils'. The word 'lead' is a misnomer and originates from the much earlier use of a lead stylus as a scoring instrument which left a black or grey mark on the drawing surface. With the introduction of true black graphite the term 'lead' was used and has continued so until today. (Similarly in German, the word for the metal lead *Blei* is used in the word for pencil *Bleistift*; in French lead is *mine de plomb* and pencil *crayon à mine de plomb*.)

In Germany one of the earliest pencil makers known was Hans Baumann of Nuremberg (c.1659). In the same city, in 1662, a carpenter named Staedtler is recorded as having applied for a permit to make pencils of graphite sticks glued between two halves of wood. Pencil holders made of brass, silver or gilt, often to elaborate Baroque designs [47] appeared at this time. There is a record of a gold-plated pencil holder dating to 1636 in which the lead was pushed out by means of a compression spring – perhaps the first propelling pencil. Double-ended holders were common in instrument cases by 1700 and are found particularly in many French cases. Wider ones had been made earlier

De figuris lapidum, &c.

stitij puto, quod aliquos Stimmi Anglicum vocare audio) genere, in mucronem derasi, in manubrium ligneum inserto.

L. Lateres e luto finguntur & coquunt, ad ædificiorum parietes, pauimenta, caminos: item ad furnos, aliosq; vsus.

46

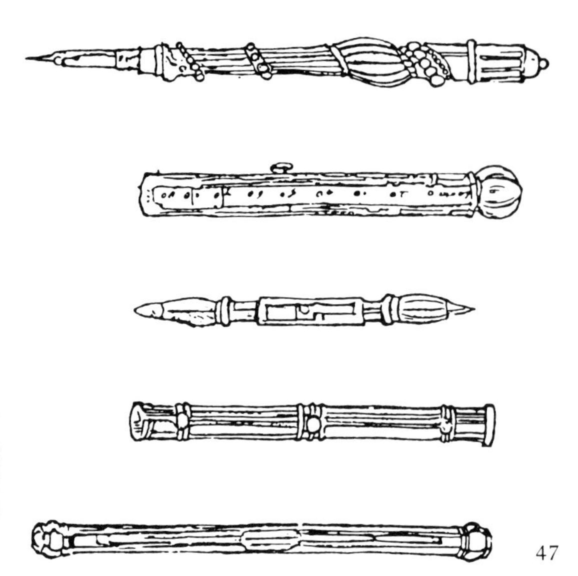

47

[46] Earliest illustration of a pencil, a wood-encased graphite stick, provided with moveable metal holder. Woodcut from Conrad Gesner's *De omni rerum fossilium genere* (Zurich, 1565).

[47] Silver or brass holders for graphite or crayon for writing and drawing dating to the 17th century.

[48] Architects' propelling pencils from A. W. Faber's catalogue dated 1896, designed to take their standard thick leads.

[49] English propelling pencils with ebonite handles, also designed to take Faber's size 'W' leads, for use when sketching or for technical drawing. 5 in and 4 in (125 and 100 mm). *c.*1900. *Private collection.*

to take the thicker wax crayons or charcoal sticks as illustrated by Giovanni Pomodoro in 1599, and by Nicolas Bion in his Plate 9 in 1709.

The well-known pencil firm of Faber-Castell was founded near Nuremberg in 1761 by Kaspar Faber, a cabinet maker, to produce graphite rods encased in wood, and this specialized skill was developed by several generations of his family. In 1840 the firm's pencils began to be sold marked 'A. W. Faber', in 1851 the firm introduced hexagonal pencils in uniform length and twelve grades of density; pencil holders to take their standard refill leads were introduced *c.*1867, and propelling pencils designed for use by architects and draughtsmen were marketed to various designs between 1870 and 1900 [48].

In Britain during the eighteenth century very small, thin – 1/8 in (3 mm) diameter – cedar-encased graphite rods were first made for use in the pencil inserts which fitted into compasses. Slim drawing pencils, usually set into silver or brass mounts, were also provided in most pocket instrument cases. The mounts were shaped for use as ink feeders or as blunt tracer points. In France, when supplies were cut off during the Revolution, the French chemist N. J. Conté sought a substitute for graphite. He invented a process, patented in 1795, in which small amounts of graphite were combined with clay and fired in a kiln; the more clay used the harder the lead became. It was now possible to establish a range for hardness of pencils. In 1830 the *Edinburgh Encyclopaedia* included an entry on pencils which describes them as being available in standard grades such as '2H for engineers; H for architects; B for shading', and the reader is advised to keep them sharp with the knife usually provided in instrument cases, although for fine drawing turning the lead in fine emery paper is recommended.

Emery powder was traditionally used from 1600 for erasing ink lines as an alternative to a penknife, and bread-crumbs were used to remove pencil lines. Rubber or gum-elastic, introduced from America *c.*1535, had since the seventeenth century only been used for its waterproof properties, in such items as boots, leggings and sheets, and the first use of India-rubber as an eraser occurred rather later than is generally thought. The instrument maker Edward Nairne (1726–1806) is credited with realizing that this material had a potential use for draughtsmen around 1788.

During the nineteenth century the pencil became a popular writing and drawing instrument, although rather expensive since supplies of graphite from the

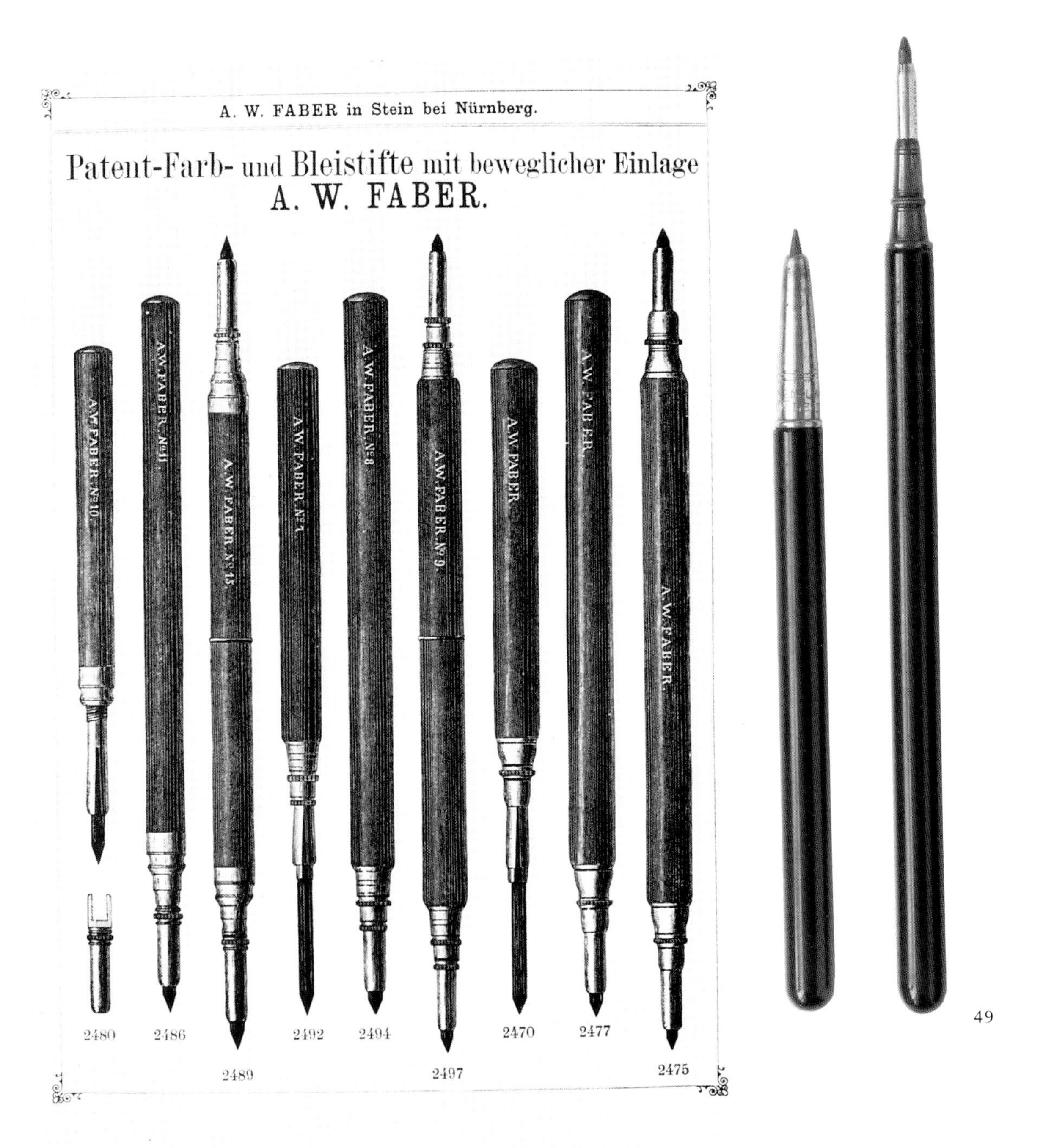

49

48

Cumberland mines were in short supply. With the introduction of clay into pencils prices came down and Britain adopted standard grades. Pencils were then made in sixteen different grades from 6B to 9H: B to signify black, F for firm and H for hard. Manufacturers used trade-names – Wolf's 'Royal Sovereign', Rowney's 'Victoria' and 'Imperial Master' – names all reminiscent of the Victorian era.

Propelling pencils for non-specialist use had been made under patent from 1822 by Mordan & Co to a variety of designs but mostly for fine leads. By the late nineteenth century Archbutt of Lambeth included a version suitable for drawing in an instrument case *c.*1865, and by 1900 British propelling-pencil holders, which took the thick drawing leads made by A. W. Faber, were available for draughtsmen [49].

Technical pencils

There was little change in the nature of drawing pencils in the first half of this century, and traditional cedarwood pencils are still made by the principal manufacturers in a wide range of grades. The main innovation for technical draughtsmen in that period was the introduction of what is now called the 'clutch pencil' or 'drop-action pencil'. In this a 2 mm or 3 mm lead is held by a spring which can be released by pressing the cap at the head of the pencil holder. Clutch pencils were marketed from the 1940s onwards by several firms who issued them with holders in their house colours (green for Faber-Castell; Blue for Staedtler; black for Caran D'Ache, and so on). Special lead sharpeners were necessary for these pencils, which varied from simple pocket versions to elaborate table-mounted rotating models. A block of emery paper proved the cheap and easy method of sharpening them but was also rather messy.

The most recent development in special drawing pencils is a plastic 'polymer' combined with graphite to produce very fine leads, only 0.3, 0.5, 0.7 and 0.9 mm thick. Originally developed by Faber-Castell in the 1950s [50] this process was soon taken over by a Japanese firm, now known as Pentel, who specialize in a range of fine leads supplied for small automatic-feed clutch pencils. There are several versions available, all of which are made with leads in metric thickness to correspond to the ink line thickness produced by technical pens. These fine-line pencils do not require sharpening and are suitable for use on tracing paper and polyester drafting film.

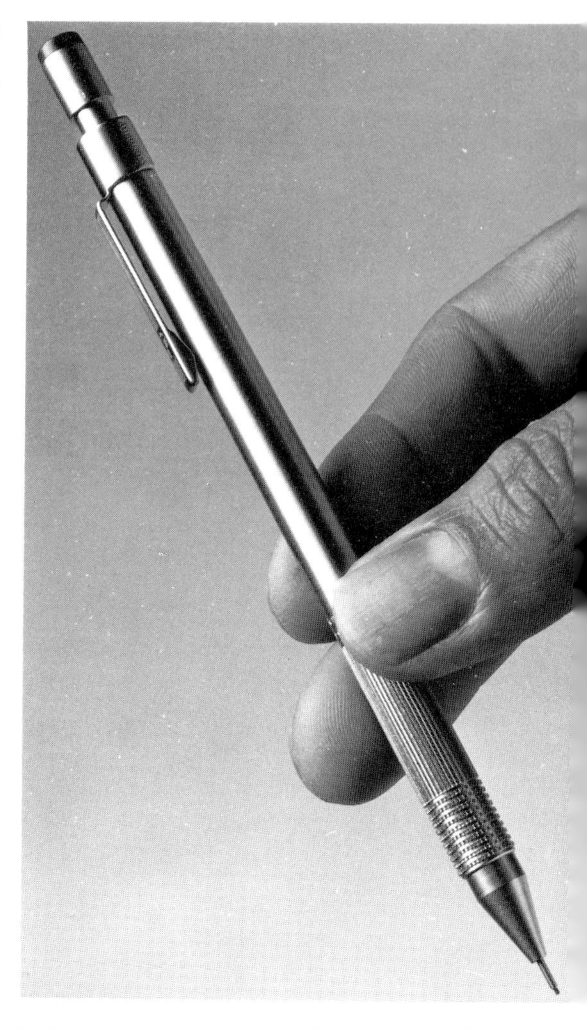

[50] Automatic technical pencil for fine-line leads by Faber-Castell, *c.*1980. First introduced in the 1960s, the latest model is known commercially as the 'TK-matic'.

4

Circles and Dividing

Compasses and dividers

From the earliest times circles could be set out with a peg or stick and piece of cord or gut, as a gardener still sets them out today. Compasses as a means of delineating circles have been known and used as tools since Egyptian times, and the Greeks ascribed their invention to the mythological Cretan Talos, son of Pedrix, the nephew of Daedalus. The Romans used dividers made of iron or bronze, and examples can be seen in some museums with Roman collections [51]. The earliest Roman compasses were very basic having a pair of metal legs held together at the head with a pin or rivet; their use can be traced back to the sixth century BC. The examples in the set of Roman instruments found at Pompeii are of three sizes, two with a riveted joint and the smallest fitted with a cottered hinge pin [10].

Of all the drawing instruments, drawing compasses appear in the widest variety of forms, designed to suit many specialized purposes. From 700 to 1400 AD compasses were used by masons and carpenters as essential tools in the form of forged iron plain or wing-compasses. Small compasses were employed in the preparation of illuminated manuscripts in the monasteries, and in engineering and architectural drawings; the drawings of Villard de Honnecourt, prepared between 1225 and 1250, show use of compasses provided with a scoring point.

During the sixteenth century a rapid improvement in the design and manufacture of compasses took place in Augsburg and Nuremberg. By 1600 their compass-smiths were producing what were then described as 'hand-compasses, hair-compasses, beam-compasses, and bar-compasses'. Elaborate versions with either a wing arc or a horizontal bar to control the setting of the opening of the legs were made in all sizes, including giant versions 14–18 in (360–460 mm) high. Some of the giant sizes were used for setting out full size details for the stonework or carpentry in cathedral drawing offices. Compasses dating up to 1600 are now highly prized collectors' items since many were decorated with either engraved motifs or finely chiselled with mouldings, combining their prime practical function with that of a decorative object [I and 52]. Simpler, less ornate examples of compasses also survive, made for specific trade purposes such as clock making, jewellery and other metal-working trades.

Compasses were first provided with interchangeable legs or an insert for a crayon-holder or ink point *c.*1550, judging from an example that was in the collection of the Mathematisch-Physikalischer Salon in Dresden until 1939. From the mid-sixteenth century onwards it is essential to differentiate between drawing compasses and *plain compasses* (later known as 'dividers') which were intended solely for use in taking and transferring measurements. Drawing compasses always include provision for a pencil or ink point and should never be confused with dividers, which have permanent steel points. Dividers were provided separately in most sets after the mid-sixteenth century and are discussed in more detail later.

The development of the various types of compasses and the introduction of new patterns can best be traced by reference to the plates in historical treatises (see Chapter 2) and makers' catalogues. Giovanni Pomodoro in 1599 and in 1709 Nicholas Bion both show several versions including some for military and marine use; Bion adds his own 'German' compasses [21], a pattern which proved very popular in France during the eighteenth century. These can be recognized easily since the legs curve like a jockey's. By 1727 Jacob Leupold illustrates a wide range of compasses, with details of the new joints and inserts then available in Germany [53]. During the 1790s both George Adams the Younger (1750–95) [29] and John Barrow [30] show similar details of small bows, which were already common in England. Adams's Plate I was revised by W. & S. Jones and re-issued in their name in 1823 to include additional items, among them tubular turnabout compasses and folding pillar compasses [54]. In 1830 John Farey (1791–1851) also features the new specialized compasses, including beam, spring bow, medium bow, pillar and tubular turnabout compasses [33].

The numerous types of compasses available by the mid-nineteenth century are recorded in W.F. Stanley's (1829–1909) treatise of 1866, which also gives details of the improved compass joints: the sector joint which supplanted the traditional English long joint to the head and the improved sleeve joint for inserts. At this time, too, needle-points to compasses and dividers were introduced to avoid blunt or damaged points scarring scales or perforating drawings. Sets of spring bows, medium bows, Swiss or pump compasses, folding and pocket compasses and beam compasses of several designs were now part of a range which remained practically unchanged in England until 1960.

In Europe new designs for compasses were introduced by Riefler with their 'round pattern' patented in 1877 [55] and by Richter with his 'flat pattern' in 1892, and similar designs were made by other firms like Kern once these patents expired [56A].

The most recent innovation in the design of compasses is quick-set compasses introduced by both Haff and Riefler by 1960. These are made in versions using either a wing-arc or a horizontal screw to effect the quick and precise setting of the opening. Both these designs have their origins in the sixteenth century. They are now available in several sizes in nickel-plated or chrome-plated brass. Staedtler and Faber-Castell both sell cheaper compasses made of electro-plated nickel on brass with injection-moulded nylon joints. However, high quality spring bows, pump compasses,

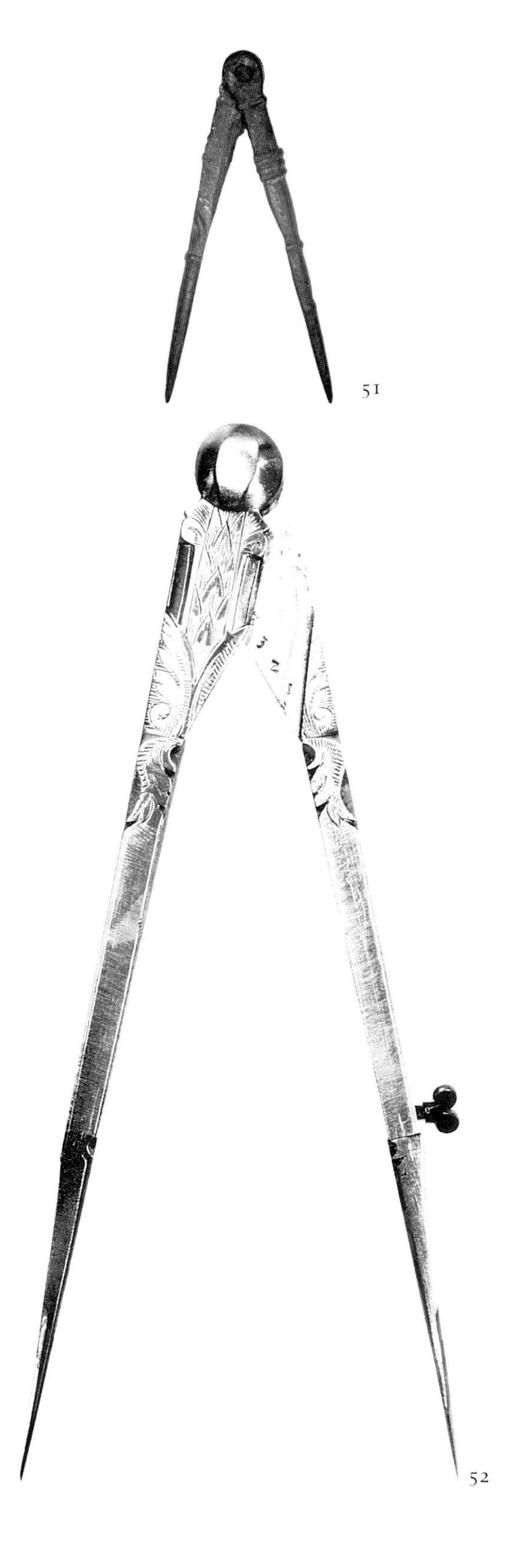
51

52

[51] Small pair of Roman dividers typical of many to be seen in museums with Roman collections, usually made of forged iron or cast brass, sometimes with decoration to the long joint and to the set-backs where the size of the legs are reduced. Height 2 in (51 mm). *Corinium Museum, Cirencester.*

[52] Pair of compasses with ball-joint of brass-gilt with some foliate engraved decoration and wing-nut to adjust the joint for the insert. Height 8¾ in (196 mm). *c.*1580. *Mathematisch-Physikalischer Salon, Zwinger, Dresden.*

[53] Early-18th-century German compasses and dividers. Fig. V shows clearly a pair of compasses with flat joint with wheel, crayon and ink inserts and the construction of the removable divider point. Similar inserts are also shown for the wing-compass in fig. X. Pl. xx from Jacob Leupold's *Theatrum arithmetico-geometricum* of 1727 (1774 edn).

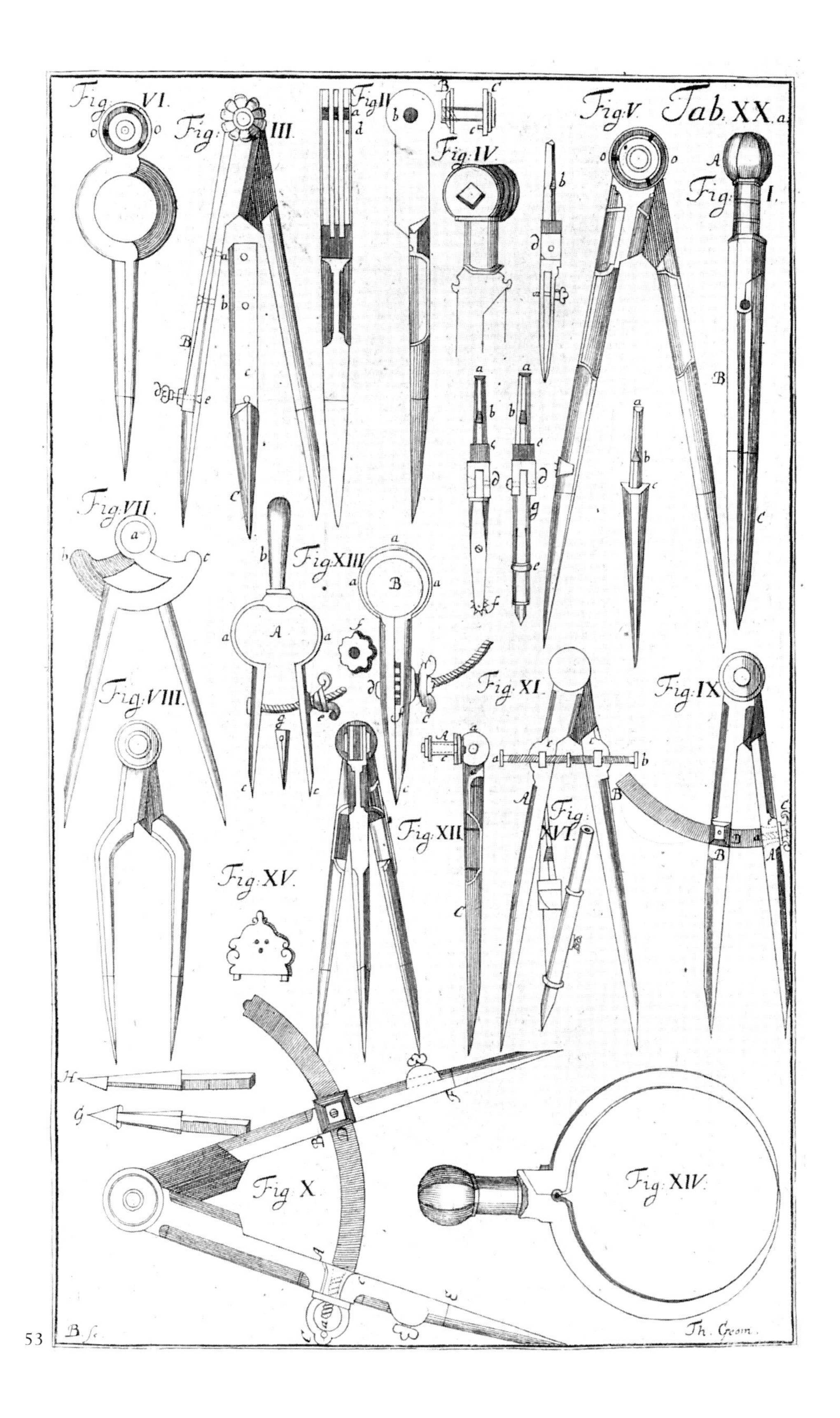
Tab. XX. a
Fig. I
Fig. II
Fig. III
Fig. IV
Fig. V
Fig. VI
Fig. VII
Fig. VIII
Fig. IX
Fig. X
Fig. XI
Fig. XII
Fig. XIII
Fig. XIV
Fig. XV
Fig. XVI
B. sc.
Th. Geom.

53

54

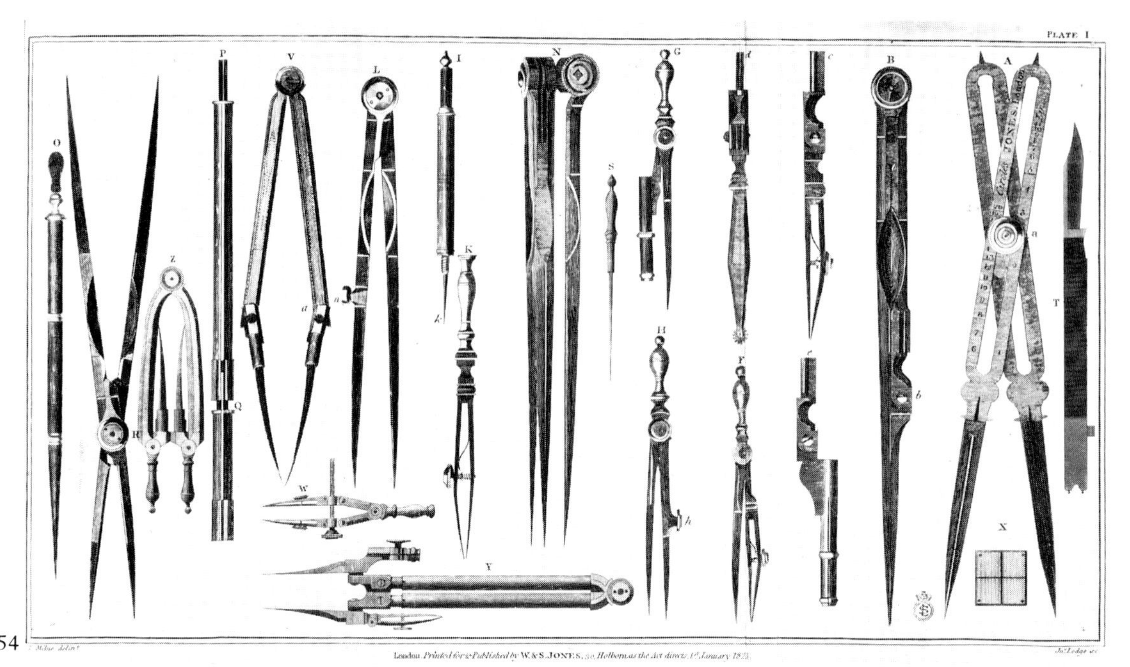

[54] Engraved Plate I from the 1823 revised edition of George Adams the Younger's *Geometrical and Graphical Essays* issued by W. & S. Jones. Note the addition of (W) small bows with screw, (X) trammel, (Y) tubular reversible compasses and (Z) folding pillar compasses. The name 'Adams' has been erased from the proportional compasses (A) and 'W. & S. Jones' substituted. *Science Museum Library, London.*

[55] Round system compasses with simplified slip-on points without screws, patented by Sigmund Riefler in 1877. The milled handle became standard for round and flat pattern compasses. *Clemens Riefler, Nesselwang, West Germany.*

[56A] Cylindrical pattern compasses included in the Kern & Co catalogue of *c.*1900. *Kern & Co, Aarau, Switzerland.*

beam compasses as well as dividers continue to be made by precision instrument makers such as Haff, Riefler and Kern [57 and 58].

Wing-compasses and *wing-dividers* were in general use by 1600. The arc together with a screw allowed more accurate setting of the opening of the legs than hitherto. They were made in a variety of materials and sizes and ranged from simple versions in forged iron for use by craftsmen to useful 6 in (15 mm) drawing compasses in brass and silver or exceptionally fine examples in brass gilt for wealthy patrons [59]. Early wing-compasses can be as elegant as versions made during the nineteenth century [60 and 61].

Screw-compasses and *screw-dividers*, where the setting is achieved by means of a long horizontal screw

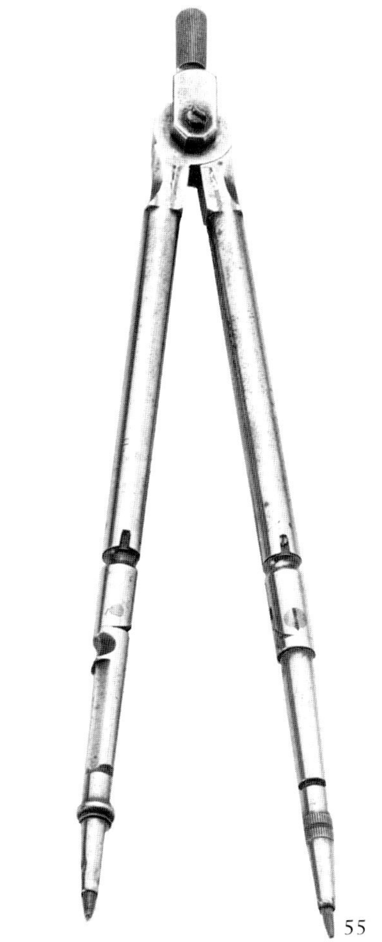

55

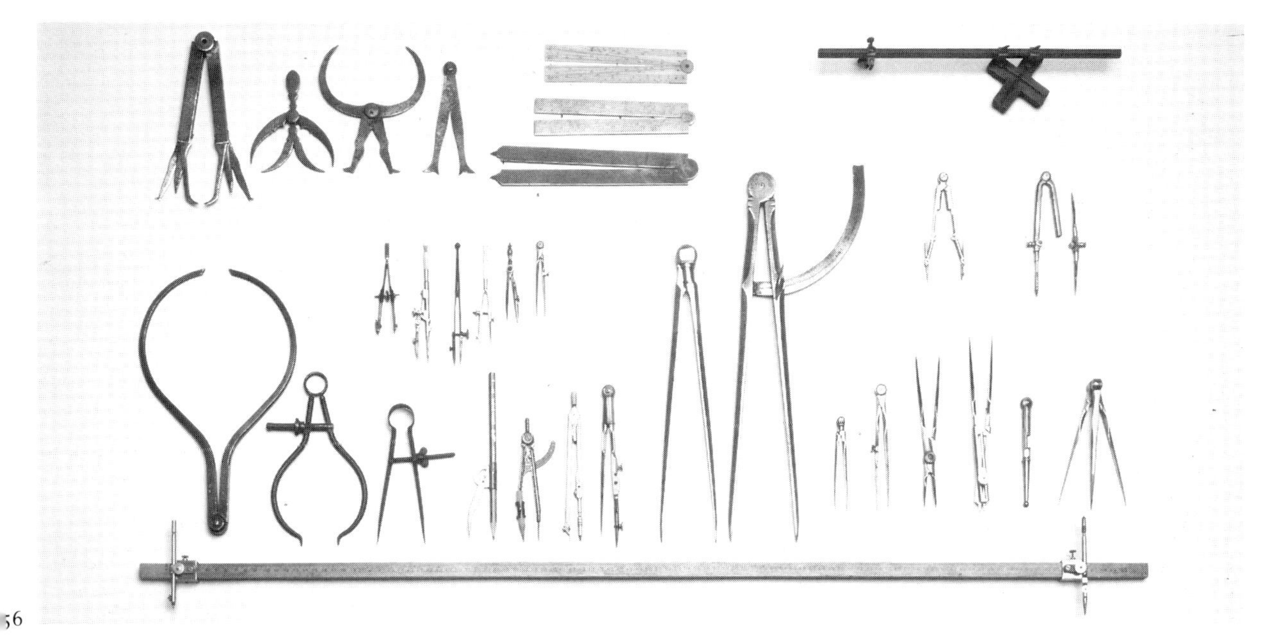

56

[56] Comprehensive selection of various types of compasses: steel dancing master and callipers, three sectors, elliptical compasses, spherical callipers and dividers, drawing compasses, large dividers and wing-dividers, folding and turn-about compasses, proportional compasses, three-legged compasses and a large beam compass. Various dates between 1700 and 1980. *Alessandro Ubertazzi Collection, Milan.*

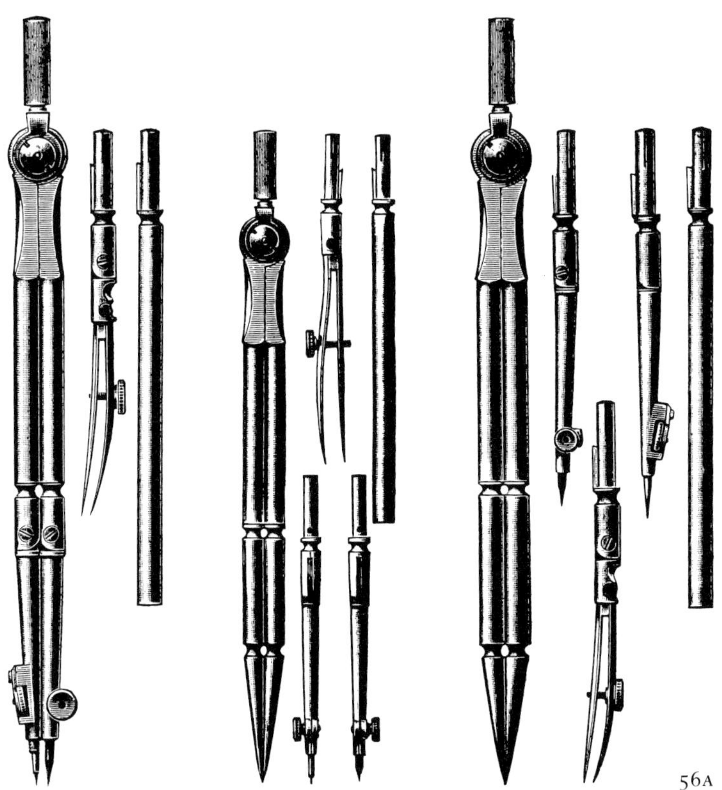

56A

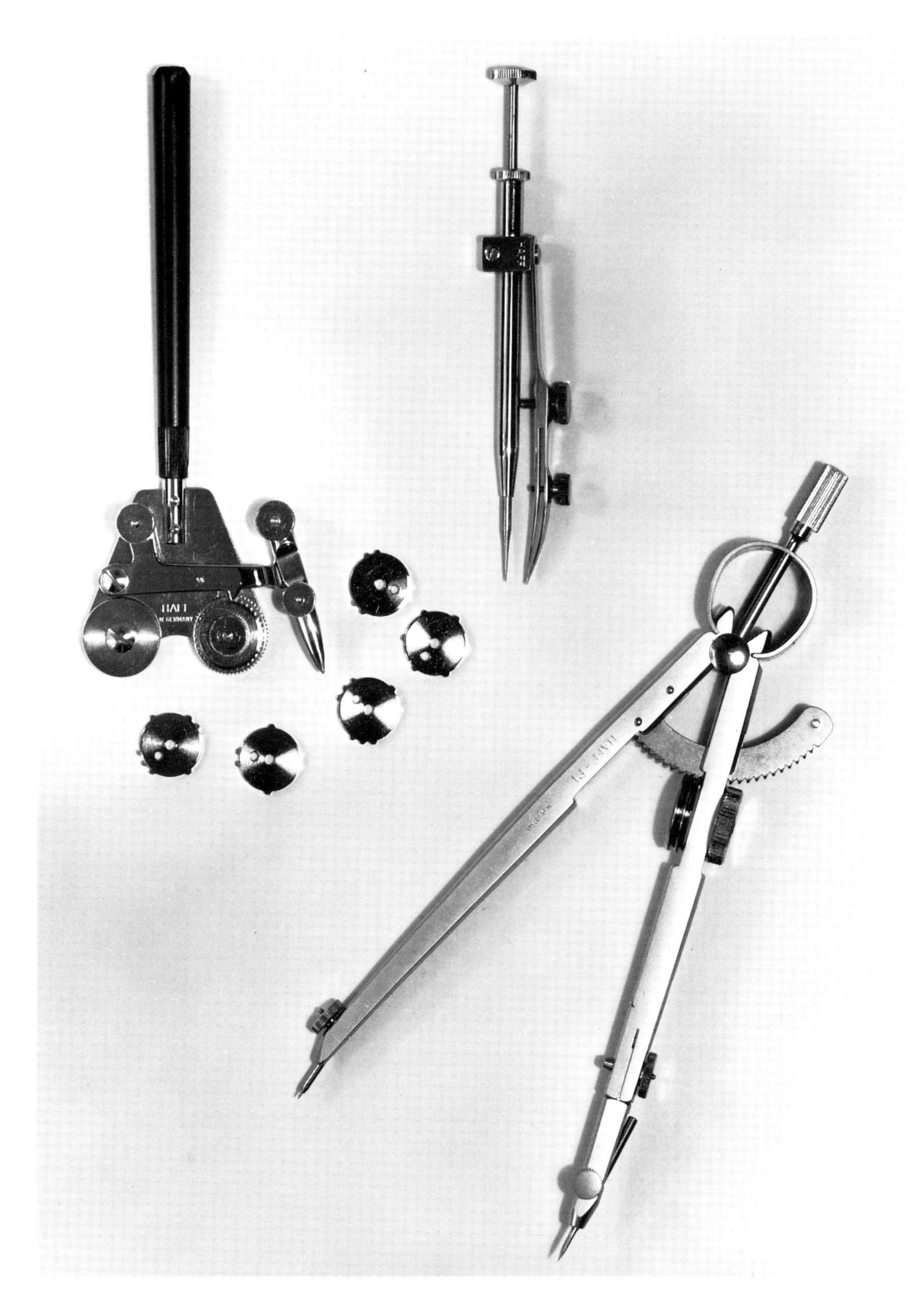

57

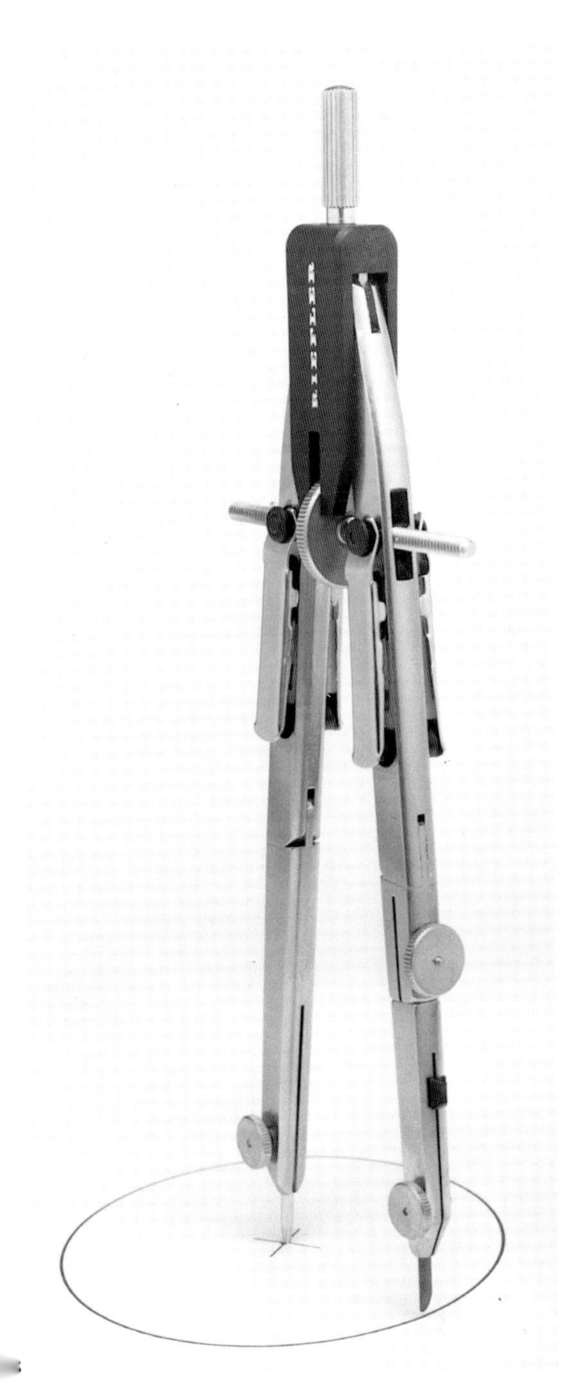

[57] Quick-setting compasses by Haff, in chrome-plated brass with fine setting screw for quick and precise setting of the opening between the point and drawing head, shown with (*above*) pump compass and special wheel pen.

[58] Quick-set compasses made by Riefler since 1980, with ball-bearing and horizontal screw adjustment; nickel-plated brass with plastic shield to the joint.

through both legs introduced at about a third of their length, were available from around 1500 and became a pattern which recurred with variations into the twentieth century. Some seventeenth-century versions were made on a similar principle to the giant dividers of hardwood and nickel silver made in the early nineteenth century [62 and 63].

Hair-compasses and *hair-dividers* (sometimes called 'spring-dividers') were in common use by 1700. In these, one point is held by a spring to one leg and the fine adjustment to the setting of the opening is made by a small screw, 'so as to be able to measure within a hair's breadth', says Chambers in his *Cyclopaedia* of 1728. By 1800, in fine quality compasses and dividers, knuckle joints were provided on the lower leg together with the springs to enable both points to be set vertically to the surface being measured or the drawing in order to achieve greater accuracy.

Beam-compasses are known to have been used since Classical times for drawing circles of large diameter. Small versions were also used when laying out and dividing scales since the same dimension could be repeated more accurately than by using dividers. In this instrument the tracing or drawing point and the centre point are provided separately as cursors and are adjustable in position by sliding along a metal rod or wooden beam. The earliest known design for beam-compasses is that by Leonardo da Vinci, in one of his notebooks *c.*1493. By 1700 beam-compasses were normally supplied in cases of mathematical instruments; a good example appears in a case by Domenicus Lusuerg [VI]. In England there are fine examples dating to the eighteenth century, including one in brass by Thomas Heath (fl.1720–72). Others with a beam of mahogany and brass fittings with points were made by Jeremiah Sisson (fl.1736–88) and Jesse Ramsden (1715–1800). Farey shows a hardwood beam with metal points clamped on in his plates for both Dr Rees's *Cyclopaedia* of 1819 and the *Edinburgh Encyclopaedia* of 1830 [32 and 33].

By the early nineteenth century most reputable makers supplied the so-called 'Swiss pattern' beam-compass fittings, which consisted of metal points clamped onto a hardwood beam. These were later available in boxed sets with alternative inserts for either ink or pencil [III and 64].

In 1866 W.F. Stanley illustrated a tubular beam-compass believed to have originated from a design by the nineteenth-century engineer Isambard Kingdom Brunel. In this the main beam is telescopic and can extend up to between 20 and 24 in (500–600 mm) in length, with the points still clamped on. When the main beam is extended to its maximum length an

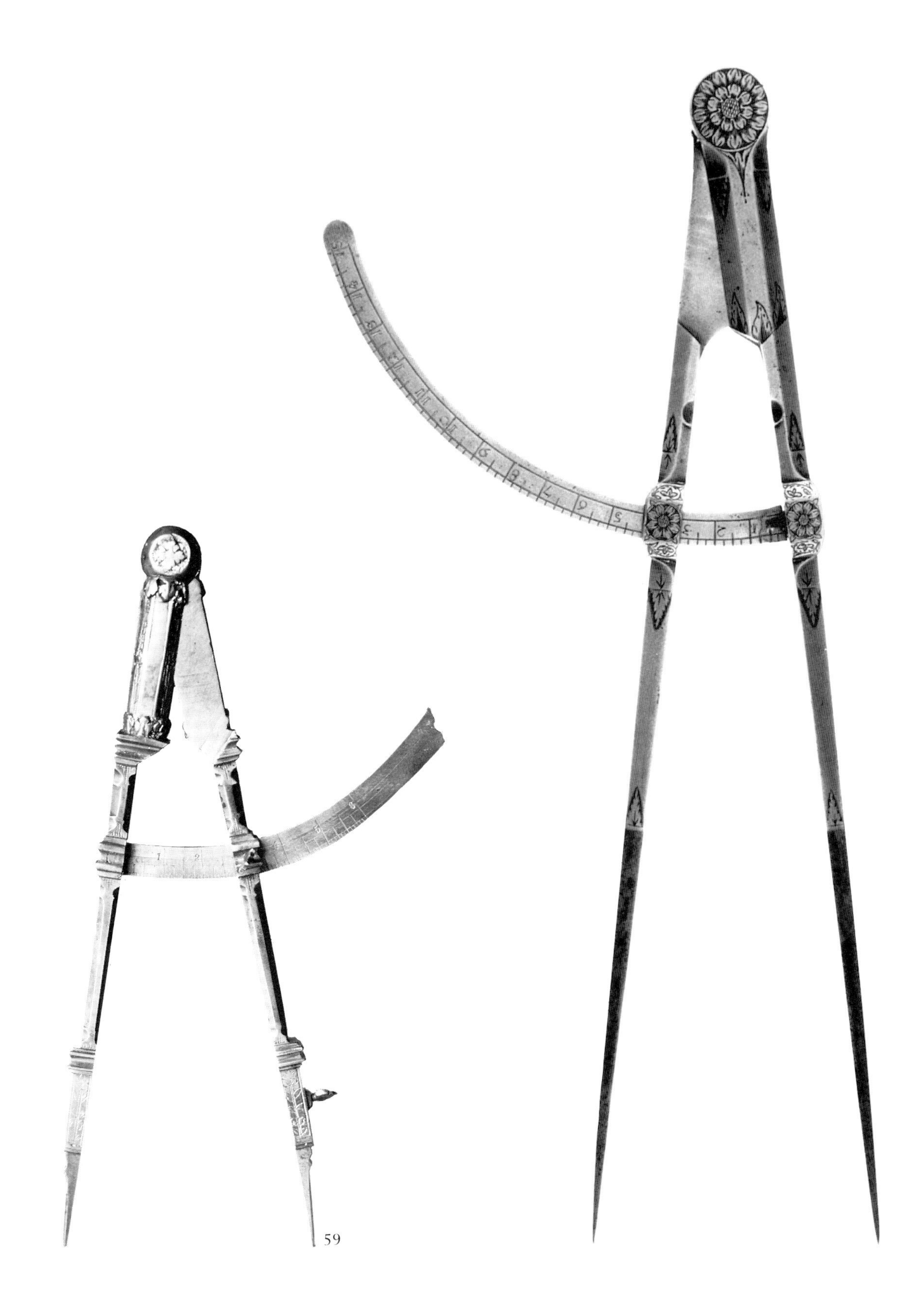

59

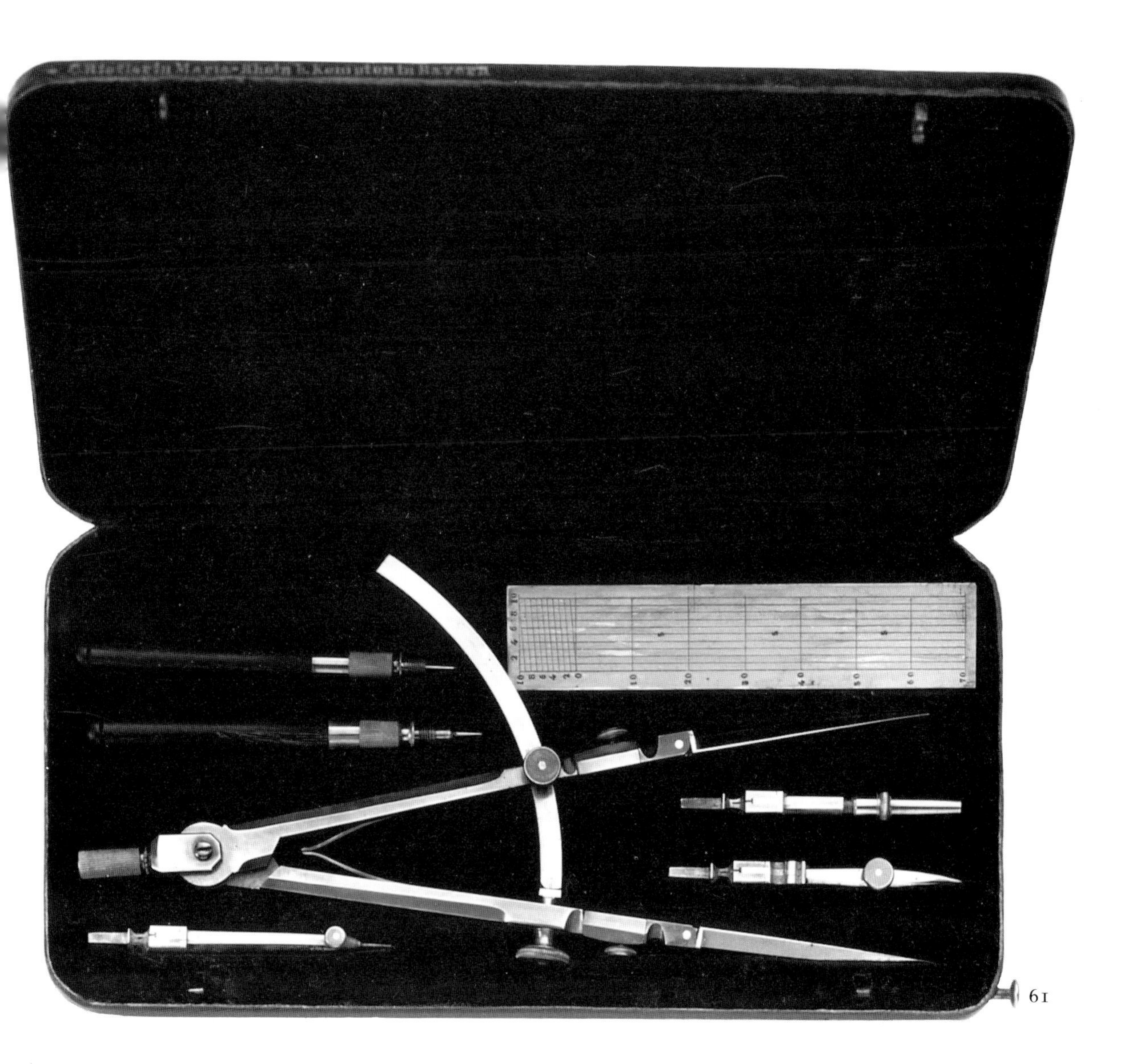

61

[59] Large wing-compasses, cast brass with steel points and an arc engraved with an inch scale, secured by wing nut; chiselled mouldings and engraved decoration. German. Height $7\frac{1}{2}$ in (190 mm). Early 17th century. *Germanisches Nationalmuseum, Nuremberg.*

[60] Large wing-dividers of brass with steel points and 45° arc graduated with inch scale and wing nut adjustment; engraved with leaves and flowers to hinge and legs. English. Height 12 in (305 mm). Late 17th century. *Private collection.*

[61] Large wing-compasses by Clemens Riefler, complete with fitted case which contains alternate inserts for ink and pencil and a metal-cutter together with 6-inch scale. *c.*1870. *Clemens Riefler Collection, Nesselwang, West Germany.*

intermediate arched support is necessary, and this is sometimes arranged on small wheels. By 1900 the best magazine cases included either the 'Swiss pattern' fittings or an entire tubular beam-compass of electrum. The latter was sometimes boxed separately [65].

Since 1960 beam-compasses have been available in square section hollow aluminium for lightness, with interlocking extension pieces. Blundell Harling of Weymouth have been producing such instruments since 1970. By contrast Haff of Bavaria now produce a small beam-compass of stainless steel with chrome-plated brass sliding points as well as a large version

[62] Large iron and gilt-bronze dividers with horizontal bar with trefoil shaped screws and pierced chiselled decoration. French. Height 9½ in (240 mm). Early 17th century. *Private collection.*

[63] Large dividers of polished rosewood with electrum horizontal threaded stay and tenoned joint. English. Height 13 in (330 mm). Early 19th century. (Shown contrasted with pair of Stanley 5-inch hair dividers.) *RIBA Collection, London.*

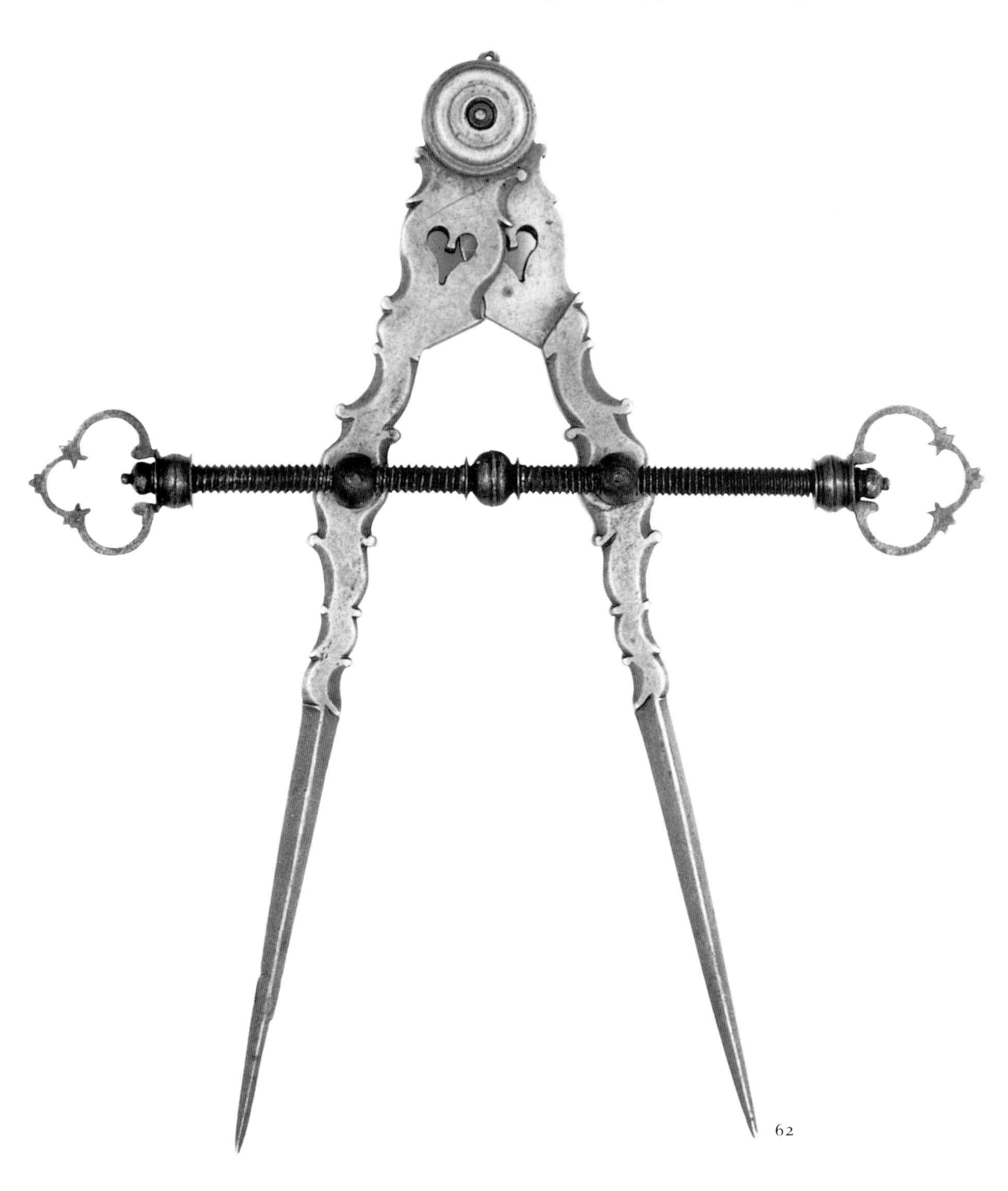

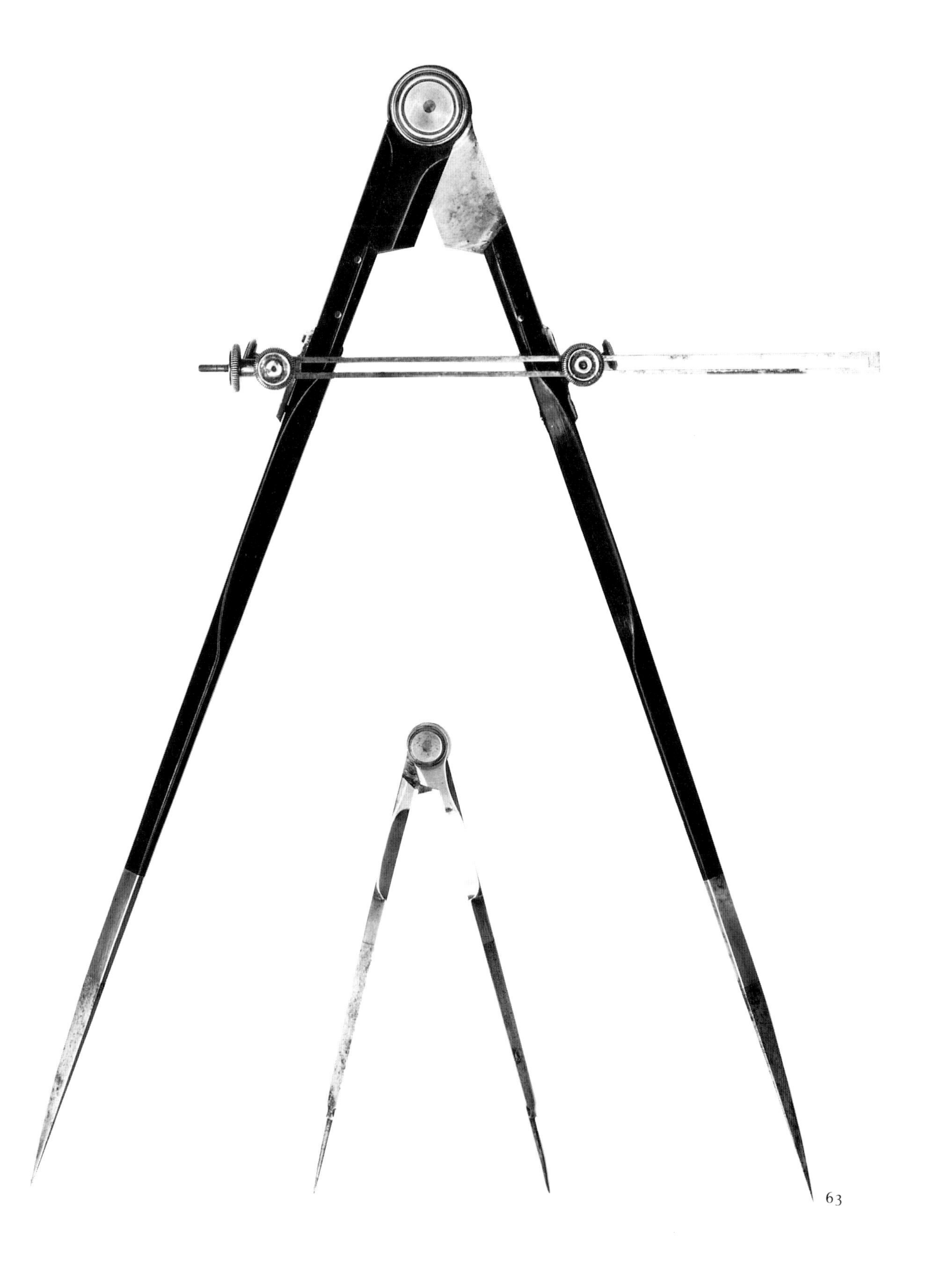

63

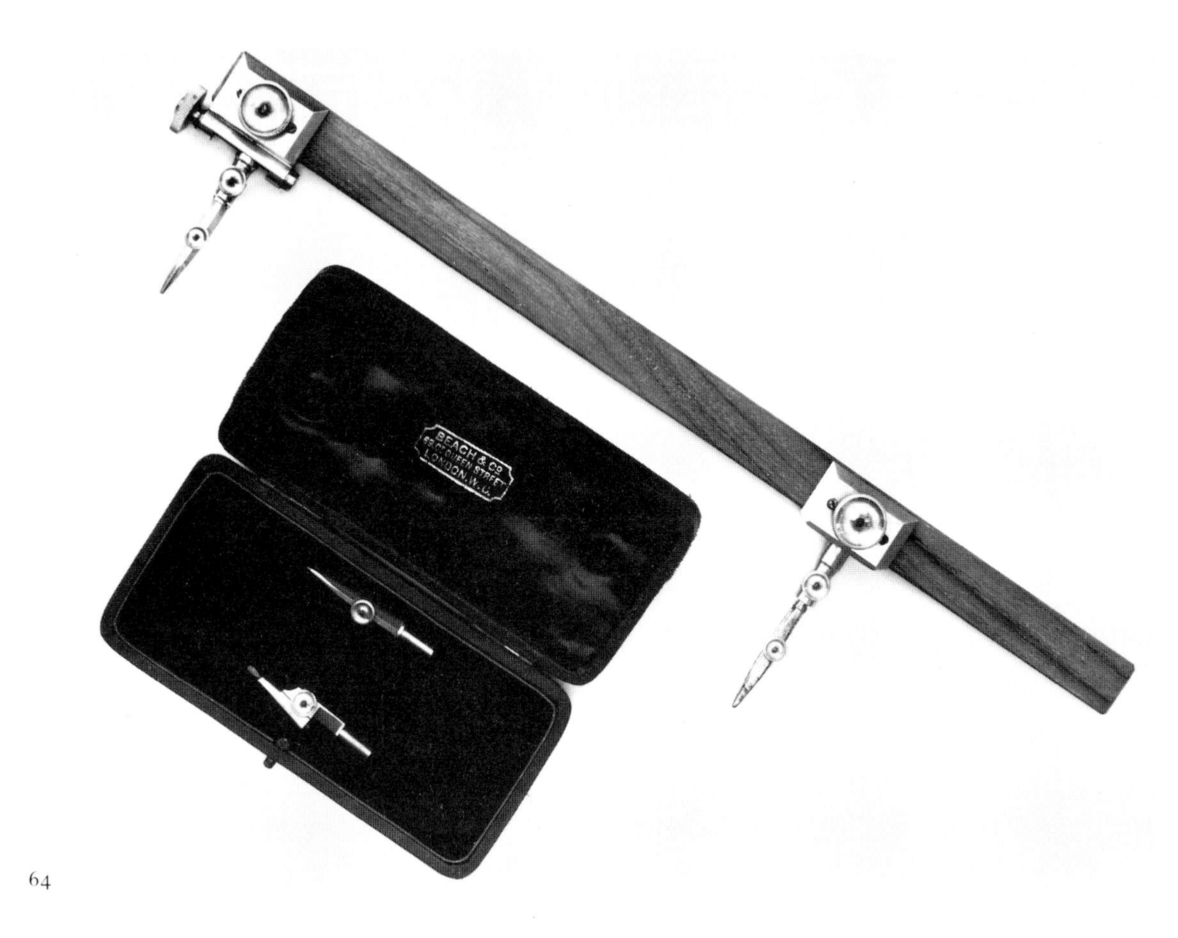

64

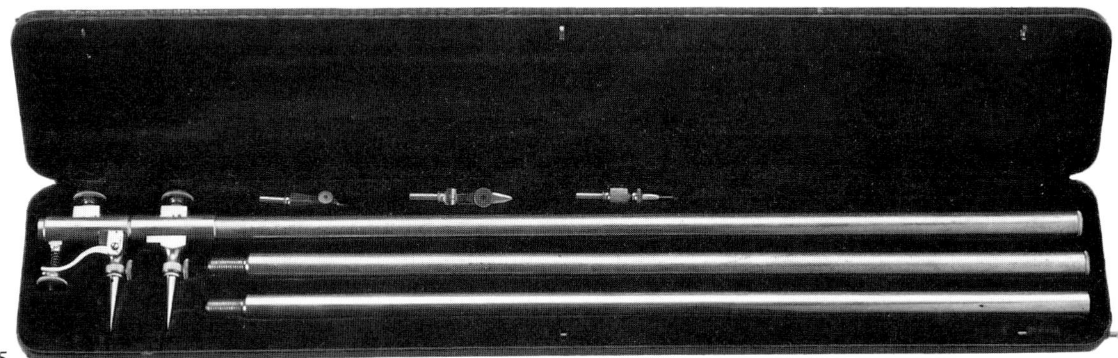

65

[64] Portable beam compass fittings of Swiss pattern with heads made of nickel silver, shown with ink point clamped onto small mahogany beam. Supplied in fitted case stamped BEACH & CO 69 GT QUEEN STREET LONDON WC. Case: $5 \times 2\frac{1}{2}$ in (128 × 68 mm). *Private collection.*

[65] Cased beam compass fittings with tubular telescopic beams and sliding points and three attachments for point, ink or pencil; nickel silver. German. *c.*1880. *Clemens Riefler Collection, Nesselwang, West Germany.*

[VIII] An elaborate case of drawing instruments of rosewood inlaid with nickel silver which contains 18 instruments of the same metal. Some of these are signed 'Renaud-Tachet, 17 rue de Richelieu à Paris'. The lower compartment is fitted for water-colours but is now empty. Swiss pattern beam fittings are also included together with distinctive ruling pens. Case: $11\frac{1}{2} \times 8\frac{1}{2} \times 2\frac{1}{4}$ in (290 × 203 × 57 mm). French, late 19th century. *Andrew Alpern Collection, New York.*

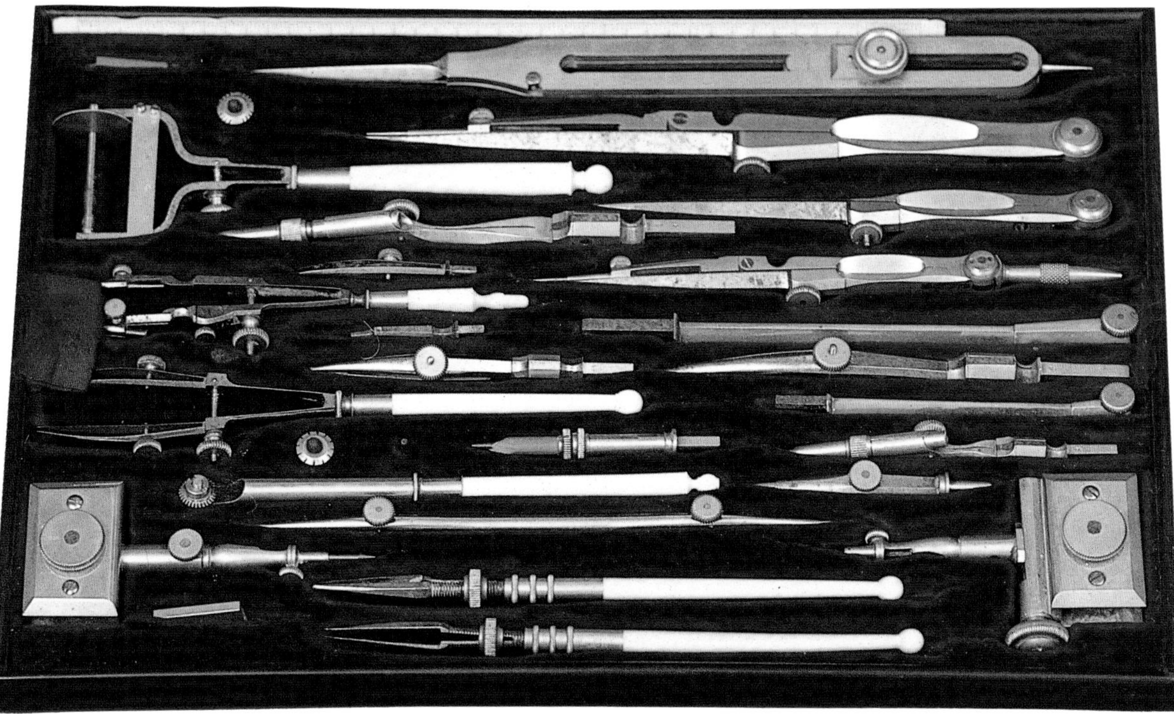

VIII

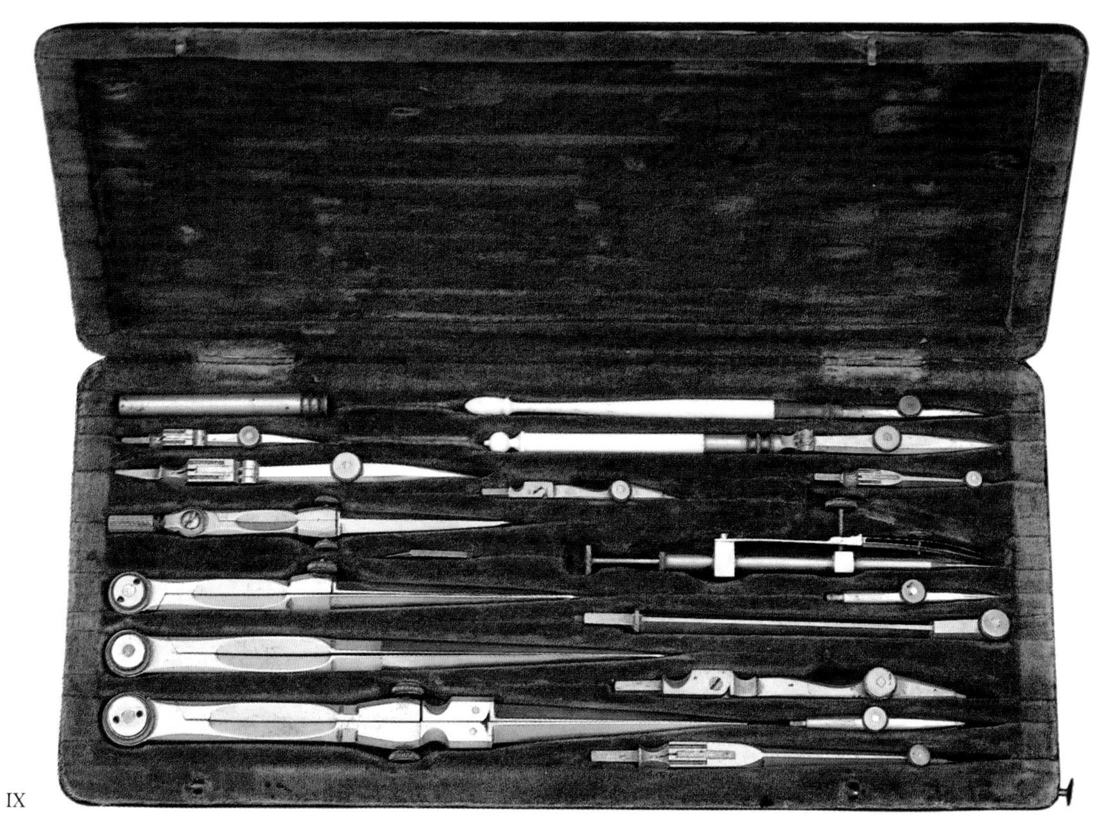

IX

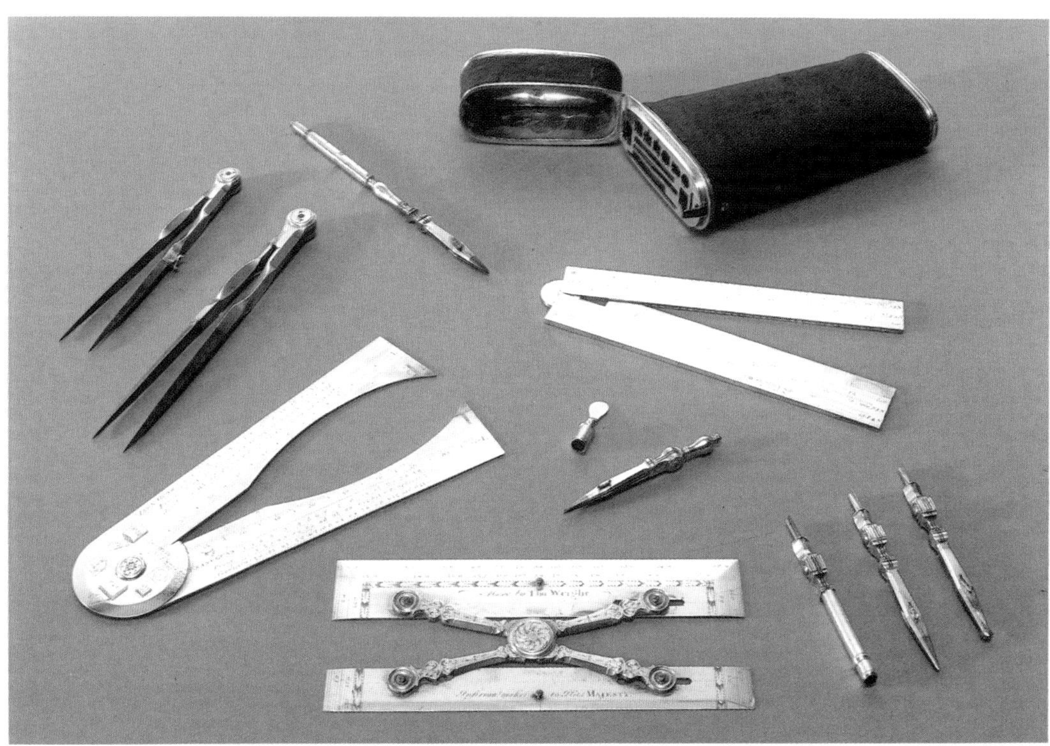

X

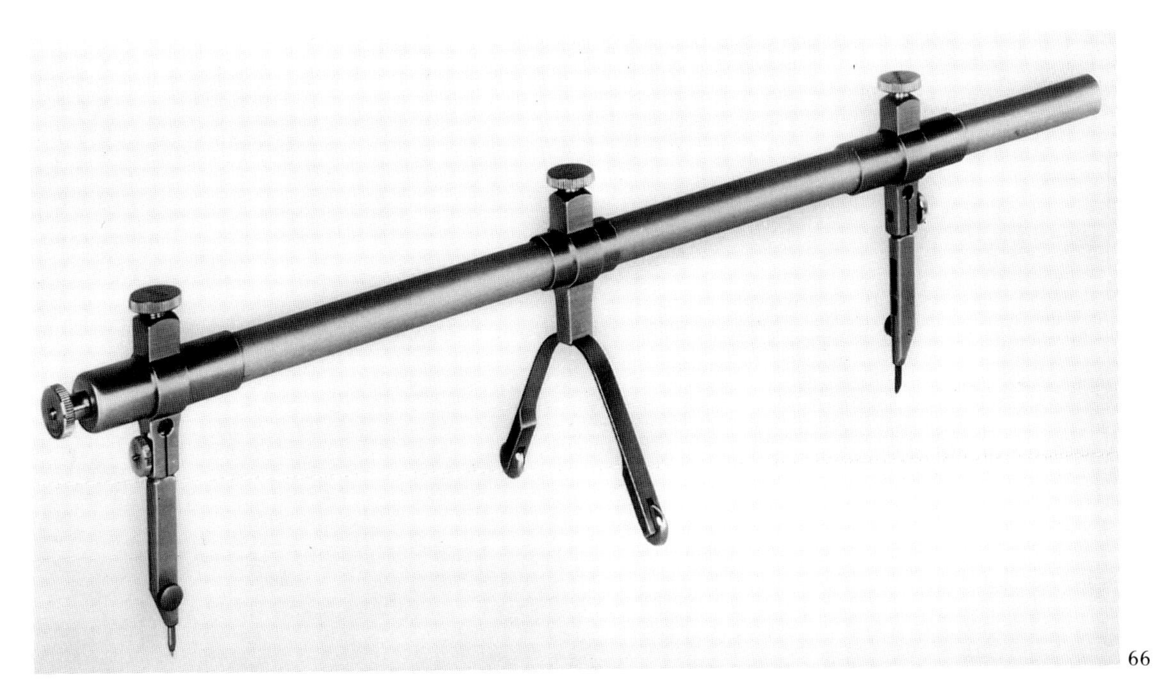

[66] Beam compass by Haff of anodized aluminium rods with chrome-plated brass points and arched support on rollers. *c.*1980. *Gebrüder Haff, Pfonten, West Germany.*

[IX] Leather-covered flat case of high quality brass and steel instruments in velvet-lined tray with ivory handles to ruling pens, including inserts to main compasses, a pump compass and an extension piece. Swiss. *c.*1900. *Kern & Co Collection, Aarau.*

[X] A black fishskin silver mounted pocket case containing a complete set of silver drawing instruments; the parallel rule and sector are signed 'Thomas Wright'. Intended for a military engineer since gunners' callipers are included. *c.*1740. *National Maritime Museum, Greenwich.*

made of hard anodized aluminium rods with central supports on rollers to prevent the beam from deflecting [66].

Bow compasses for drawing small circles make their first appearance in some larger cases around 1700. During the eighteenth century in England very small bows, 2–2½ in (50–65 mm) high, were provided in some pocket cases with different attachments for ink point or pencil holder versions [67]. Medium-sized bows, 4–4½ in (100–110 mm) high, were made later both for ink and pencil, and by 1800 they were made with an extended handle centred over the head of the joint. In France and Germany this handle was frequently made of ivory or bone; by 1850, mainly in France, the handle was sometimes of milled metal provided with projecting friction rings to form an easy grip [164].

Spring-bows became generally available in the early nineteenth century for drawing very small circles; Farey includes one in his plate of 1830 [33]. They were usually 3–3½ in (75–90 mm) high and were made of one piece of high-quality steel provided with a small milled handle, the opening of the legs being adjusted by a fine screw. Variations of these compasses can be found in most large nineteenth-century cases whether English [II], German, Italian or French. They were also sold separately in boxed sets [68], and they became common from 1850 as sets of three to provide dividers, ink and pencil bows with fine needle-points.

Pump-compasses, credited by Stanley in 1866 as a Swiss invention, were designed for drawing circles as small as a pin's head in either ink or pencil. The drawing point rotates around a tube containing a spiral spring with a handle set at the head and a fine needle-point at the centre of the instrument. Various versions can be found in nineteenth-century cases; [17] those of French or German origin often have the handle made of ivory or bone to match the spring-bows. Modern versions known as 'drop bows', designed for setting out circles down to 1/32 in

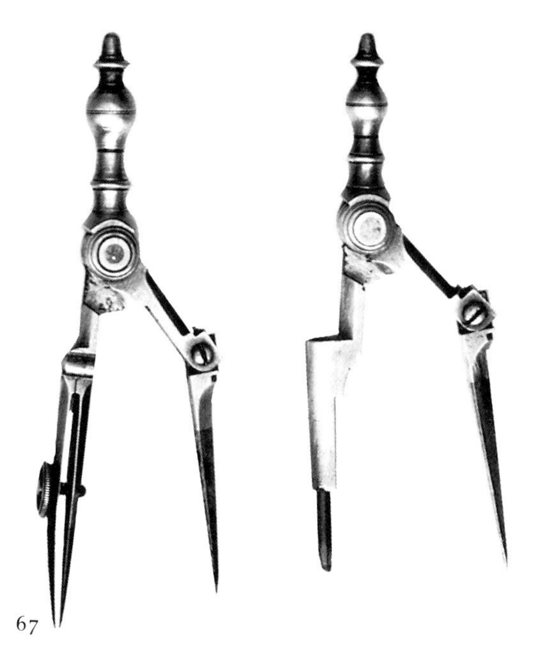

67

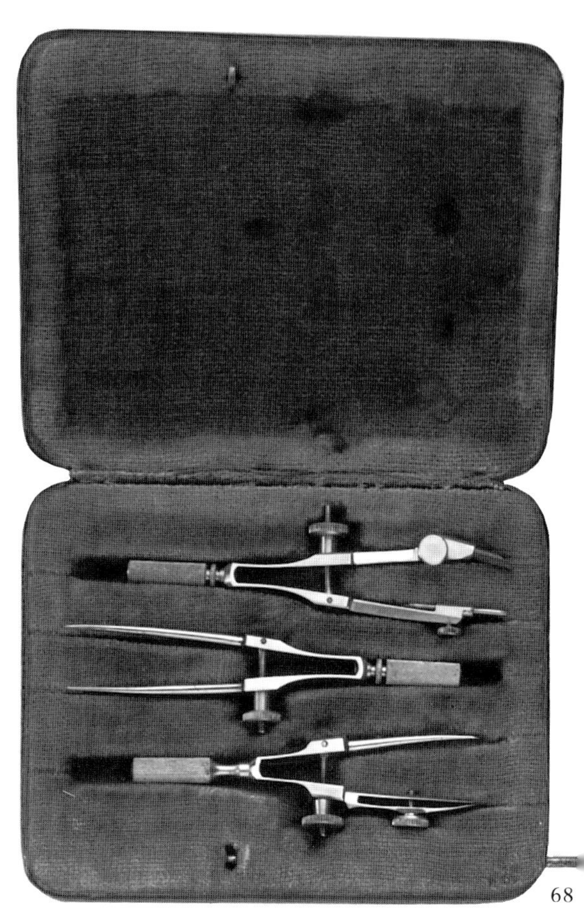

68

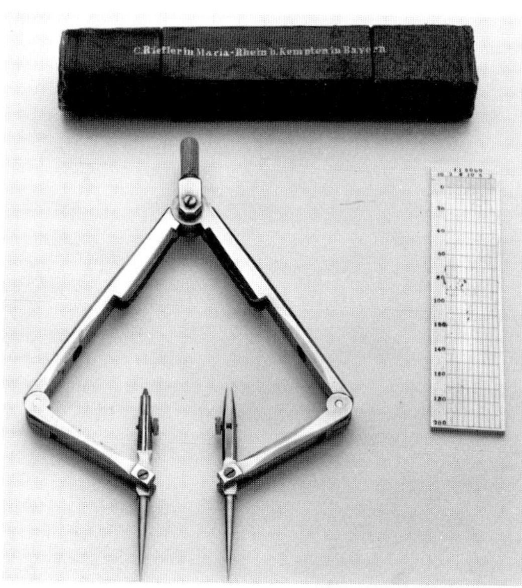

69

(0.8 mm), are still made by several European instrument makers, including Haff [57], Riefler and Kern.

Turnabout or *turn-up compasses* were described by Chambers in his *Cyclopaedia* of 1728 and illustrated as an English contribution by Edmund Stone (1700–68) in his revised edition of Bion in 1758. All these compasses are provided with reversible heads to give two points for use as dividers, or one point and a head with an ink or pencil point. They had two possible disadvantages: either the swivel joint was difficult to

[67] Small brass bows, one each for ink and pencil, both with finely turned handle and hinged joint to leg with steel point. 3 in (75 mm). *c.*1815. *RIBA Collection.*

[68] Set of spring bows by Clemens Riefler in fitted case lined in velvet with neat bolt fastener; nickel silver with finest steel points and milled hand grip to handles. *c.*1880. *Clemens Riefler Collection, Nesselwang, West Germany.*

[69] Turn-about compasses with fitted leather case inscribed 'C Riefler in Maria-Rhein b Kempten in Bayern', shown extended with reversible points which swivel to give either divider points or ink or lead-holder heads which fold away into the limbs. *c.*1860. *Clemens Riefler Collection, Nesselwang, West Germany.*

[70] Folding and pocket compasses. (*Top left*) Cased pillar compasses in electrum case stamped STANLEY GT TURNSTILE HOLBORN WC & RAILWAY TERMINUS: LONDON BRIDGE; (*top right*) large pair of pillar compasses with pencil insert set for use; (*bottom left*) pair of Napier compasses shown extended, the upper part of the limbs cut away to allow the hinged lower leg to fold up inward; (*bottom right*) pair of Swiss pattern folding compasses in fitted case also stamped 'Stanley' etc. The latter is the most compact since the legs fold away with a swivel joint in the same plane as the head joint. All *c.*1900. *David Gray Collection, London.*

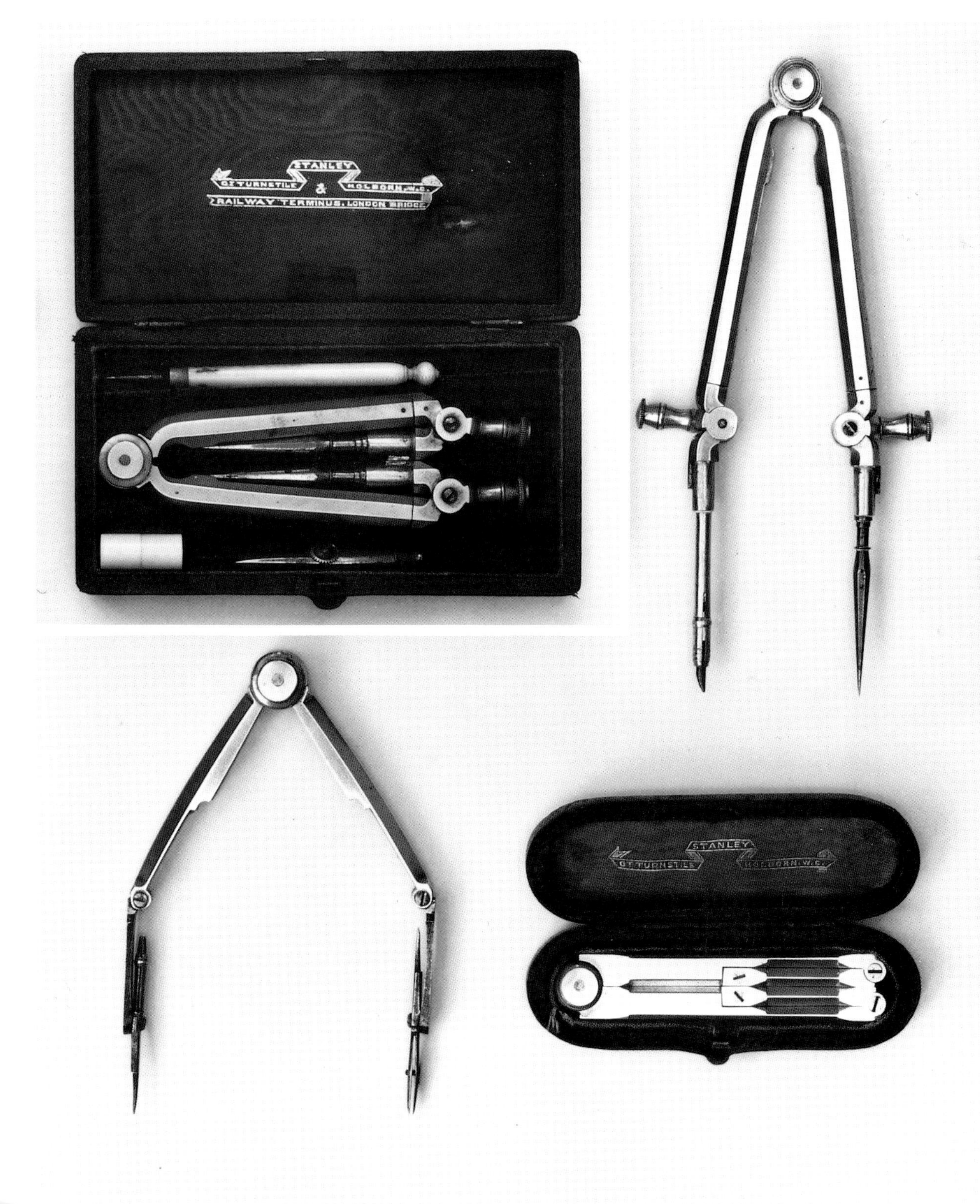
STANLEY
GT TURNSTILE
&
HOLBORN, W.C.
RAILWAY TERMINUS, LONDON BRIDGE
STANLEY
GT TURNSTILE
HOLBORN, W.C.
70

set accurately or it was impossible to prevent slight movement during their use. A fine example of silver turnabout compasses exists in a small pocket case by Thomas Heath dated to around 1740, and versions in German silver or electrum were sometimes provided in nineteenth-century magazine cases [69].

Pocket and *folding compasses* and dividers were available from the early nineteenth century [70]. In the *tubular* variety the legs contained reversible inserts again arranged for use as dividers or to provide one point and an ink or pencil head. The *pillar* variety was designed on a similar principle but the limbs were faceted, not tubular. The addition of a hinged joint enabled them to be made as folding compasses to be carried in a compact small case [72]. A third version known as *'Napier' compasses* was made with light hollow limbs into which the reversible turnabout points folded [71]. A further variant, the 'Swiss pattern', is the most compact: here the legs fold up into the upper part, as in the Napier compasses, but the swivel joint is made in the same plane as the head joint. All these were sold individually in small cases or, as above, included in magazine cases.

Dividers

From Antiquity plain compasses were used as dividers for marking off distances, taking measures off scales, dividing into equal parts and for copying dawings on tablets, parchment or vellum. Later, they were also used for copying maps and nagivational charts. (See Chapter 9 on proportion and ratio for their use with sectors.)

Medieval dividers vary from very primitive objects which resemble gypsies' clothes-pegs to versions with an octagonal ball joint similar to some Roman compasses. A flat tenoned joint appears in some dividers made during the fifteenth and sixteenth centuries, as can be seen in an example from a London case of instruments *c.*1570 [74]. From the sixteenth century onwards they were made in a variety of forms for specialist use.

Single-handed dividers evolved from plain dividers, cut back so that they could be opened by a simple pressure from the fingers of one hand [75]. They were made to several designs to serve as marine chart compasses during the sixteenth and seventeenth centuries, some with the upper part of the main limbs semicircular to allow wider separation of the points. Examples of this type can be seen in the Milanese case of *c.*1540 [148] and that by Domenicus Lusuerg of 1701 [VI]. The finest versions were sometimes highly decorated and finished in gilt brass.

Triangular compasses or three-legged dividers are

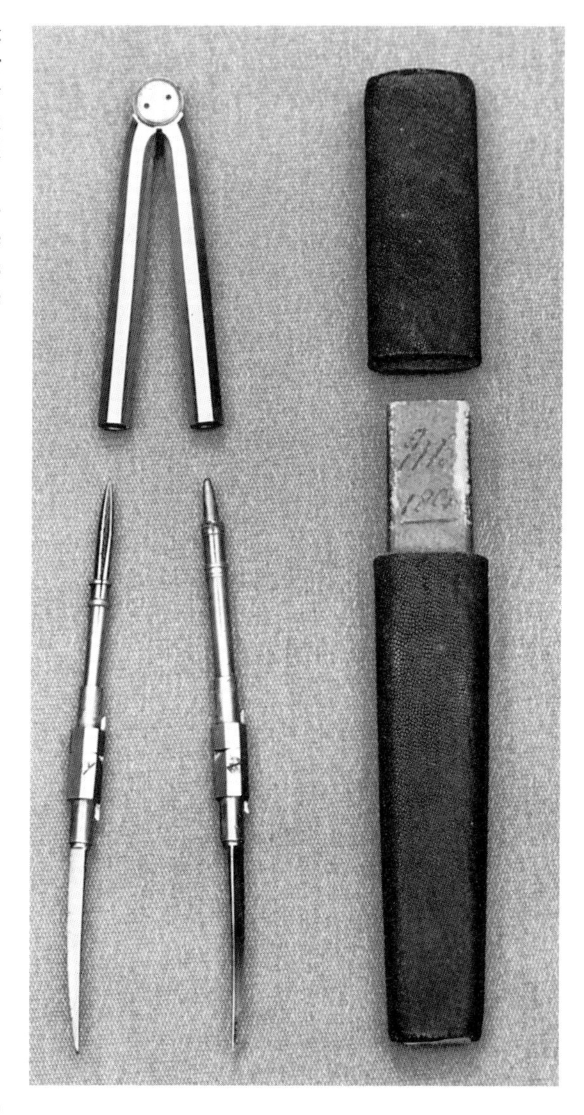

[71] Reversible compasses with interchangeable divider points to give either an ink or pencil leg. Made of brass, this example has a fitted fishskin-covered pasteboard case. Other versions have screw-on protective sheaths or a tapered cap. English. Case: $5\frac{3}{4} \times \frac{1}{2} \times \frac{3}{4}$ in (147 × 13 × 19 mm). *c.*1800. *Andrew Alpern Collection, New York* (100).

[72] Small étui of silver mounted shagreen shown with nickel silver pillar dividers with points exposed and sheath together with extension pieces in two sections and a scale inscribed 'Cary London'. $6\frac{3}{4}$ in (170 mm). *c.*1830. *Private collection.*

[73] Forged iron dividers with flat tenoned joints and chiselled decoration. 16th century. *Mensing Collection, Adler Planetarium, Chicago.*

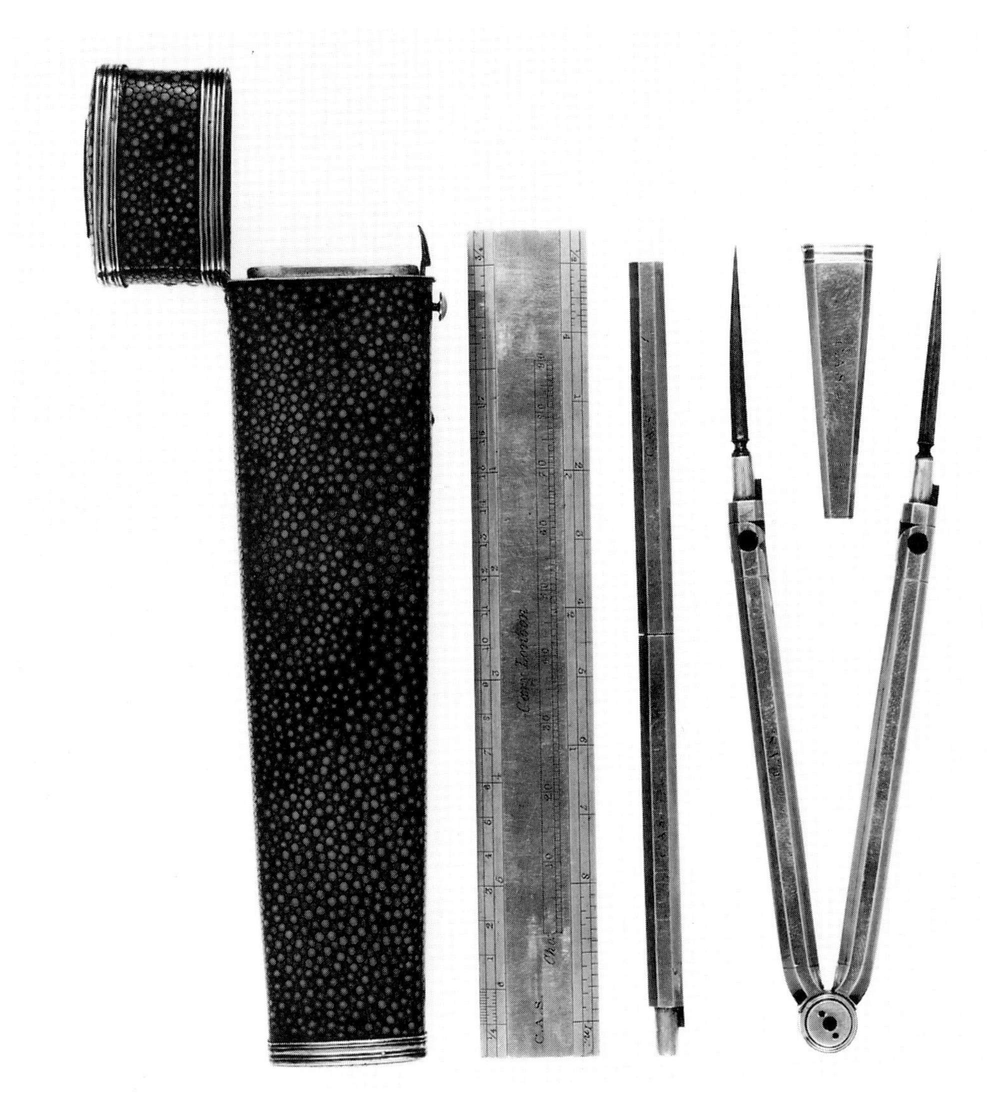

72

73

mentioned in this category since they were used as dividers. Introduced during the sixteenth century, they were widely used for transferring three points simultaneously from one drawing to another; they were also used for taking measurements from globes. These compasses are dealt with in detail in Chapter 8 on copying, however, since their main function lies in that area.

Spacing dividers serve the needs of draughtsmen wishing to divide a length into several equal parts. They superseded such devices as the brass sectograph made by Thomas Jones *c.*1810 [76]. An elegant and accurate modern equivalent is manufactured by the German firm of instrument makers Haff for use by architects, engineers and designers [77].

[74] Gilt-brass dividers with flat tenoned joint and richly decorated engraving on join and legs, from the Bartholomew Newsam compendium *c.*1570; shown in [145].

[75] Single-handed dividers of brass with semi-circular form at joint to allow a wider separation of the points. English. 17th century. *Science Museum, London* (1937–163).

[76] Sectograph in brass for dividing lines into equal parts, arranged as a parallelogram with a sliding diagonal arm engraved with inches and degrees; signed THO^{S} JONES's No 70. *c.*1810. *Museum of the History of Science, Oxford.*

[77] Spacing dividers by Haff in stainless steel with eleven points to enable a line to be divided equally into ten accurately and quickly. Height 6¼ in. (160 mm). *c.*1980.

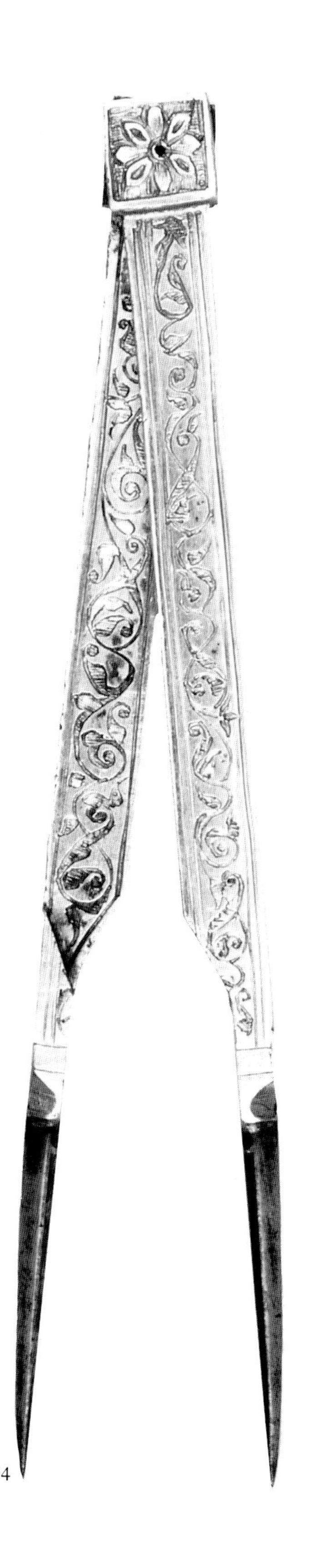

74

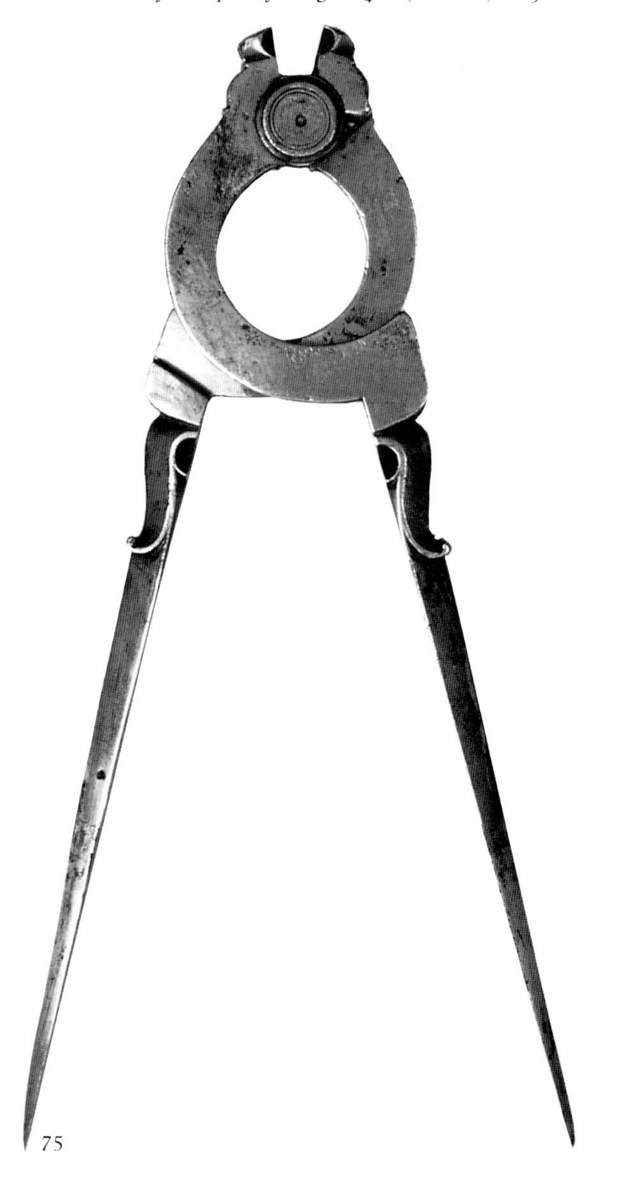

75

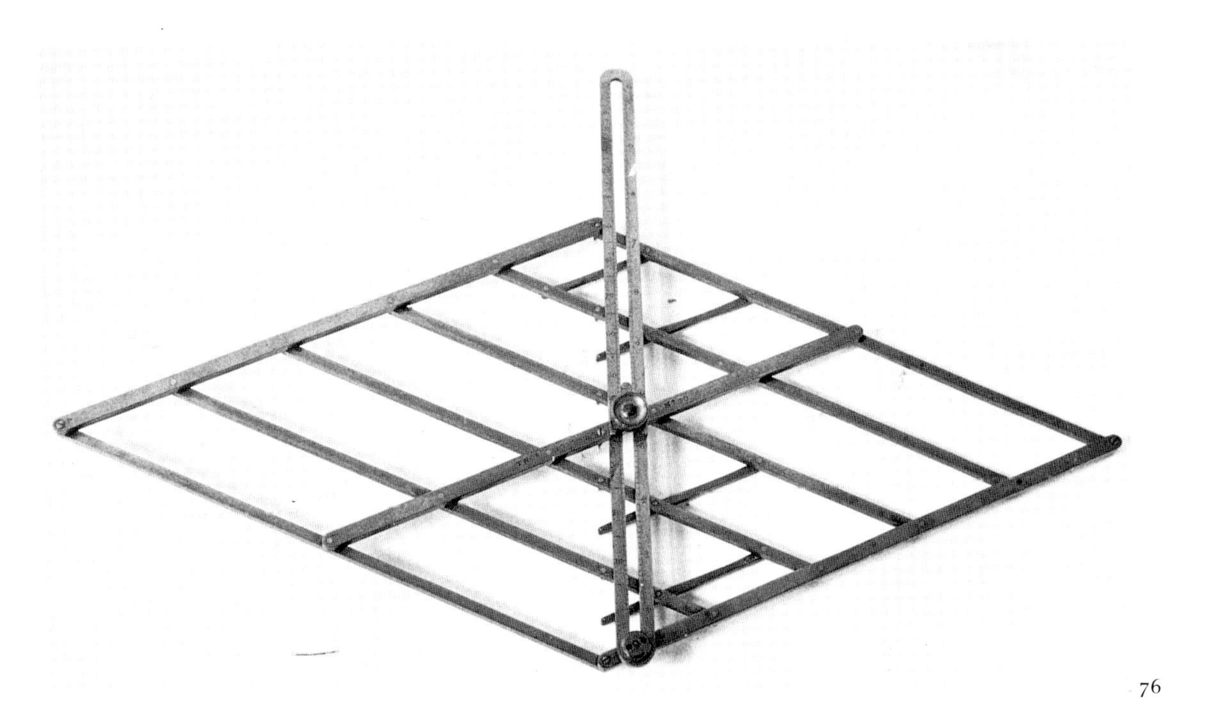

76

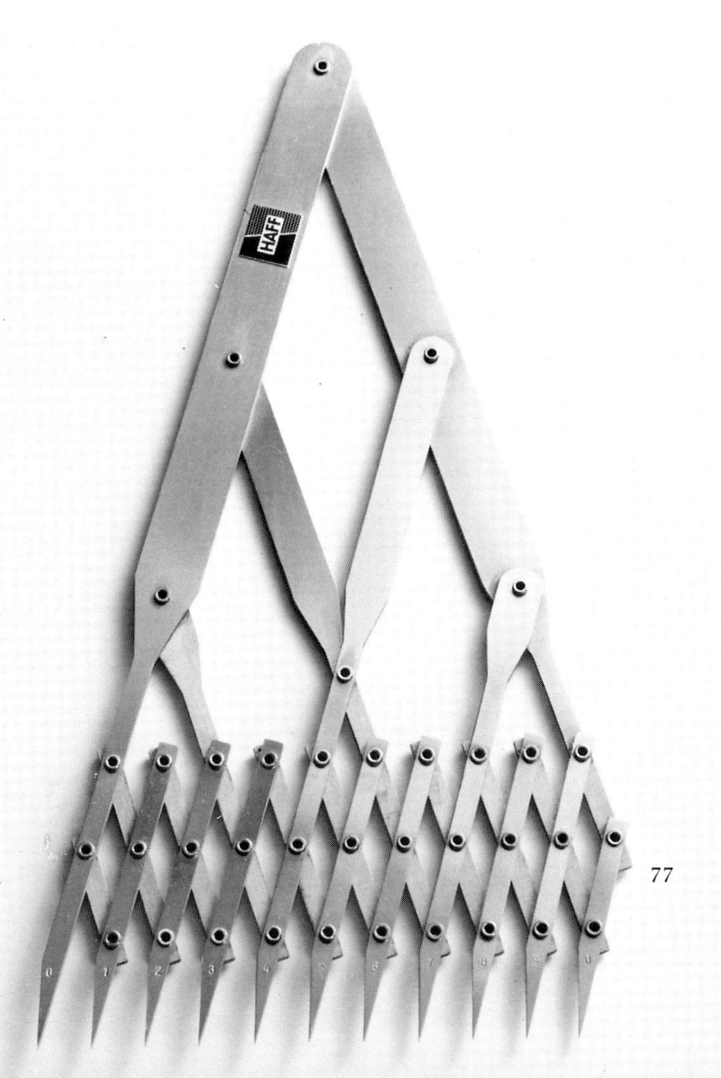

77

Callipers/cylindrical compasses

Callipers or calliper blades made as inserts to compasses were used by the Romans, as can be seen from the spherical hollow-legged variety found belonging to the set of instruments from Pompeii [10]. They were not strictly used as drawing instruments, their purpose being to measure solid objects of cylindrical or spherical shape, hence their use by military engineers for measuring cannon-balls from 1500 onwards. Calliper blade inserts were made for use with large compasses, as can be seen from the Roger North case of *c.*1680 [150] and they are found in many eighteenth-century French and German drawing instrument cases. Gunner's callipers were also provided for calculations in connection with gunnery in pocket cases intended for military use [78]. Callipers designed for measuring the internal diameter of tubes or cylinders were also sometimes included in cases of mathematical instruments.

[78] Gunner's callipers signed 'I Rowley Fecit' and engraved with scales, emblems and the owner's monogram; shown with fitted pasteboard case covered with simulated fishskin. English. Case: 12 in (305 mm). *c.*1720. *Private collection.*

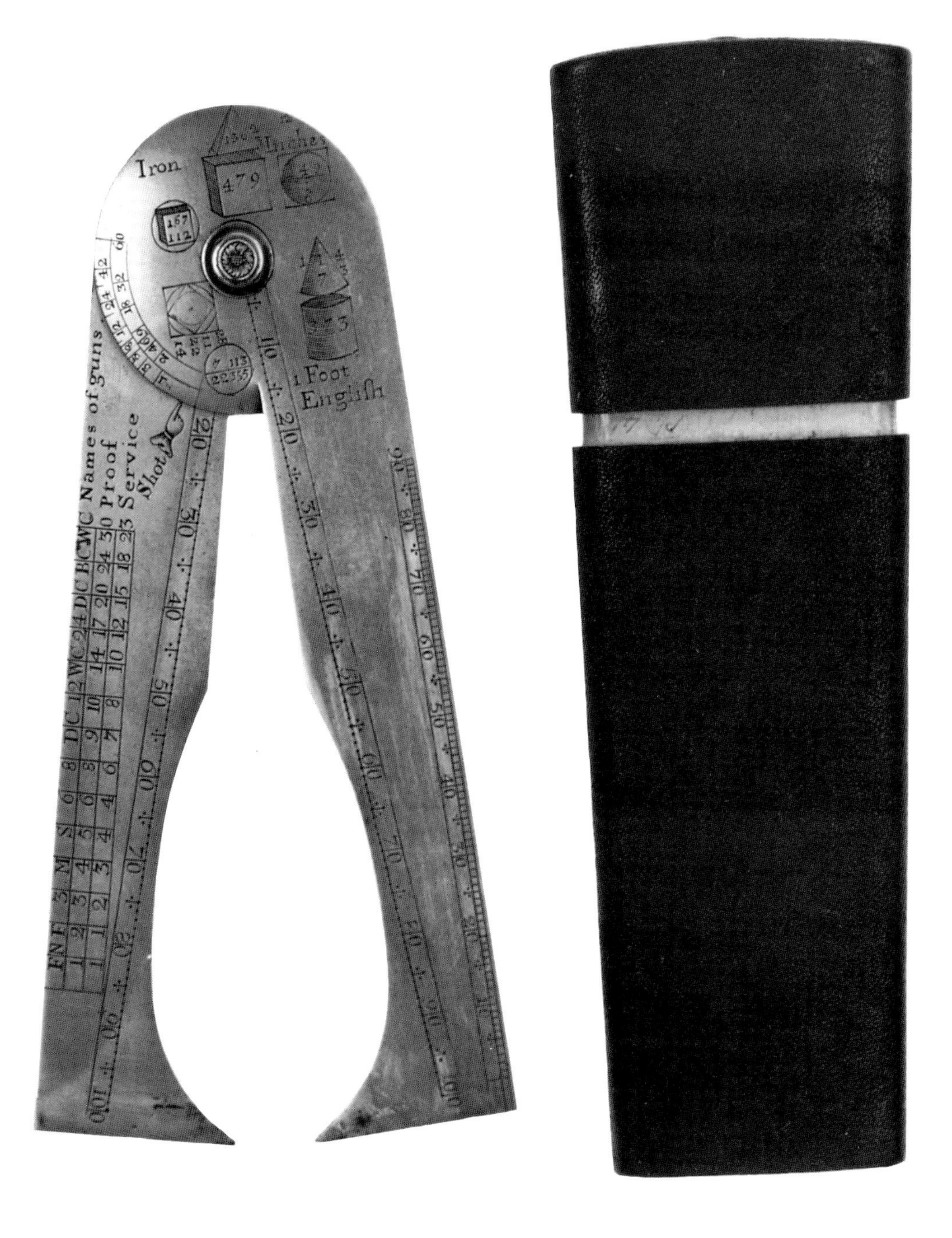

5

Curves

Ellipses

The primitive way of setting out an ellipse is that still used by gardeners: two stakes or pins are placed at the foci and some endless cord restrains the stick or drawing implement used to form the oval. The ellipse, being a conic section, was known to the Greeks and used by the Romans, but it was not until the Renaissance that the desire to draw a circle in perspective accurately gave the impetus to the invention of the earliest devices for depicting ellipses. Ellipses were required by engineers in the design of bridges and arches and by architects when drawing or setting out ceilings, stairs, etc. in this form.

ELLIPTICAL TRAMMELS

An elliptical trammel consists of a cross-shaped base, usually formed of grooves or channel section brass, approximately 3½ in (90 mm) square, that can be pinned to a drawing surface. It has a long bar or arm, with a pen or marking point at one end, running through two sliding heads which slot into the channel tracks that form the cross. The pen is restrained on its bar enabling a perfect ellipse to be drawn. Since the curve is always drawn outside the cross this instrument only draws large ellipses, with a minimum size of 5 in (125 mm) on the major axis. The semi-elliptical trammel which, like the elliptical trammel, was made from 1600 onwards, uses a tee-shaped base, produces smaller ellipses and has to be set up in two halves.

Dürer illustrated his invention for a compass to draw ellipses *c.*1540, which by its form we would now call a semi-elliptical trammel. The English scientist Robert Hooke mentioned 'elliptical compasses and swashworks' in his diary of 1674. Early versions appear in cases dating from 1600 onwards, and Nicolas Bion illustrates an example of an elliptical trammel in 1709 [21]. These trammels are the simplest instruments in this category and have continued to be used in a modified form until this century. An example of a fine early semi-elliptical trammel can be seen in the case by Christoph Schissler dated *c.*1599 [149]. Domenicus Lusuerg provided elliptical trammels together with drawing arms in some of his cases of mathematical instruments *c.*1700 [VI].

In England Joseph Moxon (1627–91) included elliptical compasses in his *Description of Mathematical Instruments* of 1701, illustrated by Thomas Tuttell (fl. 1695–1702) [20A]. A similar trammel was shown by Ephraim Chambers in one of the plates for his *Cyclopaedia* of 1728 and he also includes a brief description of elliptical compasses. By the mid-eighteenth century trammels were included in instrument cases by the best London makers. There is a fine example of a circular trammel in a casket by Thomas Heath (fl.1720–72) and a semi-elliptical trammel in a small magazine case by George Adams the Elder is to be seen in the Oxford Museum of the History of Science [151].

During the nineteenth century W.F. Stanley supplied both the semi-elliptical and elliptical varieties, which were both easy to operate. This firm were still including models in their catalogue as recently as 1960 – four hundred years after the instrument was first developed. The German firm of Riefler made both varieties of trammel between 1870 and 1900 [79].

ELLIPSOGRAPHS

Designing an instrument to draw small ellipses precisely fascinated several inventors during the first half of the nineteenth century, who were stimulated by the needs of those wishing to draw tilted circles in technical illustrations or circles in perspective.

One of the earliest surviving ellipsographs is a French version signed 'Gourdin à Paris' of *c.*1790; but little is known of its origins [80]. The first English ellipsograph was devised by John Farey *c.*1810, who used it when drawing circular objects in perspective. The son of an exceptional geologist and surveyor of the same name who published *A General View of Agriculture in Derbyshire* between 1813 and 1817, he was

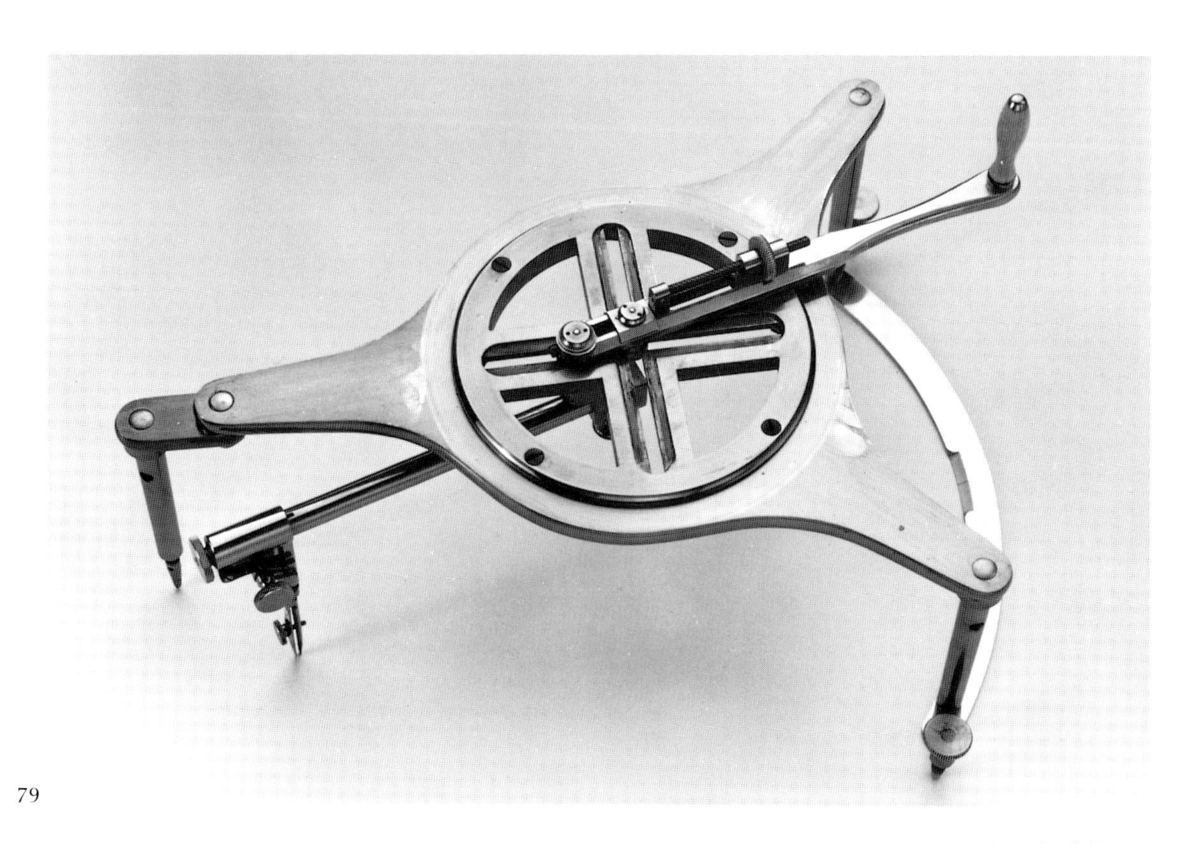

79

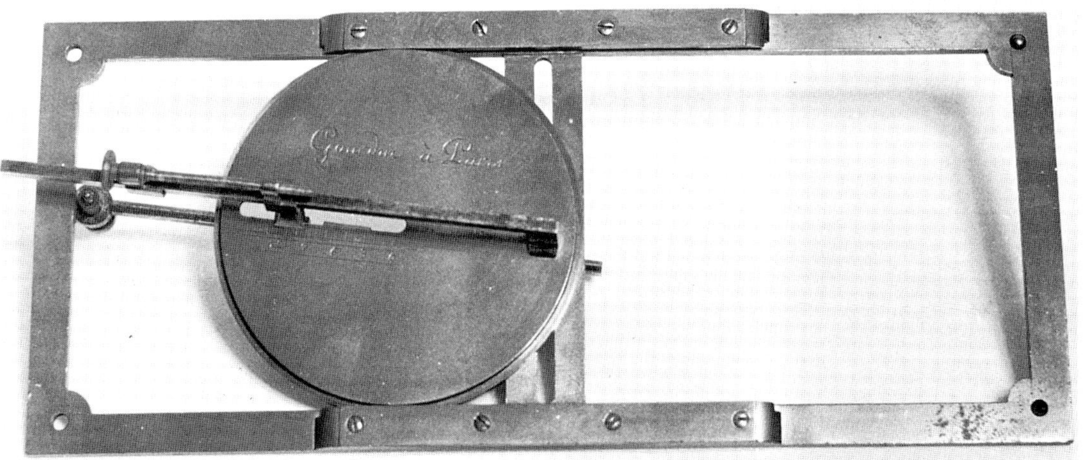

80

an engineering writer who commenced drawing plates on technical subjects for Dr Abraham Rees's *Cyclopaedia* in 1805 when he was only fourteen. He subsequently drew many plates for other publications including Sir David Brewster's *Edinburgh Encyclopaedia* (1808–30). Farey was awarded a Gold Medal by the Society of Arts in 1812 when he presented his prototype ellipsograph together with a paper on its use (published in *Transactions of the Society of Arts*, Vol.31, 1813). Farey's instrument was made of brass and consisted of a frame of parallel rulers and concentric circles 4 in (105 mm) in diameter with a central crossbar and socket to hold the pen or pencil. The circles could be moved by a small rack and pinion with a pair of milled screw heads which enabled different varieties of ellipse to be drawn. Examples of Farey's ellipsographs can be seen in English museum collections; several were made by W. & S. Jones, some numbered;

[79] Elliptical trammel by Clemens Riefler in brass set on a tripod stand with adjustable drawing arm below and the operating handle above the circular trammel. *c.*1890. *Clemens Riefler Collection, Nesselwang, West Germany.*

[80] Ellipsograph of brass and steel inscribed 'Gourdin à Paris' with frame and circular plate designed as a trammel slotted to take the drawing arm; the four adjustable feet at the corners are missing. *c.*1790. *Museum of the History of Science, Oxford.*

[81] Ellipsograph designed by John Farey inscribed 'Farey Invt London'; a prototype similar to this was awarded a Gold Medal by the Society of Arts in 1813. *Private collection.*

the later models have improved rack and pinion adjustment [81 and V]. In 1818 Joseph Clement, an engineer who trained under Henry Maudesley, presented his design for an ellipsograph to the Society of Arts and like Farey was awarded a Gold Medal. Clement's model was twice the size of Farey's and a more complex instrument since it performed several other functions besides drawing ellipses. There is a boxed version in the Science Museum in London.

Further variations on the ellipsograph were introduced from 1840 onwards. One, designed by James Finney *c.*1855, had an overhead frame on a raised

81

82

[82] Ellipsograph designed by James Finney as made by W. F. Stanley with improvements to render it easier to use. Stanley illustrated this in the 1873 edition of his *Mathematical Drawing Instruments. Science Museum, London.*

[83] An unusual compass designed for drawing ellipses, consisting of an elaborately fretted bracket on the main shaft operated by a turned handle. This device relies on a chord similar to that used with a helical compass, to restrain the drawing points. English. *c.*1800. *Museum of the History of Science, Oxford.*

[84] Plate by John Farey devoted to 'Ovals', dated 1815, engraved by Wilson Lowry for Dr Rees's *Cyclopaedia* including Farey's ellipsograph (fig.3) and an elliptical compass (fig.2)

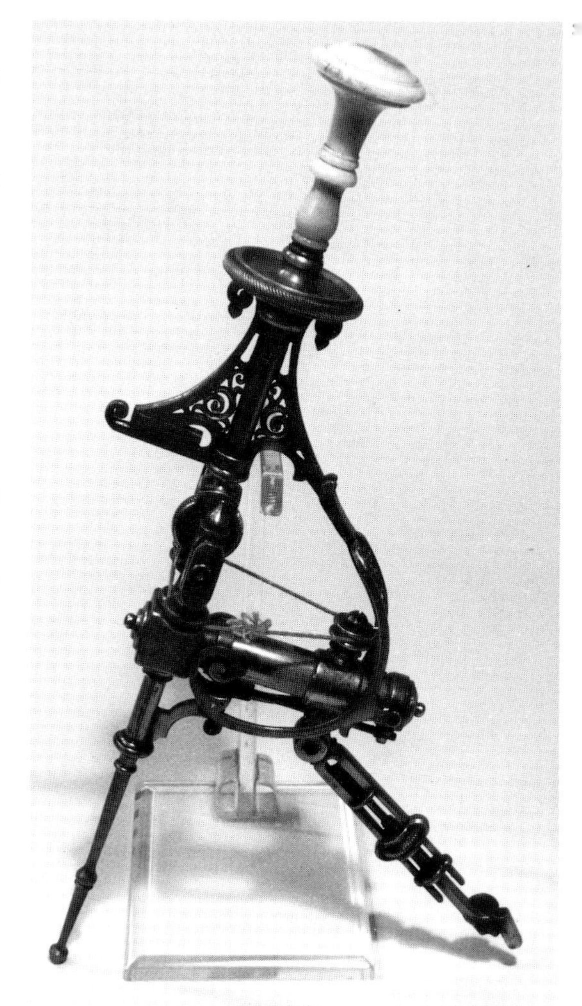

platform which proved simpler to use than Farey's and was capable of producing small ellipses from 6 in (152 mm) down to ¼ in (6 mm) on the major axis [82]. Edward Burstow, an architect, contributed another design, fully described by W.F. Stanley in the 1873 edition of his treatise. Both these ellipsographs were made in improved versions by Stanley and sold by his firm.

Christoph Schissler of Augsburg made a vertical device for drawing ellipses *c.*1580. Some instruments based on a similar principle appeared in England after 1800.

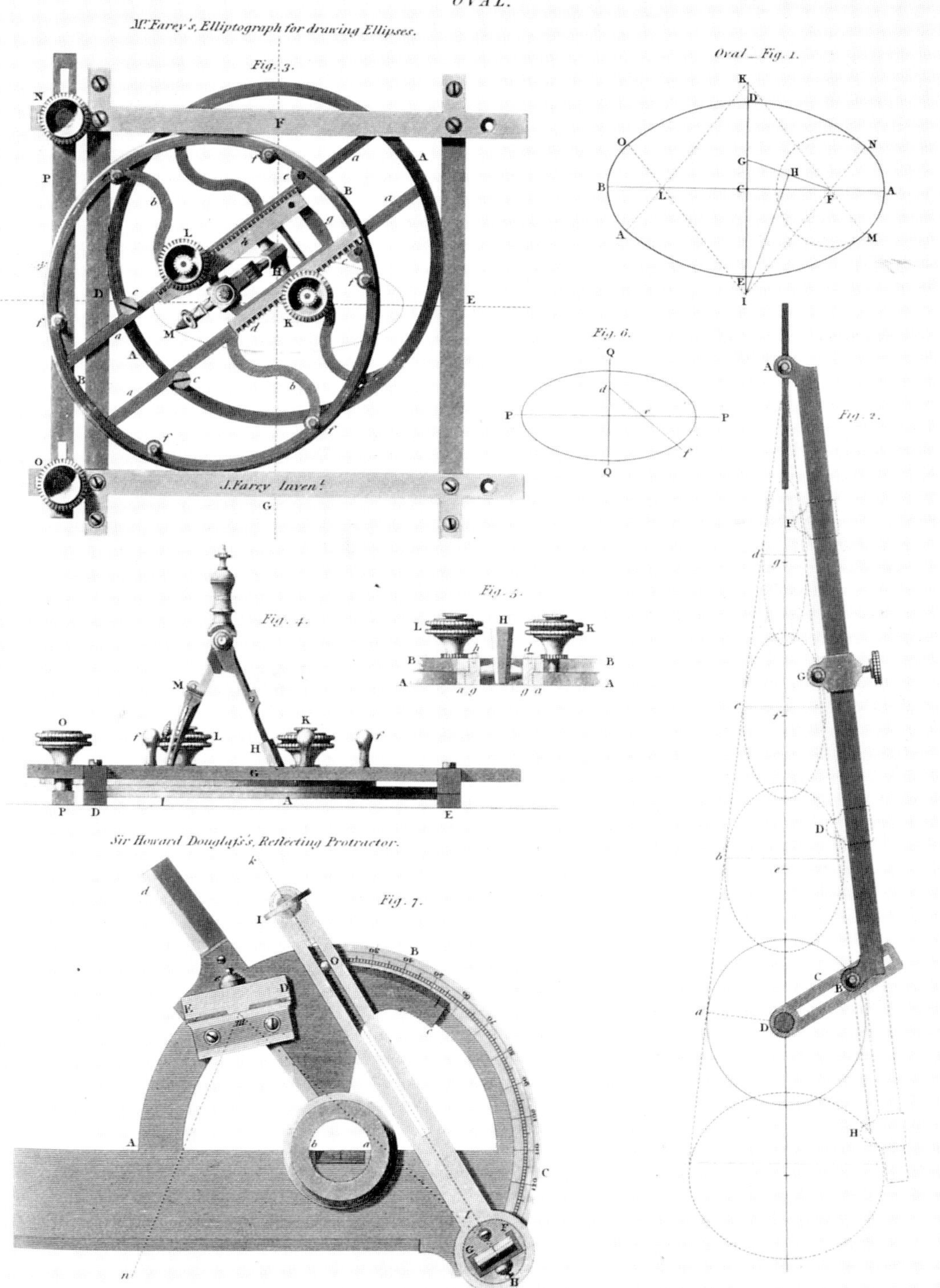
DRAWING INSTRUMENTS.
OVAL.
Mr. Farey's Elliptograph for drawing Ellipses.
Fig. 3.
J. Farey Invent.
Oval _ Fig. 1.
Fig. 6.
Fig. 2.
Fig. 4.
Fig. 5.
Sir Howard Douglas's, Reflecting Protractor.
Fig. 7.
Published as the Act directs, 1815, by Longman, Hurst, Rees, Orme & Brown, Paternoster Row.
Lowry sc.

84

John Farey illustrates one in his plate devoted to 'Ovals' for the Rees *Cyclopaedia* [84]. Another design of *c.*1800, with an elaborately fretted bracket to the central shaft, can be seen at [83]. Other, simple vertical ellipsographs set up for use with templates were introduced by John Hicks of Bolton *c.*1840 and by James Nasmyth, the engineer responsible for inventing the steam-hammer, both using trammels stacked one above the other [85A]. Finally, a remarkable mid-nineteenth-century ellipsograph of brass was made by Troughton & Simms of London, consisting of a three-legged platform with a raised setting circle for the drawing arm [85B]. This epitomizes the earnestness with which nineteenth-century instrument makers tackled the problem of the ellipse, but one wonders how many of these ellipsographs were ever used regularly since it required application and considerable skill to obtain an ink drawing in one operation.

For the more precise needs of engineers or graphic artists when drawing small ellipses or tilted circles for such manufactured items as dashboards for flight-decks, the German instrument makers Haff have, since 1972, manufactured a high quality ellipsograph, similar in principle to Farey's, which is easy to use and which describes an ellipse in one movement [86]. The facilities of computer-aided draughting systems can now deal with the graphical problems of these complex curves by a simple programme.

TEMPLATES

Another way of drawing ellipses to scale is to use numerous individual templates. During the nineteenth century pearwood elliptic curves were made, to be followed at the end of the century by the first celluloid templates. The firm of W.F. Stanley still offered a range of sets of hardwood elliptic curves in their 1925 catalogue. Since the 1960s templates have been manufactured in acrylic and sold in groups, the

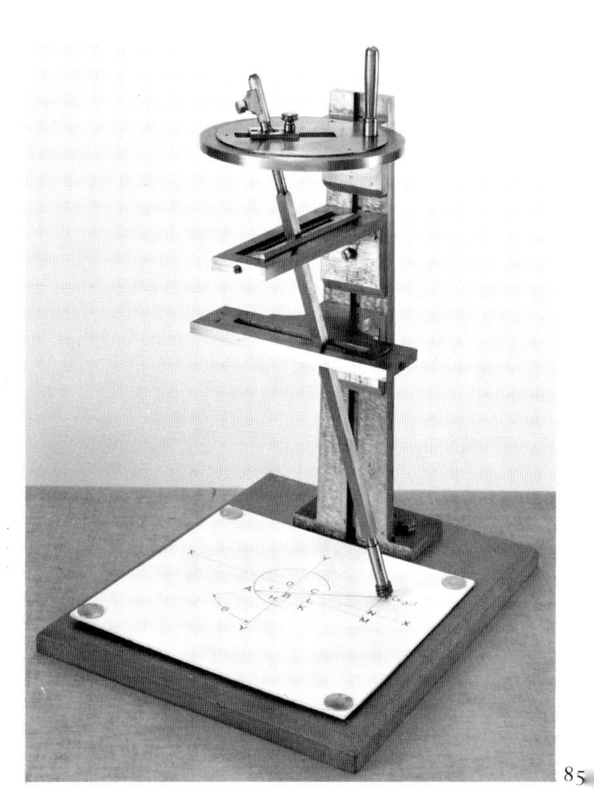

85

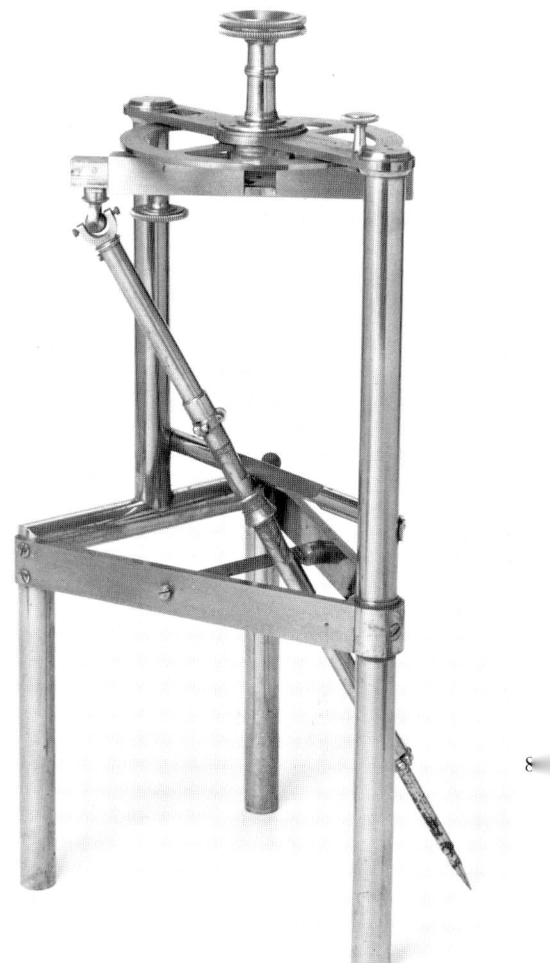

8

[85A] Ellipsograph by James Nasmyth, designed to be operated vertically, with a circular trammel at high level set above two plates with slots whose axes are at right angles to each other. Mid-19th century. *Science Museum, London.*

[85B] Ellipsograph signed 'Troughton & Simms London', of lacquered brass. An unusual design (by Airy with Wm. Simms) shown at the 1851 Exhibition, with a circular trammel set on a high platform consisting of three columns; the extending pen, located via a knuckle joint, runs within three roller-castors and is fitted with an extension arm and clamp; all contained in a mahogany fitted case with spare drawing points. Case 15 in (203 mm) wide. Mid-19th century. *Science Museum, London.*

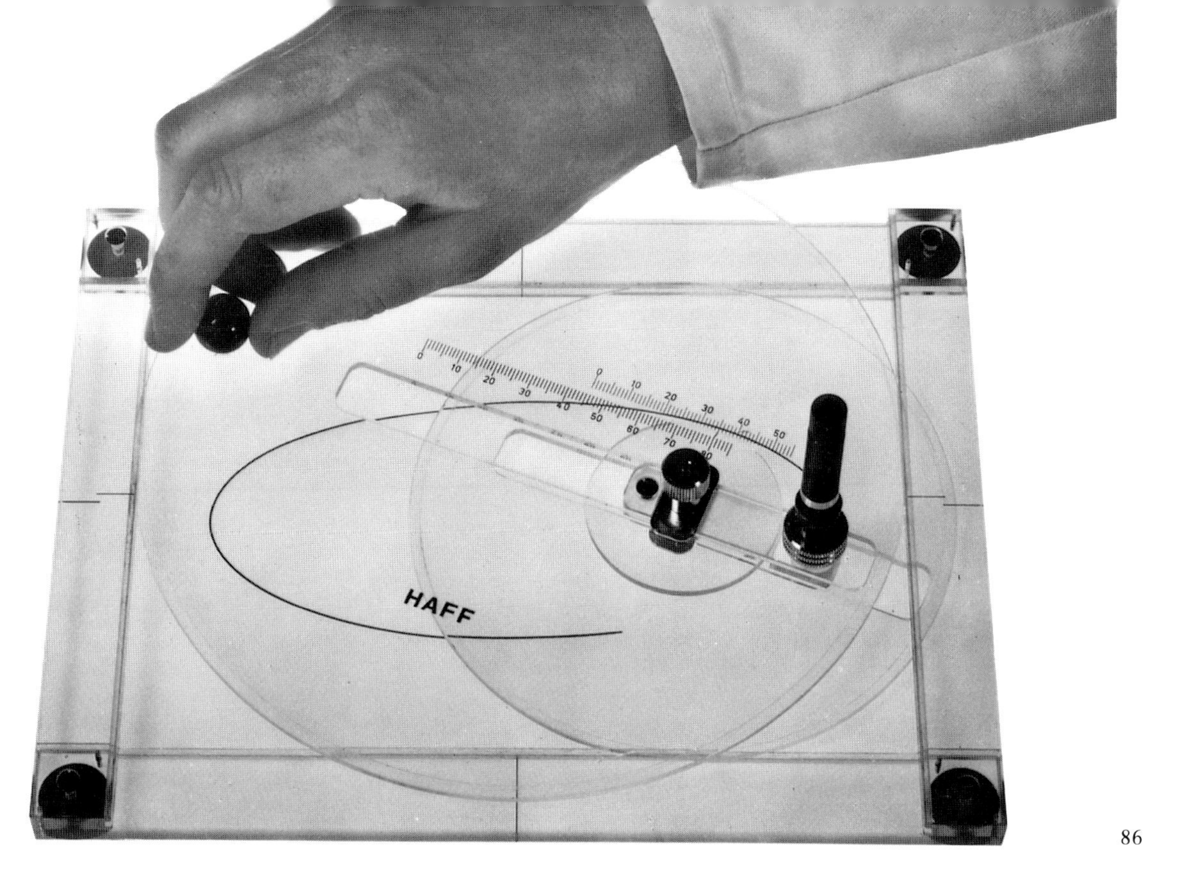

86

[86] Ellipsograph by Haff in transparent acrylic sheet with chromeplated rotating operating knobs, for use with either ink, pencil or a technical pen. The semi-axes of the ellipse are set using two engraved scales. After the drawing point has been inserted and lowered into position the ellipse can be drawn in one complete movement simply by rotating the knob on the upper circle. Small version $6\frac{3}{4} \times 4$ in. (170 × 110 mm). *c.*1980.

range covering every possible angle from shallow to full ellipses. These have become standard aids to draughtsmen.

Spiral curves

The need to draw or set out an accurate spiral dates from the Classical period when volutes had to be formed in the Ionic order. Alberti's *De re aedificatoria* (1485), based on the writing of Vitruvius, was the first work to include the precise method for setting out this spiral form of the Ionic capital. By the end of the seventeenth century information was available in French, Italian, Dutch, German and English treatises used by architects, and by the mid-eighteenth century it was to be found in many of the popular patternbooks and manuals of geometry available to builders [87].

The first English instruments for this purpose seem to be the volute compasses and helicographs devised during the eighteenth century. The object of these instruments is to arrange that the marking or drawing point should advance or recede to or from the centre of the spiral in regular proportion, either by equal degrees or by accelerated motion, during the revolution of the instrument. Several versions of volute compasses were made which employed helical drum guides of various sizes and a helical spring which, with the aid of cat-gut, could be arranged to draw spirals of differing sizes [88]. An illustration of the *helicograph* was included by George Adams the Younger in his *Geometrical and Graphical Essays* of 1791 [89]. In this complex instrument the drawing point is moved towards the centre with the revolution of the instrument by a pair of pulleys, one of which is stationary upon the axis and the other fixed some distance from it. A line passing over the pulleys is attached to the drawing point, which is carried along by its action. A similar instrument, also a 'helicograph', was devised by Penrose and Bennett in 1850, but in this case all the operational parts were in one instrument and its movement could be easily

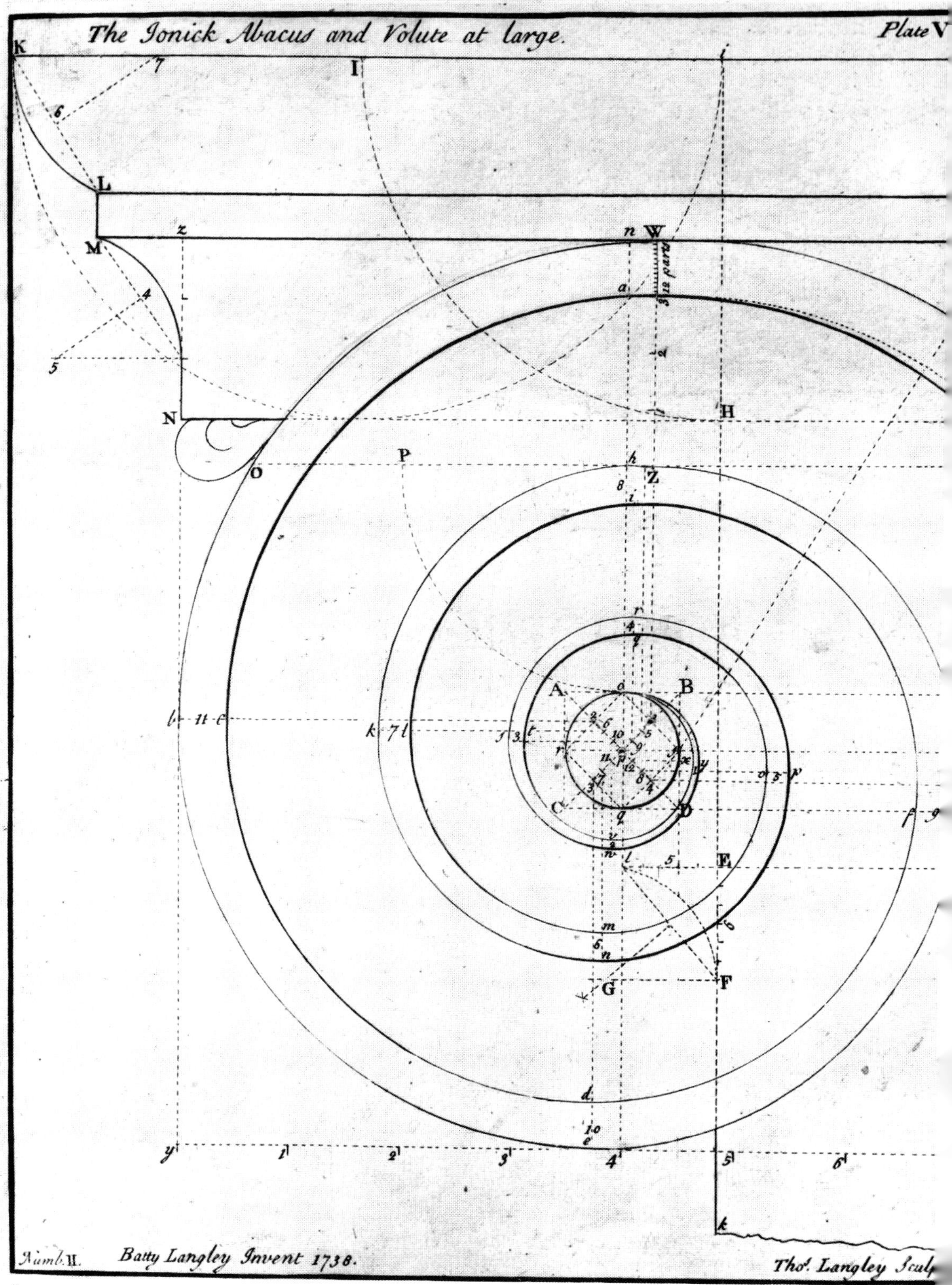
The Ionick Abacus and Volute at large.
Plate V
Numb. II.
Batty Langley Invent 1738.
Thos. Langley Sculp

87

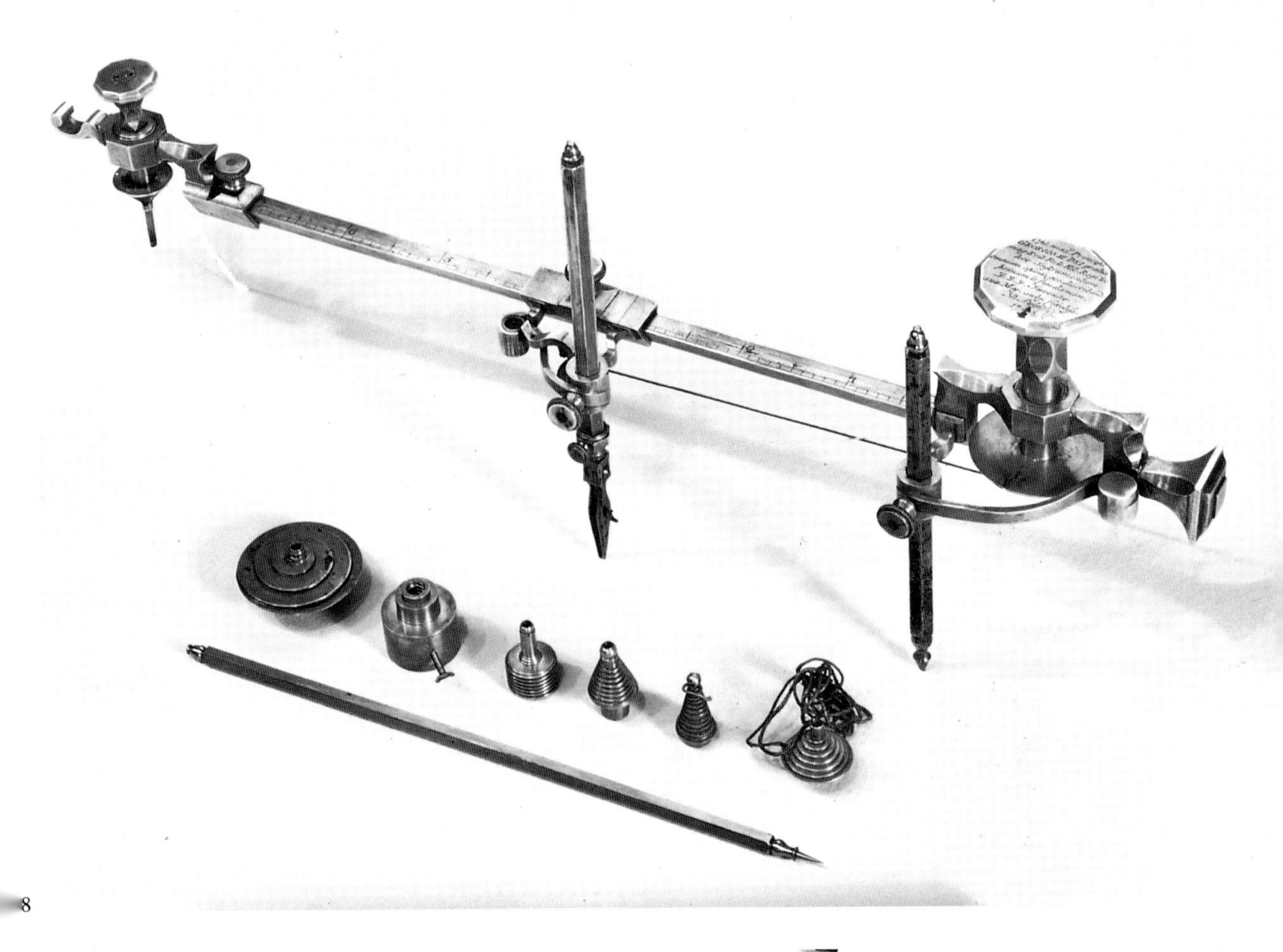

88

[87] Plate from Batty Langley's *Treasury of Designs* (1740) which shows the method of setting-out a volute for the Ionic order of architecture. Note the 'eye' from which the spiral springs.

[88] Volute compasses in silver made for George III and signed 'D. Lyle 1760'. These consist of a beam divided into inches similar to a beam compass, but with a helical drum unit fixed to the plane of the beam. A catgut thread connects the end of the helical curved spring to the pencil-holder. The beam is rotated with the centre fixed, and the drawing point traces a spiral curve. Alternative helical drums are included in the shagreen-covered fitted case for drawing different spiral curves. Beam length $7\frac{1}{2}$ in (190 mm). *George III Collection, Science Museum, London.*

[89] Helicograph designed by George Adams the Younger, shown in Plate XI (fig.6) of his *Geometrical and Graphical Essays* (1791 edn). The drawing point is moved towards the centre of the spiral by means of a pair of pulleys, one of which is stationary upon the axis while the other is fixed to revolve some distance from it. A thread passes over the helical drum and two pulleys to the drawing point.

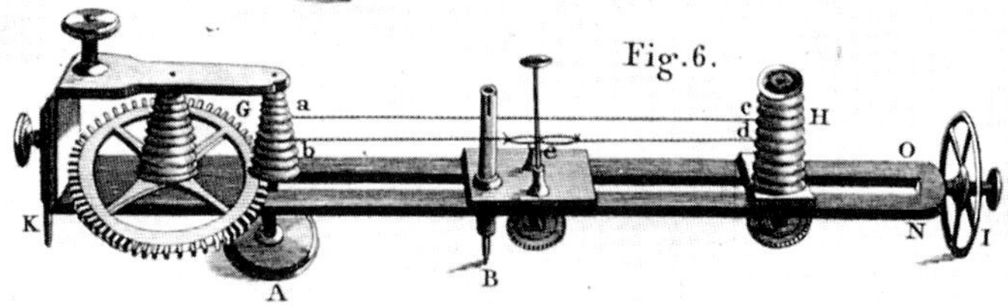

89

set by an exact scale engraved on it. Stanley stated in 1866, 'This instrument produces its lines with considerable accuracy but its defects are that it will not draw a spiral except near the centre of a moderately large drawing.' It was not suitable for small spirals and drew most easily in ink, unlike most of the other instruments.

In 1857 an instrument called a 'volutor' was patented by H. Johnson. This, like volute compasses and the helicograph, had to be placed centrally on the drawing paper. It was operated by a large handle, and the drawing point rotated anti-clockwise with a cord

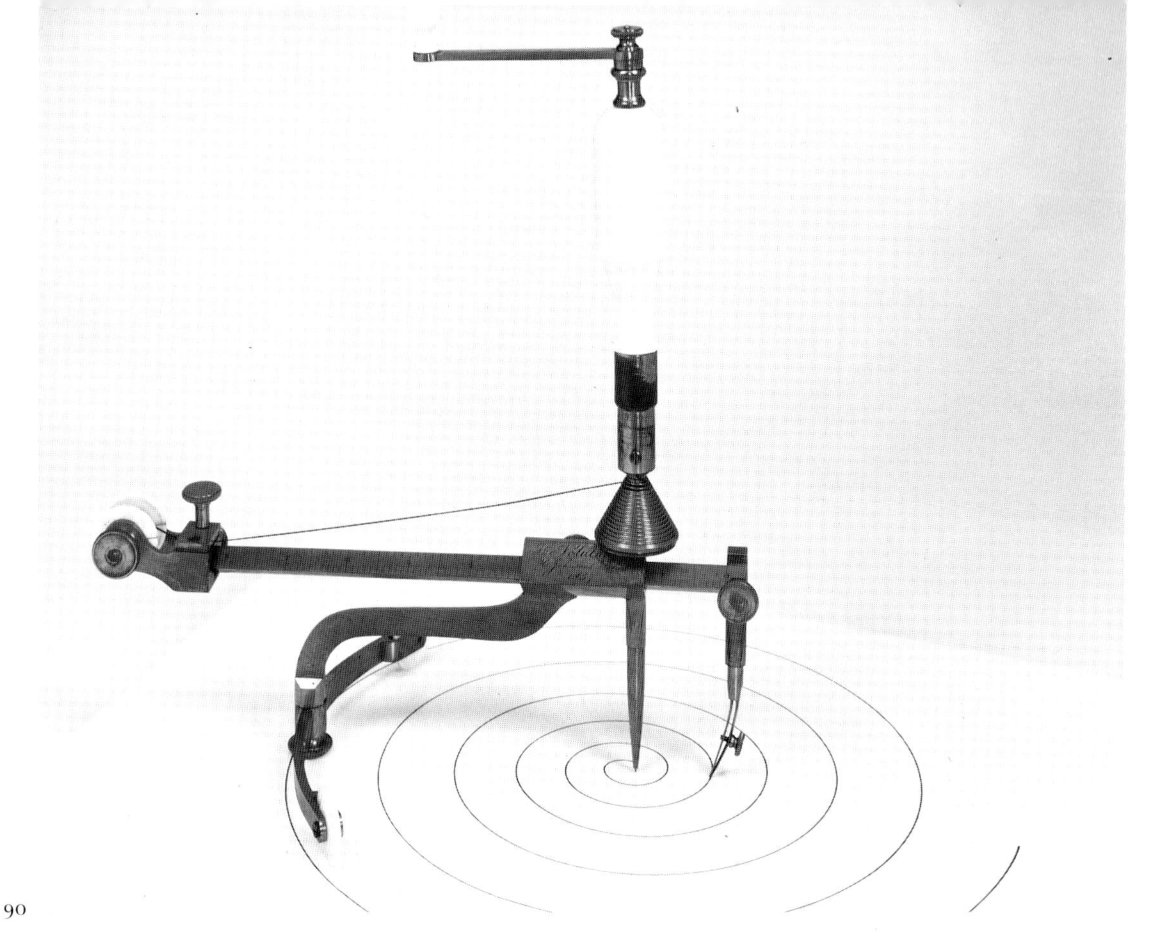

90

[90] Volutor inscribed 'The Volutor H Johnson's Patent 1857' in lacquered brass with a beam graduated 1–8 inches having horn wheels on the stand and a white china handle to operate the central drawing points. The set contains several helical cones to give differing spirals and a chord passes over the bone pulley. *Science Museum, London.*

[91] An early method of setting up a parabolic curve, as drawn by Leonardo da Vinci in a notebook now in the Ambrosiana Library, Milan.

[92] Parabolagraph designed by J. Payne of London University and made by Coradi, consisting of a series of adjustable rules operated from a horizontal frame raised slightly from the drawing surface. Late 19th century. *Science Museum, London.*

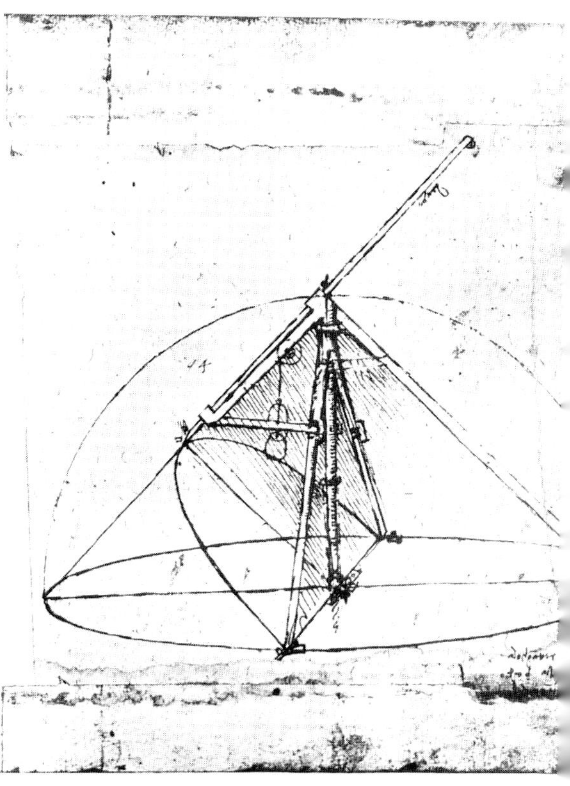

91

92

attached to one of several grooved helical cones to control the pen which drew the spiral [90].

Parabola and hyperbola

Two conic curves, parabola and hyperbola, were known to Apollonius in the second century BC. A facility for setting them out is extremely useful in forming or drawing arches, vaults, and so on, since these curves recur in their construction. Geometrically, this can be done with the aid of a straight edge or tee-square, a pin, some string and a pencil. Stanley describes a simple method in his *Mathematical Drawing Instruments* of 1866. An early attempt to design an instrument to set out a parabola is shown in a drawing by Leonardo da Vinci now in the Ambrosiana Library in Milan [91]. The geometry of conics (or cone-shaped objects) was first analysed in detail by the French geometrician, Gérard Desargues (1593–1662), a contemporary of René Descartes, and was later explored by the Englishman Peter Nicholson (1765–1844) at the end of the eighteenth century. Nicholson recognized that Greek mouldings were all based on conic sections, and he prepared plates on the geometry of conics for both Rees's *Cyclopaedia* of 1819 and the *Edinburgh Encyclopaedia* of 1808–1830. There seems to have been little interest among makers in devising instruments for plotting parabolas and hyperbolas, but late in the nineteenth century J. Payne of London University invented an elaborate instrument called a 'parabolagraph', which consisted of a series of adjustable curves [92].

Conchoid curves

Conchoid curves also date back to Classical times. The word conchoid derives from the name of the spiral conch shell; the conchoid is a plane curve invented to solve the problem of trisecting a plane angle. The earliest method of drawing a conchoid is attributed to Nicomedes, the Greek mathematician *c.*150 BC and is described by Peter Nicholson in detail in his *Five Orders of Architecture* of 1825, where he states that it enabled one to set out the flutes of a Classical column [93]. (Flutes, which increase the appearance of slenderness in a column, and the subtlety of entasis, which corrects the eyes' distortion of a column's vertical lines, were both introduced in Classical Greece.) Stanley refers to

TO DRAW THE FLUTES OF COLUMNS.

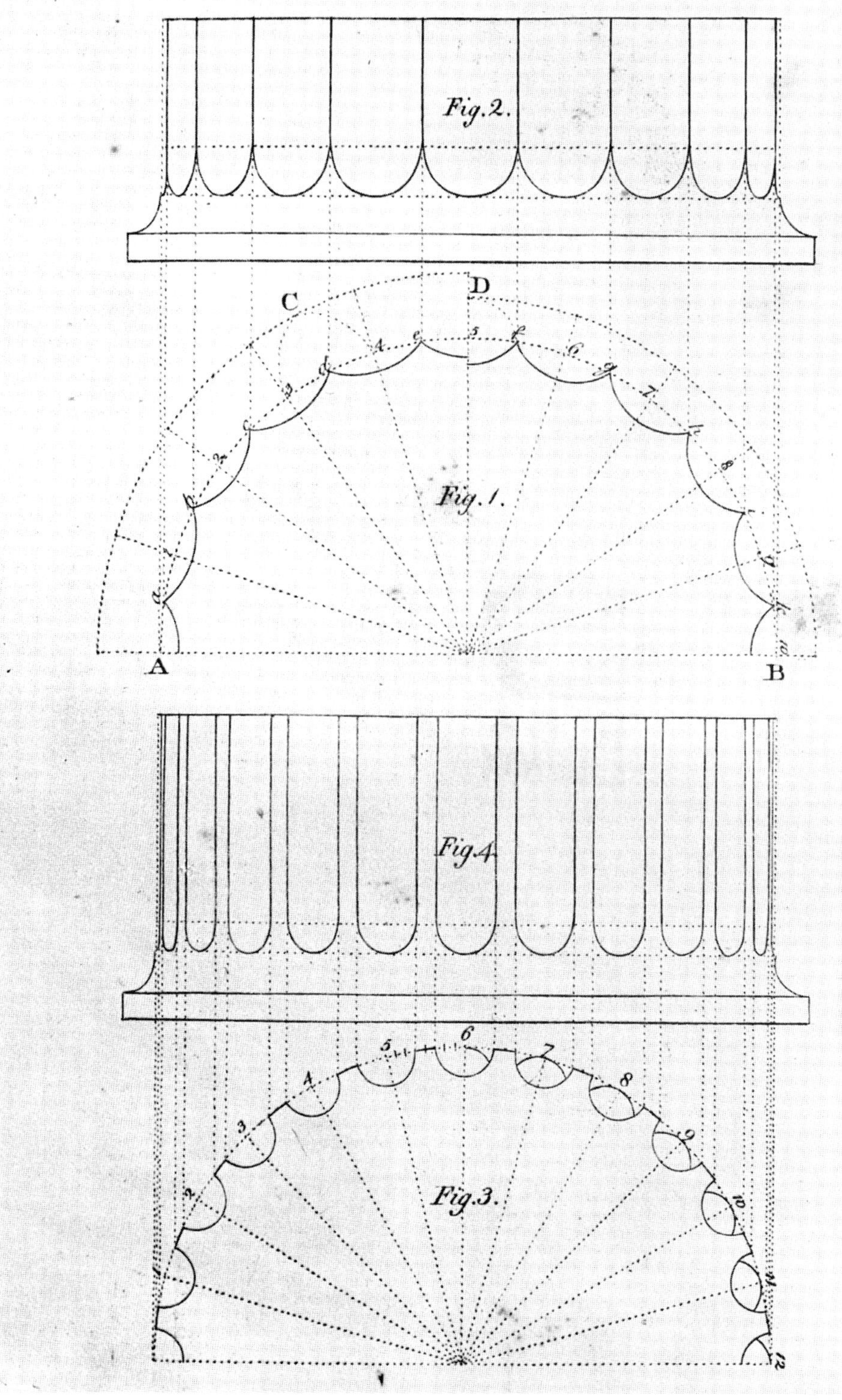

93

[93] Engraved plate by Peter Nicholson, originally included in his *Student's Instructor* of 1795. This shows the method of setting-out the flutes of a Doric column and the diminution in the diameter of the column in order to achieve slenderness. Plate 204 from Joseph Gwilt's *Principles of Architecture*. (1848 edn). *British Architectural Library*.

[94] W. F. Stanley's design for a conchoidograph as illustrated in his treatise *Mathematical Drawing Instruments* (1868 edn).

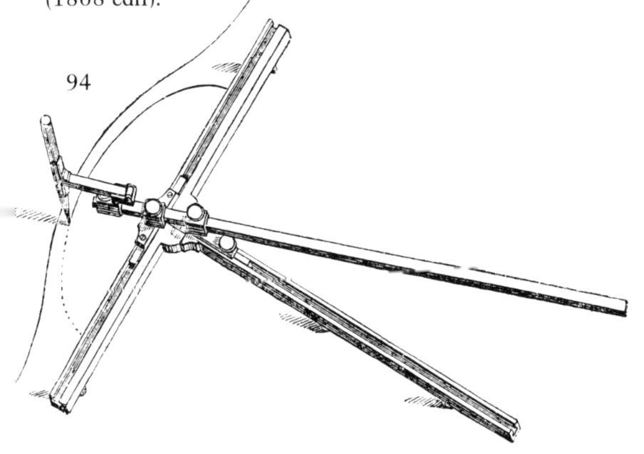

Nicholson's contribution when he describes his own design for an instrument called a 'conchoidograph' in 1866, which was sold by his firm until 1900 [94].

Large radius curves

Some curves of large radii, beyond the capacity of even a large beam-compass, were achieved using various devices including simple straight edges, pins and string. George Adams the Younger illustrated an instrument in 1791 for producing arcs of high radii.

John Farey's version of a similar instrument consists of a hinged rule which is held by weights to allow a pencil placed in a hole at the fulcrum joint to draw a flat arch [32]. In 1866 Stanley illustrated his 'centograph', designed to deal with the same problem.

Irregular curves

Iregular curves are required in both architectural and technical drawing. Smooth curves between two points which are not geometric could be achieved using carpenters' templates, and already by the sixteenth century ship's curves and 'sweeps' – templates cut either full-size or to scale to the outline required – had been introduced. Late-seventeenth century bow curves for the same purpose are more complex as can be seen from the timber version at the M.H.S., Oxford, which is adjustable by means of five spacers to form a variety of flat curves for designing window heads, arches, etc. A slightly smaller version of this type of bow curve, but made of ivory, was provided in a casket of instruments by Thomas Heath. From 1866 Stanley made a bow curve to give an outline for minimal curves. Slip curves were also made in which a thin slip of timber could be set into notches on the outer frame to give smooth curves of differing heights.

Individual drawing curves appear to have been made from 1700 onwards as aids to drawing the outline of complex curves found in domes, onion shaped roofs, etc [95]. By the early nineteenth century drawing curves were being made in France and Italy from pearwood, lime or similar stable woods. Irregular curves, or 'French curves' as they were called in Britain, were devised for drawing various intricate curved lines required in decorative drawings. These were originally made in pearwood by makers in France and sold in sets to give a range of sinuous lines. W. F. Stanley, who commenced in business with the manufacture of hardwood drawing aids, began producing his architectural curves, of rather squiggly outline, from *c.*1860. At the end of the nineteenth century sets of small French curves were available in Britain made of vulcanite or pearwood [96]. They were expensive and were usually kept in the lid or base compartment of a magazine case. Although celluloid was introduced after 1870 for curves, protractors and triangles, pearwood curves continued to be made until well after 1900, and Stanley still offered both pearwood and vulcanite in addition to celluloid curves in the 1925 catalogue. Acrylic sheet was introduced during the 1960s, from which date French curves in small sets were made in natural or coloured acrylic, the best being stamped; they form part of a draughtsman's standard equipment.

Railway curves or parallel curves were marked out by beam-compasses and cut from pearwood to be sold from 1850 onwards by such makers as Elliott, Stanley and Cary, packed in hardwood boxes containing 25, 50 or even 100 in a set. Similarly, ship's curves and those derived from helix, ellipses and parabolas were issued by the Admiralty. In Europe ship's curves were also made in series to suit the outlines required by different shipyards. In Munich curves were produced *c.*1905 in sets to the design of Professor L. Burmester (1840–1927).

Free curves

From the earliest times large continuous irregular curves have been set up by using a flexible strip of wood and blocks or weights to hold this in position. W. F. Stanley illustrates his versions of what were called 'weights and splines' in 1866. The weights were usually made of lead covered with mahogany and the splines of thin pieces of lancewood or red pine from

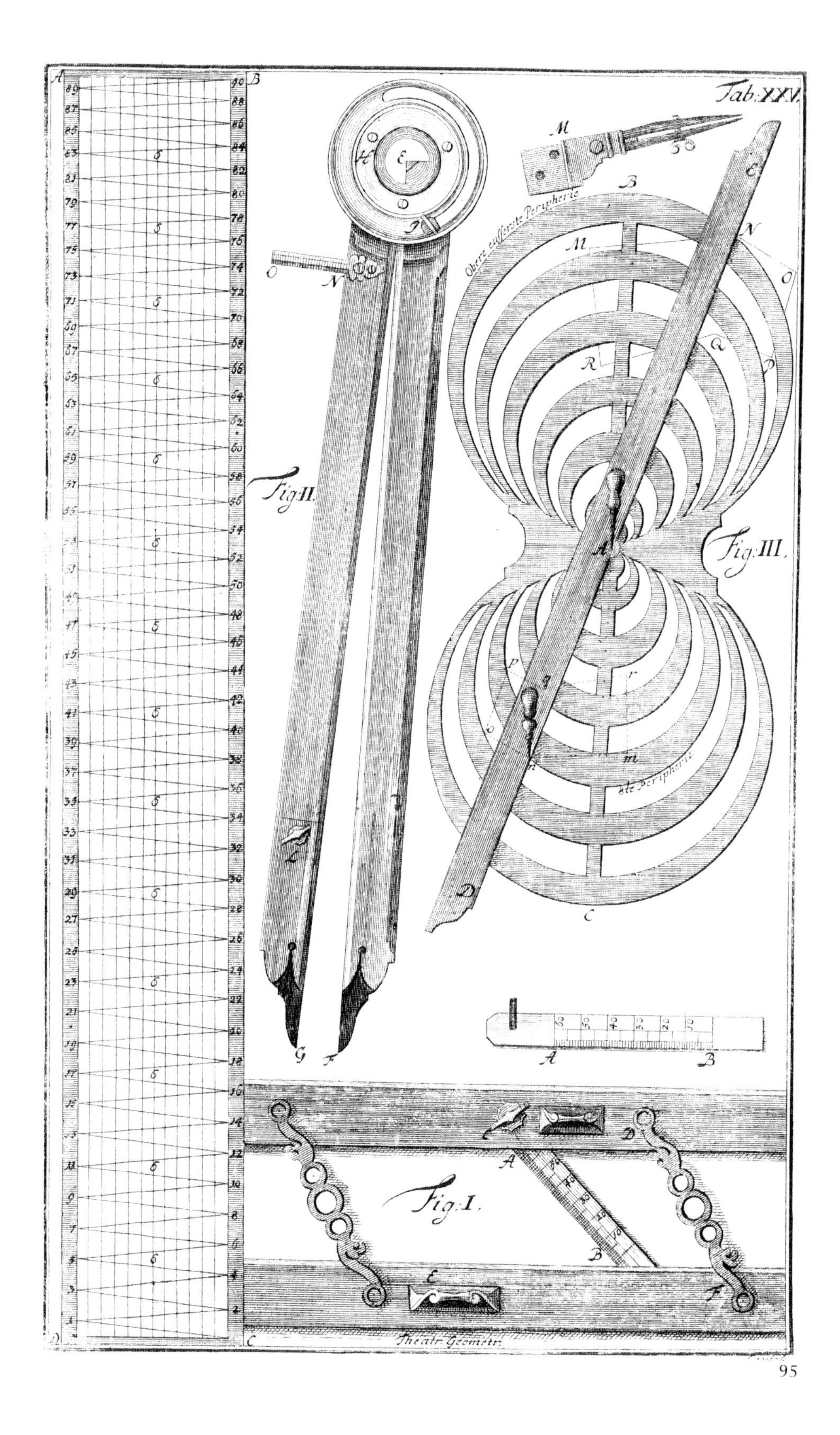
Tab. XXV.
Fig. II.
Fig. III.
Fig. I.
Oberz eusserste Peripherie
Theatr. Geometr.

95

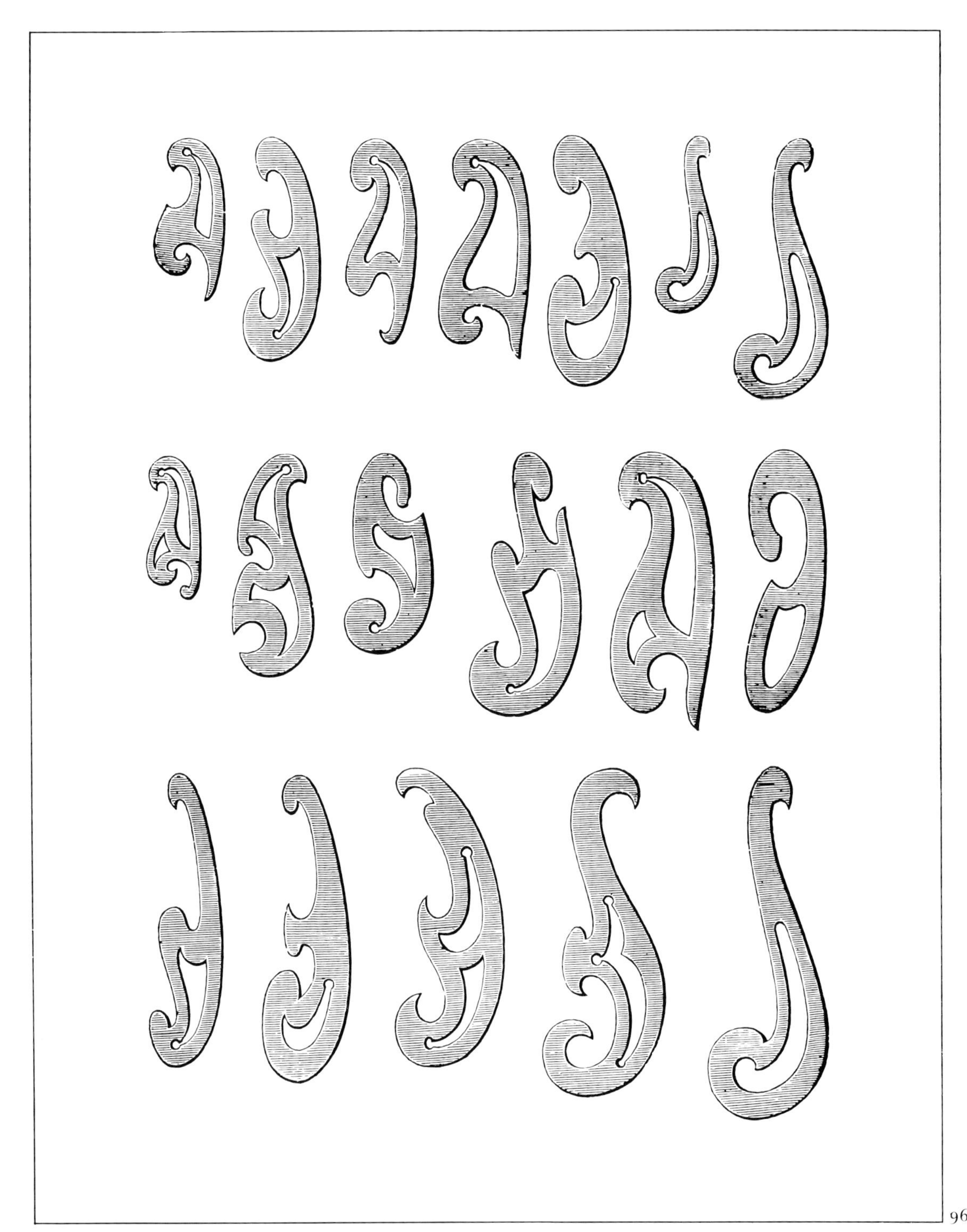

96

[95] Engraved plate from Jacob Leupold's *Theatrum arithmetico geometricum* (1727), which illustrates an unusual template, probably made of pearwood, as an aid to drawing the outline of complex curves found in domes, and onion-shaped roofs etc.

[96] Architectural drawing curves offered by Reeves & Sons, London, made of pearwood in 18 different shapes and sizes from 6 to 14 in long (152–356 mm). As illustrated in Reeves' catalogue dated 1904.

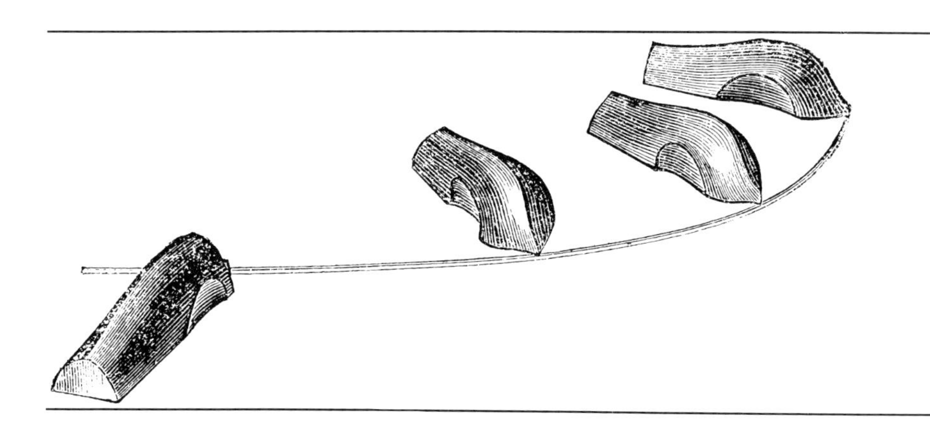

97

98

18 in (460 mm) to 8 ft (2440 mm) long [97]. The US instrument makers Keuffel & Esser produced a modern version of this until 1984, with lead weights and plastic splines.

Other versions of flexible curves can be found dating to the nineteenth century which consist of brass lazy tongs which set out a steel strip to act as a drawing edge. The bars were fitted with stiff friction hinges to retain the instrument in position. One design introduced by Brookes *c.*1900 was still included in the Stanley catalogue of 1925 in 9 in (230 mm) and 18 in (460 mm) long versions. This catalogue also includes the Stanley flexible curve ruler which consisted of a lead core with steel stiffeners sheathed in either metal or rubber casing. Flexible curves of this kind are still made by several manufacturers but usually sheathed in PVC colour coded to represent the firm which markets them. Keuffel & Esser produce an elegant black acrylic adjustable curve with an excellent drawing edge [98].

[97] 'Weights and splines' as used for drawing long free curves. The weights were made of lead covered with mahogany and the splines of thin tapered pieces of lancewood or red pine, from 18 inches to 8 feet long (457–2440 mm).

[98] Flexible curve rule made by Keuffel & Esser of flat section black acrylic perforated to allow it to form free curves strengthened by a metal wire spine; available in 12, 18, 24 and 30 inch lengths.

6

Squaring and Ruling

Squares

The carpenter's timber angle square and the mason's forged iron set square were the craftsman's traditional tools for setting off right angles. The Romans used a set square with a refined decorative shape to the exposed ends of each arm [10], a detail which was revived during the Renaissance [99].

By 1600 folding rules with either a sector hinge or a mitred hinge were designed to open into a right angle, and some had a brace to hold the arms in position. Giovanni Pomodoro included a fixed angle set square and details of the hinged version in his plate of 1599 [19]. Nicolas Bion illustrated both versions in his Plate 9 of 1709, where 'O' shows a brace and a plumb-bob with a line for use in surveying [22]. Joseph Moxon in 1701 describes the 'Square' as being 'made of brass or wood; sometimes made with a joint to fold or for use on a Drawing Board'. These folding rules, hinged to form set squares, were sometimes provided in instrument cases from 1700 onwards, and examples by diverse makers survive. Several eighteenth-century French makers supplied set squares with the plumb-bob aperture, which became a formalized shape as can be seen from eighteenth-century examples by Canivet [100] and Quillet, and early-nineteenth-century examples by Surçou and Lenoir [163]. Fixed angle set squares were provided in some eighteenth-century cases, usually of brass, though in Germany these were often made of hardwood or ebony.

TRIANGLE SET SQUARES

Triangle set squares first appear in the seventeenth century as an aid to drawing at specific angles. An interesting surviving example from the period is the 60°/60° metal version in Sir Roger North's case of mathematical instruments of *c.*1680 [150]. There are two brass triangle set squares in a case by Richard Glynne (fl.1705–30) of *c.*1730; one made to give 45° and the other 30°/60°. hardwood triangle set squares are to be found in many eighteenth-century German instrument cases; one was illustrated by Johann Penther in his Plate I of 1732 [25]. The French architect Jean-Jacques Lequeu shows a small ebony-edged triangle set square in his plate on drawing aids and media of 1788 [7]. George Adams the Younger shows triangles in 1791 but there are none by John Farey in any of his early-nineteenth-century plates on drawing instruments.

Triangles came into common use in the early-nineteenth-century with the general introduction of larger drawing boards and large tee-squares for technical drawing. To begin with versions in pearwood were imported into England from Italy and France, but W. F. Stanley set up in business in 1853 by making pearwood and mahogany triangles, and by 1860 he had introduced his improved framed mahogany triangle, provided with ebony bevelled drawing edges. These continued to be produced by the firm of Stanley until 1940 [101A]. By 1900 small triangle set squares made of vulcanite were quite common, usually kept in the lid or base of a magazine case. Glass was tried but it did not prove a practical material. From 1900 celluloid was more commonly used since it combined lightness with transparency – a great advantage for draughtsmen; plain triangle set squares continued to be made of celluloid until the 1960s when acrylic sheet was introduced. Today the best quality and the most accurate set squares are those which are moulded and provided with a bevelled edge for ink drawing. In the larger sizes they remain standard items of drawing equipment; the cheaper ranges are stamped.

Mention should be made here of the various special set squares made from 1860 onwards as aids for drawing certain common angles used regularly, such as 'slopes and batters' made for railway engineers for embankments and a choice of 'roof pitches' made for architects' use, usually of vulcanite (a rubber treated with sulphur).

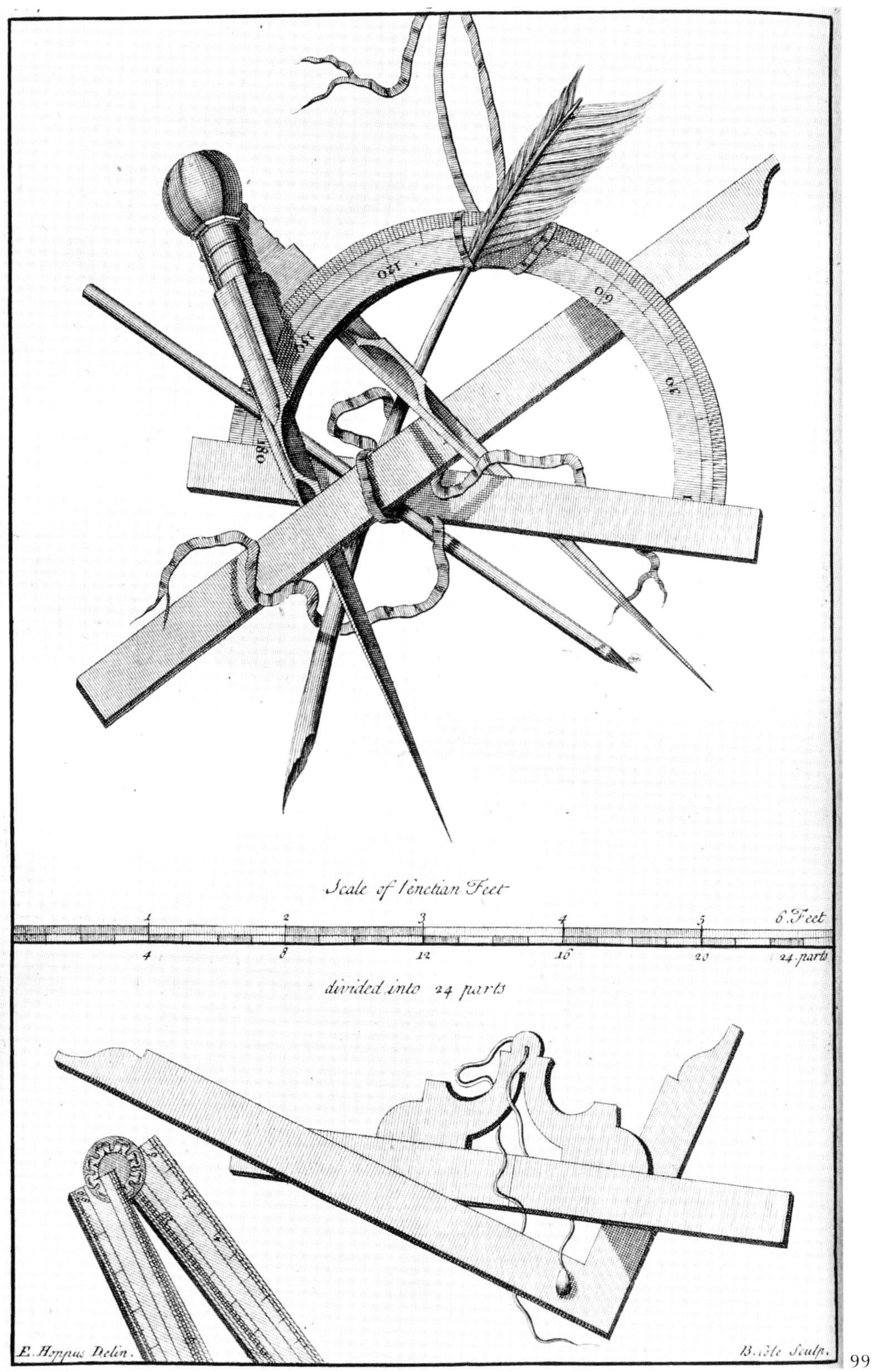
Scale of Venetian Feet
1
2
3
4
5
6 Feet
4
8
12
16
20
24 parts
divided into 24 parts
E. Hoppus Delin.
B. Cole Sculp.

99

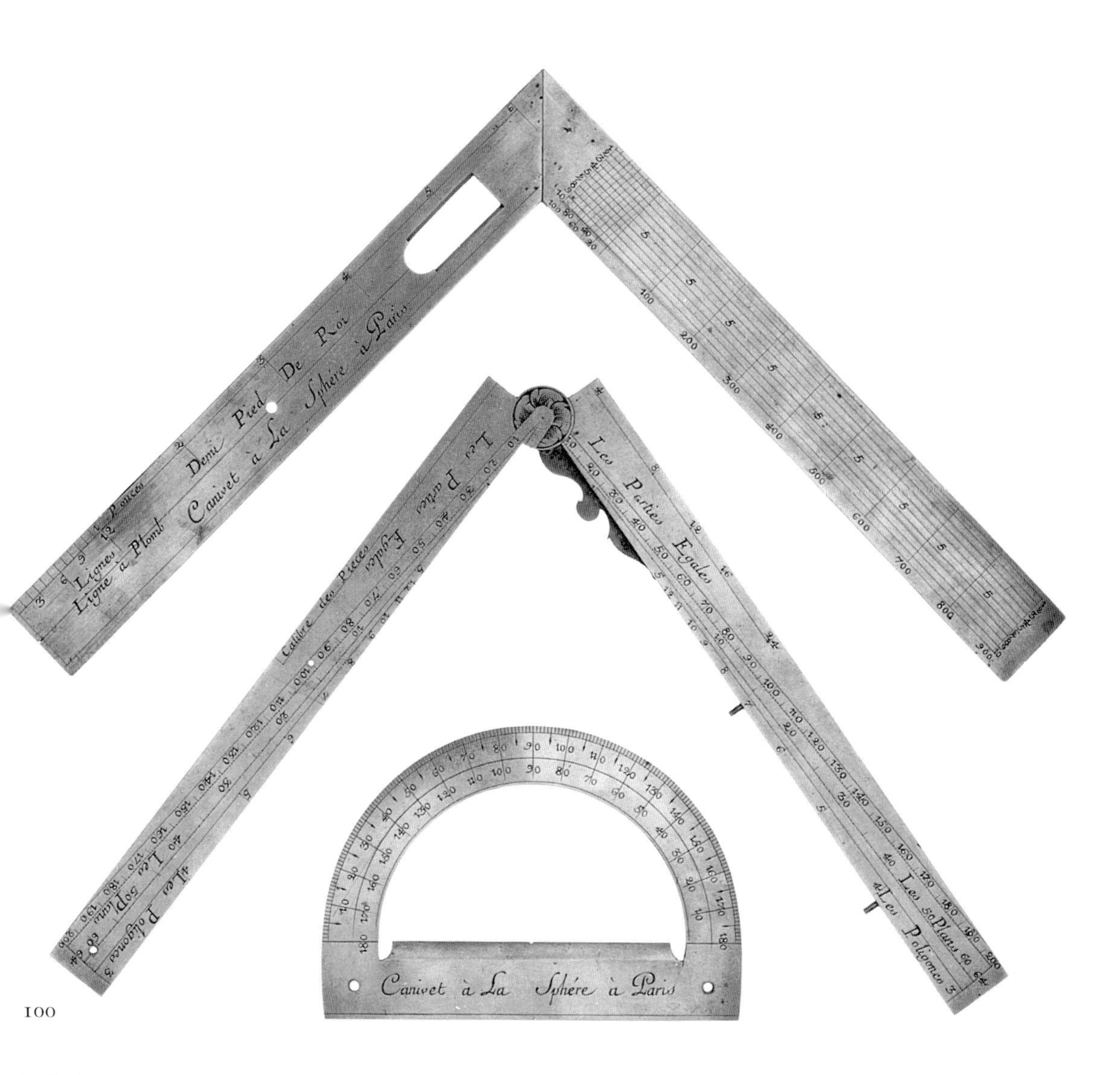

100

[99] Plate by Edward Hoppus, engraved by Benjamin Cole, from *Palladio's Architecture* published in London in 1733, showing a set square and rule together with a plumb-level and sector. Above the scale, which is given in Venetian feet, is a protractor, with rule and dividers, pencil and quill pen.

[100] Folding brass rule hinged to form a set square, inscribed 'Canivet à La Sphére à Paris', graduated with a scale of *Demi Pied de Roi* and provided with a cut-out to take a plumb-bob and line; shown with a protractor by the same maker. *c.*1750. *Private collection.*

ADJUSTABLE SET SQUARES

From 1600 onwards several attempts were made to provide hinged set squares with graduated arcs or protractors which enabled them to be set to any desired angle. There are examples of early instruments made of ivory with black indices in some museum collections and the various triangulation instruments which date from 1600 to 1700 combined sighting devices together with the purpose of drawing surveys and setting off known angles. The German geometrician Jacob Leupold illustrated an unusual adjustable folding rule in 1727.

Further efforts were made after 1800 to provide simple yet accurate instruments that could adjust to any angle, internal or external. John Farey included mention of a 'bevel' in his text for the *Edinburgh Encyclopaedia* of 1830 and illustrates his version [33]. The name 'bevel' continued to be used by English engineers into the twentieth century. W. F. Stanley's version of the bevel was what he called an 'isograph'. This

[101A] Stanley framed mahogany set squares with bevelled ebony drawing edges: 45 and 30/60. Late 19th century. *John Cook, Oxford.*

[101B] Assorted set squares: 45° mahogany with dowels to the mitred joints; small versions 30°, 60° and 45° in black vulcanite; Marquois $22\frac{1}{2}$° and $67\frac{1}{2}$° in boxwood marked ELLIOTT BRO^S LONDON, 11 × 4 in (272 × 100 mm). Late 19th century.

101A

101B

102

[102] (*Above*) Isograph designed by W. F. Stanley to provide an adjustable set square giving the corresponding angles so often required in architectural and mechanical drawing; boxwood, with brass plates to the hinge which incorporates a Vernier protractor. Usually 12 in (305 mm) long. (*Below*) Rolling parallel rule of ebony with ivory bevelled drawing edges graduated as scales of 1, ½ and ¾ inch, brass rollers and cross bar; inscribed BAKER HIGH HOLBORN LONDON. 12 × 2⅝ in (305 × 68 mm). *c.*1900. *RIBA Drawings Collection, London.*

[103] Adjustable set square of clear acrylic sheet with bevelled drawing edges, chrome-plated setting arc graduated 0–90° and a milled setting knob. True-Angle by Blundell Harling. 10 in (250 mm). 1980.

consisted of a folding boxwood rule with a brass Vernier protractor incorporated into the hinge so that the rule could be set to any desired angle [102]. Stanley's firm also sold a simpler set square called a Clinograph *c.*1924 for drawing repeated angles.

It was not until the 1920s that a really practical version of an adjustable set square was mass produced in England. W. F. Stanley included their version, made of transparent celluloid with a white setting-arc, in their 1924 catalogue. A. G. Thornton of Manchester produced their 'Kinwest' pattern in various sizes from the 1930s until the 1960s. This form of instrument was, surprisingly, unique to Britain until the 1970s; until then neither North America nor Europe seemed to value its use so much as did British architectural and engineering draughtsmen. Since then adjustable set squares have been made by several European manufacturers in a range of sizes from 4 to 12 in (100 to 300 mm), in acrylic sheet with either a stainless steel or chrome-plated setting-arc on precision models. These are simple and effortless to use, and consequently protractors are now seldom needed by architects, engineers and graphic artists for general purpose drawing [103].

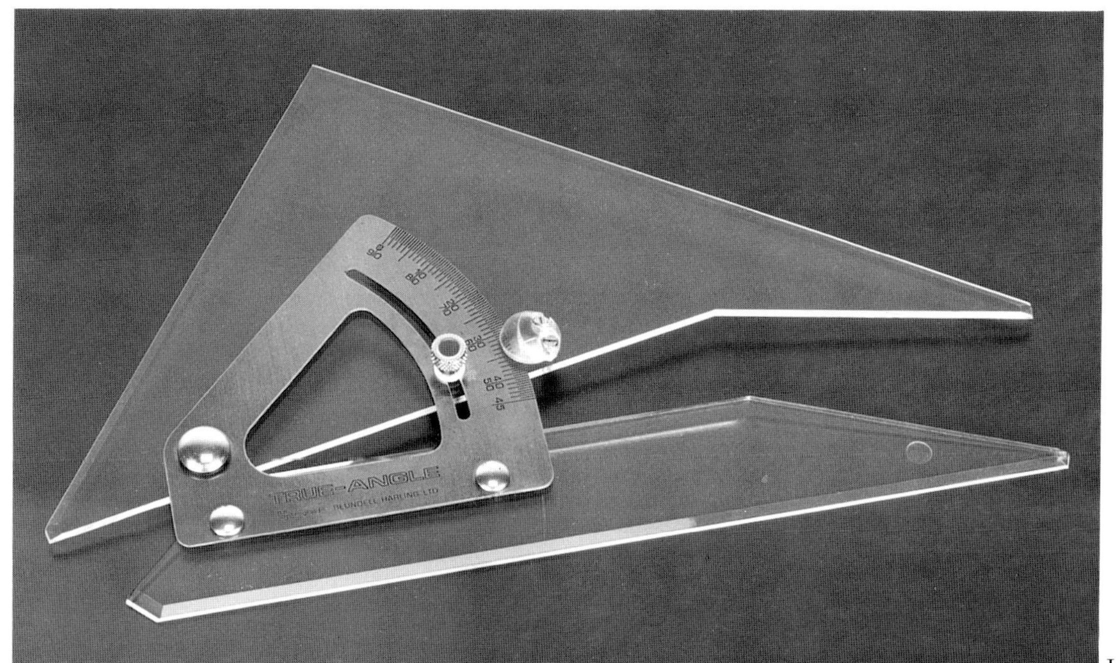

103

Rules

The carpenter's rule or straight edge performed the function of a ruling edge (an improvement on the use of a piece of cord covered with chalk which, when released against a flat surface, would leave a straight guideline for primitive craftsmen). Rules of brass, bronze and iron were used for setting out straight lines in Roman times, just as latte or laths were during the medieval period and brass and hardwood rules during the early Renaissance.

By the seventeenth century many sets of instruments included rules made of brass for use as a straight edge or, combined with measuring scales or folding rules, for use when surveying. A separate rule with one bevelled edge for drawing was sometimes provided in eighteenth-century instrument cases. The bevelled edge on any instrument gave a better drawing edge for use with a ruling pen since it prevented the pen from flooding against the edge. The small ivory or boxwood scale rule provided in pocket cases from this date was not so reliable since its edge tended to become notched or uneven.

PARALLEL RULES

By 1700 parallel rules of brass had been introduced to assist in drawing parallel lines accurately with an even, unscarred drawing edge. These were used by architects, engineers and cartographers together with a scale rule which gave the ratio reductions of standard measures in order to produce orthogonal drawings. Bion illustrates two versions in his 1709 Plate 9 [22], one with plain parallel links and the other with scissored links. Throughout the eighteenth century variations of these were made in brass, silver, ebony, ivory or mahogany, with the links made of brass or silver. [104] In England Richard Glynne, Thomas Wright and Thomas Heath among others made pierced and engraved parallel rules of silver of exceptional quality [170 and X] which fitted neatly into their pocket cases.

The range of rules available at the end of the eighteenth century can be seen in George Adams the Younger's Plate II of 1797 [105]. Parallel rules do not appear to be so common in French pocket cases or small boxes. Double parallel rules, usually made of ivory or ebony, became popular in England in the late eighteenth century since the ruling edge moved a greater distance across the paper [106]. Both types of parallel rule were used without a tee-square and were moved up the drawing by hand. They were therefore liable to error when used for large drawings. Parallel rules are still used with nautical charts, however, but these are normally laid out on a grid.

ROLLING PARALLEL RULES

According to John Robertson in the 1775 edition of

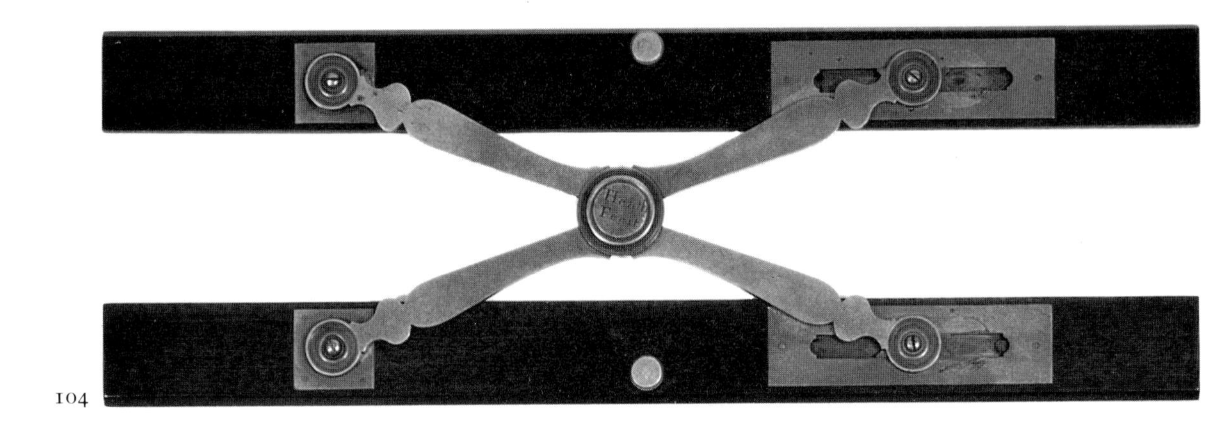

104

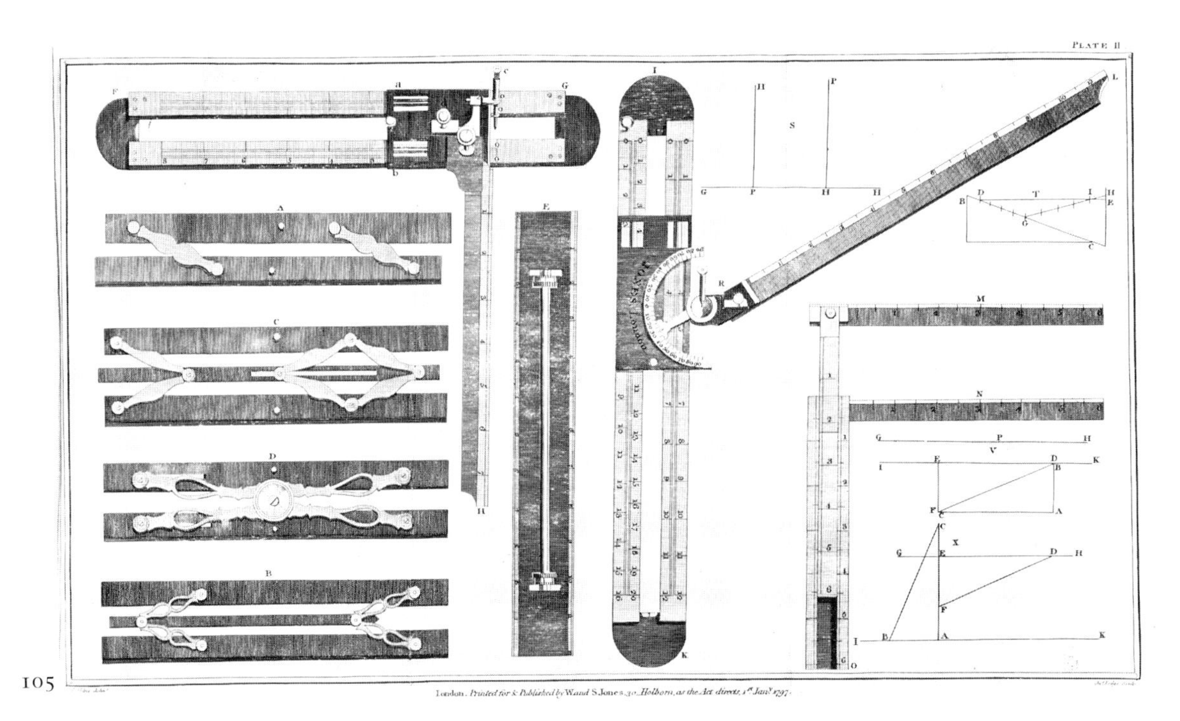
PLATE II
London, Printed for & Published by W and S Jones 30 Holborn, as the Act directs, 1st Jany 1797.

105

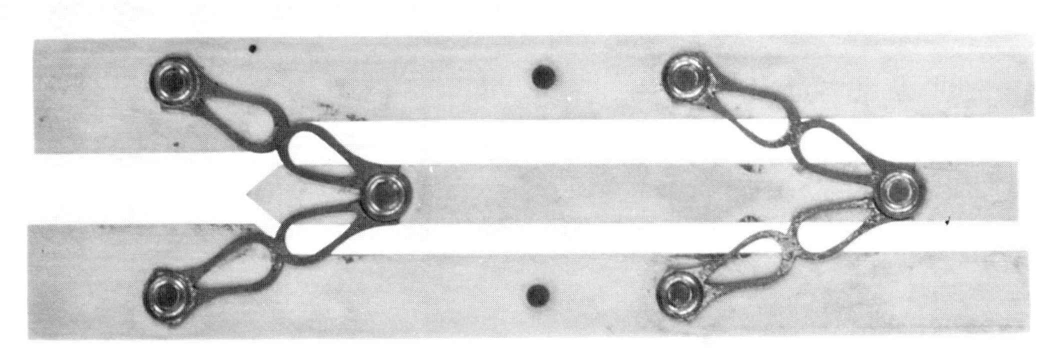

106

his treatise, A. G. Eckhardt invented the rolling parallel rule in 1771, and left the patent with Peter Dollond. An example by Dollond is in the Oxford Museum of the History of Science. The instrument soon became popular judging from small versions in ivory to be seen in cases by John Berge (*c.*1742–1808) and Jesse Ramsden. (The latter combined it with a rectangular protractor [161B].)

During the nineteenth century rolling parallel rules were frequently made of ebony with ivory scales set to the bevelled drawing edges. Usually 10 in (250 mm) or 12 in (305 mm) long, they were provided with brass or nickel-silver serrated wheels to ensure perfect rolling contact with the drawing surface. A piece of metal or hardwood fixed over the axle could be used for moving the ruler along [102]. However, even the best were difficult to use and, once truly aligned tee-squares became available, they were no longer used for large drawings.

Like the sector, the rolling parallel rule continued to be provided by tradition in some comprehensive cases of drawing instruments of the first half of the twentieth century, and it was still included in W. F. Stanley's last catalogue of 1960.

TEE-SQUARES

The history of the tee-square is quite separate from that of the other rules since it has its origin in the sixteenth-century carpenter's blade and stock fixed at right angles to each other. One of the earliest illustrations to show a tee-square used with a drawing board appears in Jean Dubreuil's *La perspective practique* of 1642 [5]. An English eighteenth-century handbook by William Salmon, *Palladio Londinensis* of 1734, illustrates a plain tee-square and a tee-square with an adjustable blade [107]. These simple tee-squares, used with a drawing board and large sheets of paper, were available for early technical drawings and can be seen in the German work by Leupold of *c.*1727 (Plate XVIII) and in Lequeu's French Plate [7] 1782.

In the early nineteenth century Farey illustrates a tee-square combined with protractor for drawing lines at desired angles set on a drawing board together with a bevel. Some tee-squares were made where the stock and blade were adjustable by means of a large milled screw. Others were – and still are – made with a protractor, sometimes incorporating a Vernier.

It is to W. F. Stanley that we owe the form of the British mahogany tee-square, now commonplace. Stanley was responsible for the improved joint where the blade is tapered and set into the stock with counter-sunk screws as permanent fixing, the bevelled ebony drawing edges and carefully seasoned mahogany. Tee-squares are still made today using prime seasoned mahogany since the true alignment of the blade to the stock must be maintained throughout the instrument's life or an inaccurate drawing will result [108]. Stanley also improved the drawing board to provide an even surface with ledged braces, which prevent the wood from warping, and ebony drawing edges.

The mahogany tee-square has remained a common item of drawing equipment in the twentieth century, available in sizes to suit the drawing boards which, in turn, are usually based on standard Imperial paper sizes. (The latter sizes were traditional until 1972 when the international standards based on metric 'A' sizes were introduced. Before this drawing papers in Britain were made to Royal, Imperial, Elephant, Double Elephant and Antiquarian sizes among others.) Since 1930 tee-squares have been made with celluloid bevelled drawing edges (in lieu of ebony) to enable a clear view of the lines being drawn. More recently they have been marketed with the entire blade made of acrylic sheet so that none of the drawing is obscured.

PARALLEL MOTION RULES

A hint of the principle of parallel motion straight edges used for drawing long parallel lines can be seen in early perspective machines or devices [139]. Some of the first drawing machines made in the late nineteenth century used a rule device restrained at both edges of the drawing board. W. F. Stanley illustrated a drawing machine with a parallel motion rule operated by piano wire guides in their 1924 catalogue but it did not prove very satisfactory. There are now numerous ver-

[104] A parallel rule of mahogany with brass scissored links and slotted plate with knobs to adjust the distance between the rules, signed 'THeath Fecit'. Length 14 in (362 mm). Mid-18th century. *Private collection.*

[105] Parallel rules: four versions of 6-inch parallel rules – (A) plain, (D) with scissored links, (C) double parallel rule with parallel links, (B) double rule with scissored links; (E) a 12-inch parallel rolling rule; (F), (G) and (H) parallel rule/set square for setting off right angles; (I), (K) and (L) protracting parallel rule for setting off any angle; (M), (N) and (O) Haywood's parallel rule which resembles a gauge. Pl. II from the revised edition (1797) of George Adams the Younger's *Geometrical and Graphical Essays.*

[106] Double parallel rule in ivory with brass scissored links. From Troughton pocket case, *c.*1780. 6 in (152 mm). *Private collection.*

sions using this principle and it has become widely accepted for use in large drawing offices. The blade or ruling edge can be made of hardwood, anodized aluminium or transparent or opaque acrylic. A variety of mechanisms for movement are used, from guide tracks or wires to axles with toothed belts fitted to the edges of the drawing boards. A simple but effective version is made by Mayline in the United States in which a black acrylic blade is raised away from the drawing paper by miniature nylon rollers so that it does not drag any dirt onto the paper. This system uses neat chrome pins and guides for the piano wires to fix it to the edges of the drawing board, which is usually maintained in a flat position. It retains the parallel motion automatically, and the blade can be moved up and down with only slight pressure at any point of its length.

Since 1980 several manufacturers of plastic drawing aids, such as Rotring and Marabu of Germany, have produced a range of small drawing boards or small drawing machines with acrylic tee-squares or parallel rules incorporated. The large complex drafting machines introduced since 1900, now commonly used in engineering offices and graphic design studios, are not within the scope of this book.

107

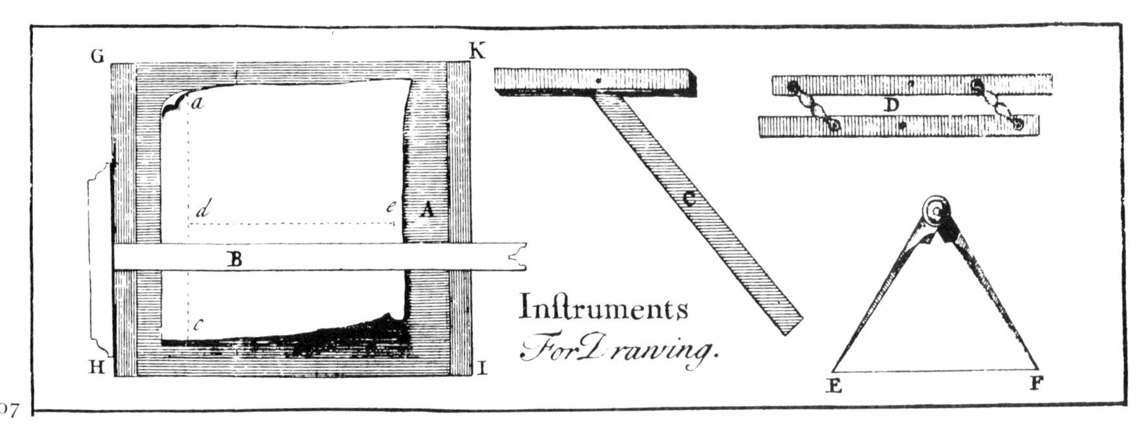

108

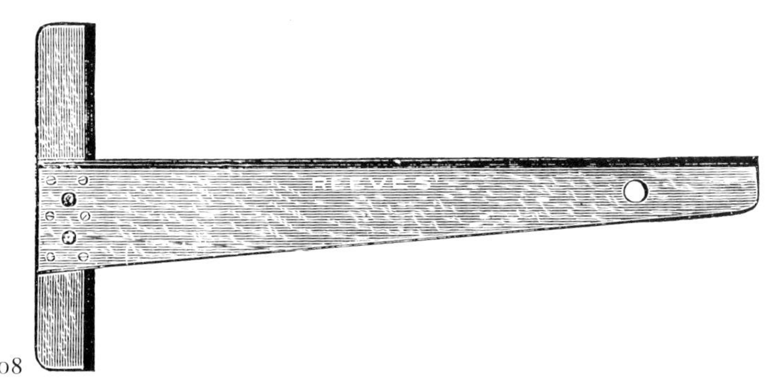

[107] Engraving from William Salmon's *Palladio Londinensis* of 1734 which shows a plain tee-square and its use with paper on a drawing board together with an adjustable version, a parallel rule and dividers.

[108] Mahogany tee-square, with ebony drawing edges: introduced in mid-19th century, this design continued in use for over one hundred years.

7

Measurement

Measuring to scale

Measuring to scale has ancient origins as is witnessed by the plotting scales depicted on relief panels found at the base of statues from Gudea in Babylon of *c.* 1230 BC (now in the Louvre in Paris). Early civilizations are known to have had various standard measures based on anthropomorphic dimensions which related to parts of the human body as do the Imperial measures still in use today. The thumb relates to the inch; the foot is self-evident; and the arm's length or ell, later called a yard, is three times the foot. The Greek and Roman foot continued in use throughout Europe until the medieval period and beyond in various local variants. In fact versions of feet and inches remained the basis for most European measures for building until the nineteenth century and for some craftsmen until after World War I.

Bronze or iron scale rules were the earliest linear measures, and by 1500 most European cities had their own version of a foot-rule or yard-stick, fixed either to the wall of the town hall or to the city gates to proclaim its common use within a certain boundary.

SCALE RULES

Normal *measuring scales*, usually provided with local versions of foot divisions, were provided as straight or folding rules made of brass, bronze, ivory or boxwood from Roman times. These rules were for taking measurements of objects, land or buildings and for setting out purposes, but although they were sometimes included in instrument cases, they cannot really be considered as drawing instruments. Measuring scales have also often been incorporated on the arms of other drawing instruments such as squares, sectors, parallel rules, rolling parallel rules and pantographs.

Drawing scales enable one to represent a subject on a drawing to a recognizable reduction or constant ratio of the actual or proposed size. This degree of sophistication was not reached until the Renaissance, i.e. *c.* 1450 in Italy and *c.* 1550 in North Europe. Scales made of either brass or silver, based on local variations of a standard foot, are to be found in most European early mathematical instrument cases. At first these scales were crudely divided but later often finely engraved, and a maker's skill was judged both by the accuracy of the divisions and the marking of the indices with numerals. (This was made easier once Arabic numerals were introduced *c.* 1500.) Scales dating from 1500 to 1600, sometimes embellished with engraved decoration, are often testimonies to both their makers' mathematical and artistic skills [149]. Drawing scales with personal decoration by the maker continued to be made during the seventeenth century and later, as can be seen from examples by Nicolas Bion, Michael Butterfield, Thomas Tuttell and Edmund Culpeper (fl. 1660–1738) [109]. By the mid-eighteenth century, however, their form had become more functional; they were made of brass, silver, ivory or boxwood, and usually only 4½ or 6 in (114 or 152 mm) long when included in a small case. These small drawing scales were often combined with a rectangular protractor or included on a parallel rule; the arrangement of individual scales needs close examination.

English drawing scales were set out in inches, usually with one face divided into a scale of equal parts, sometimes given as six lines of inches divided into 25, 30, 35, 40, 45, and 60 equal parts. (By 1700 decimal ratio divisions of an inch were common for drawing purposes.) Diagonal scales were also included, sometimes on the reverse side, for use when plotting land measures of chains and links. These enabled the user to divide any given quantity into one hundred parts by transversals (usually 1 in or ½ in long). Proportional scales (usually described as 'Gunter's scales') were also given on some drawing scales, for logarithmic calculations involving chords, sines, secants, tangents, etc [110]. The introduction of fractions of an inch for both architectural and engineers' drawings commenced before the end of the eighteenth

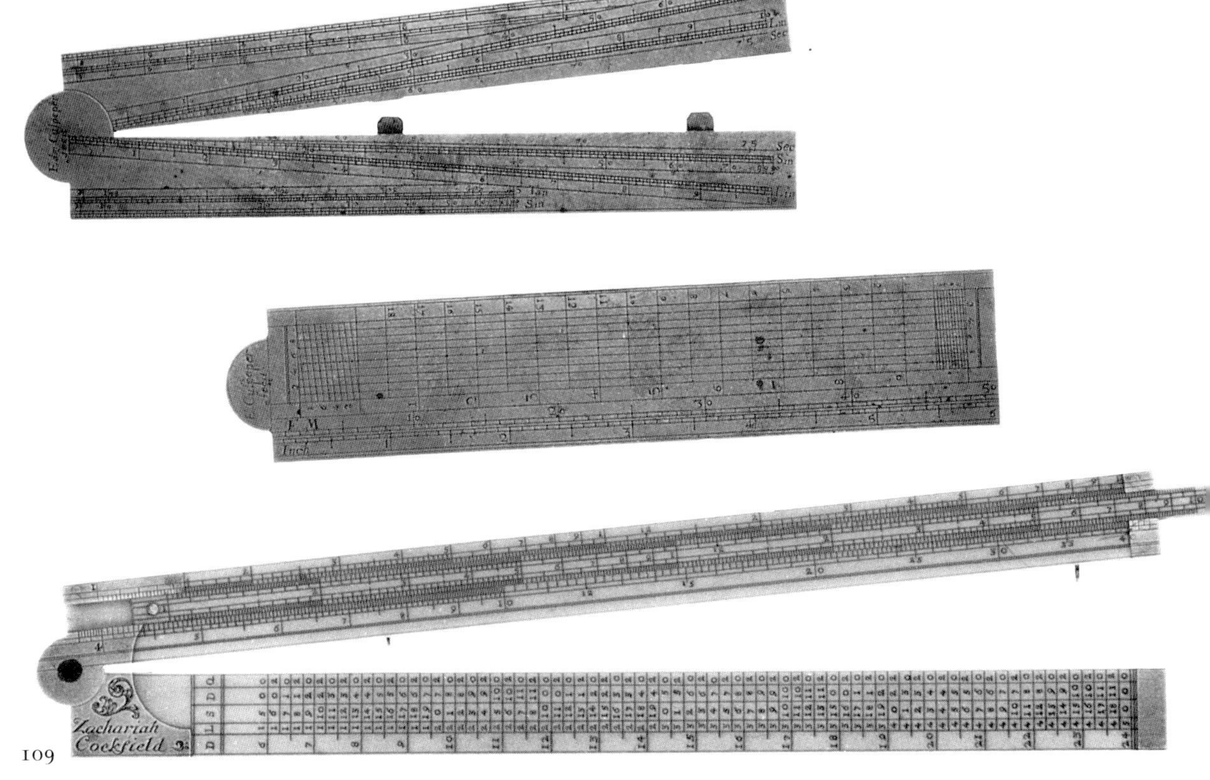

109

[109] Brass scale signed 'E Culpeper fecit,' graduated with diagonal scales and an inch scale to one edge. Shown with sector also by Culpeper and a boxwood combined scale rule and slide rule. Early 18th century. Length 6 in (152 mm).

[110] Engraved plate of instruments by Jonathan Sisson showing both faces of a 6-inch sector (A and B): a protractor combined with diagonal scales (C), and decimals of an inch and proportional logarithmic scales (D). *c.*1740.

century, and early-nineteenth-century scales often combine the decimal divisions of an inch with the new fraction scales. In his *Practical Builder and Workman's Companion*, of 1837, Peter Nicholson illustrates this transitional form of scale [111].

Small French drawing scales were usually inscribed *demi pied du roi*, being only 6 in (152 mm) long, and were sub-divided into *pouces* and *lignes*. Diagonal scales were often included on the reverse side.

From 1600 onwards various European drawing scales were made with comparative indices for the inch or foot scales of different local cities or areas. One late-seventeenth-century German scale included inch scales for six local cities. The reverse of this scale by Brander & Hoeschel gives a diagonal plotting scale. In 1775 Georg F. Brander (1713–83) recorded the complexity of the European situation when he made a comparative scale with divisions for the versions of an inch scale of 68 different cities and districts. A boxwood scale of *c.*1800 includes a number of local inch measures, among them Saxon, Hamburg, English, Prussian and old French, together with English standard measures, and compares those with the new metric measure of centimetres. This practice continued well into the nineteenth century, and a comparative scale board made by Elliott *c.*1840 is still divided into inches, *lignes* ($\frac{1}{12}$th inch) from fifteen European localities together with centimetres [112].

The French standard measure – the *pied du roi* – was used until the introduction of the metric system in 1794 (just after the Revolution). On some scales after 1800 the centimetre scale was included together with the old scale, renamed *pied de France*. The metre as the official linear measure was established in France by decree in 1799 as part of the decimal system. It was based on scientific measurements related to calculations of the exact diameter of the earth, and it was part of a system which included the rationalization of all weights and measures in France. The metre was taken as being a ten-millionth part of the quadrant of the earth from the equator to the pole. Despite the period of Napoleonic control over Europe

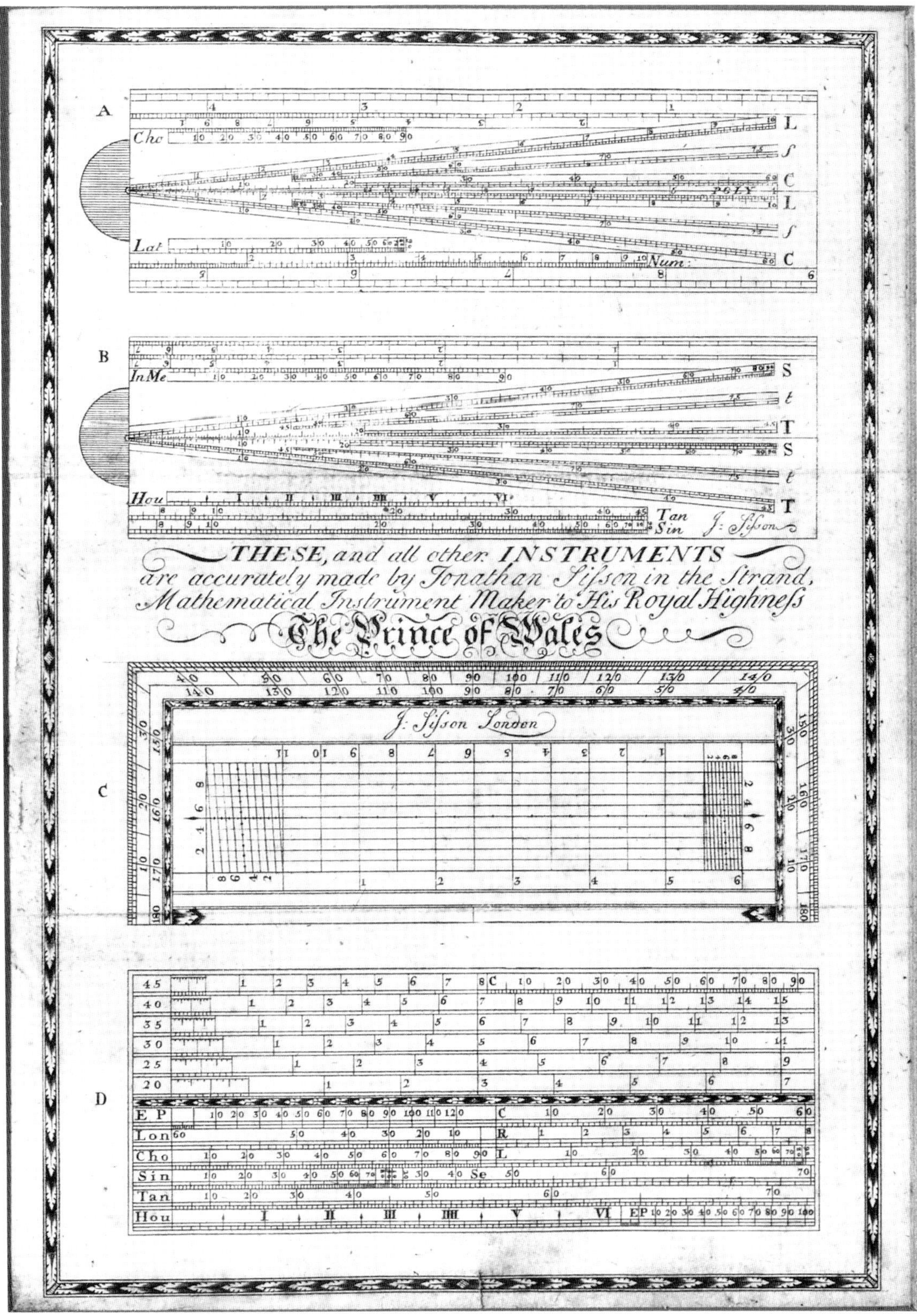
A
B
C
D
THESE, and all other INSTRUMENTS
are accurately made by Jonathan Sisson in the Strand,
Mathematical Instrument Maker to His Royal Highness
The Prince of Wales
J: Sisson
J: Sisson London

110

GEOMETRY.

THE PLANE SCALES &c.

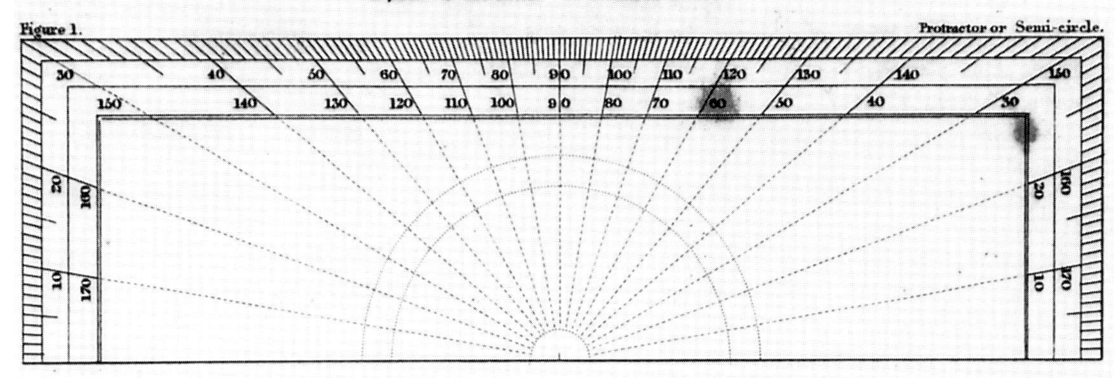

Figure 2. Equal Parts and Decimal Diagonal Scale.

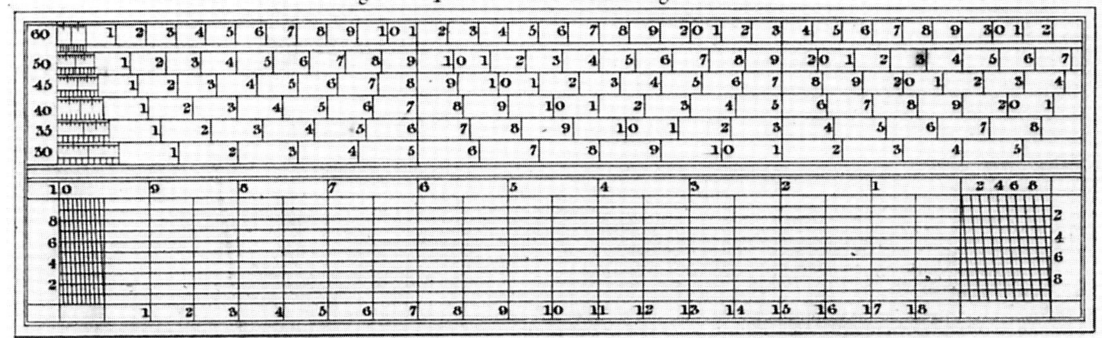

Fig. 3. Chords. Equal Parts for Feet and Inches.

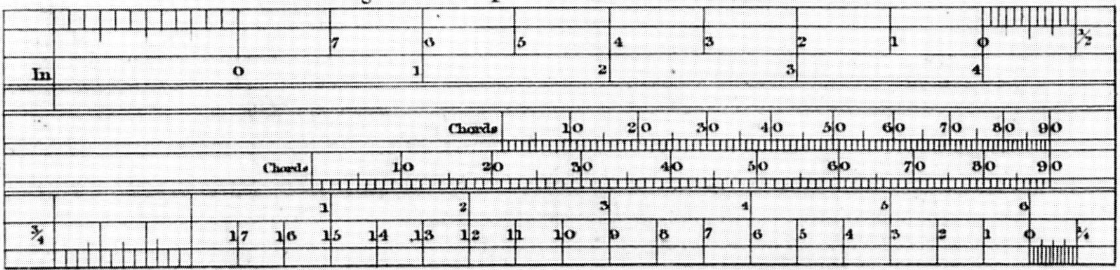

Fig. 4. Diagonal Scales for Feet, Inches, and Parts of an Inch.

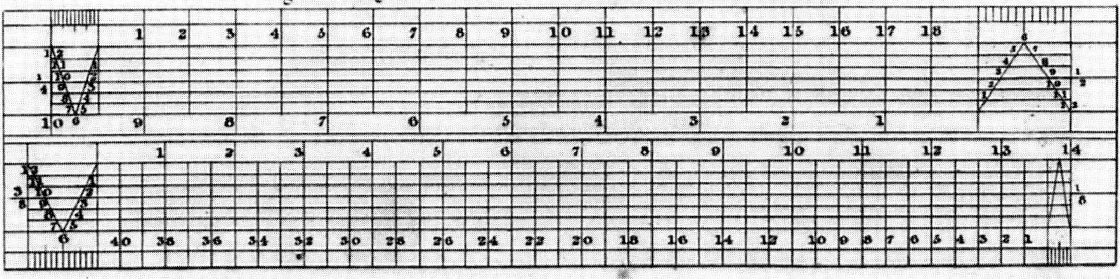

III

between 1800 and 1815, it took some time for the metric system to be adopted legally in France and other European states. Holland, in 1816, was the first country to adopt the metric system; the Federal German State of Prussia proposed its adoption in 1868 but it was not confirmed by law until 1873. In Italy it was not until after unification of all the states in 1871 that the French metric system was established by law. In Britain a Metric Act was passed in 1864 to recognize some metric measures, and a standard metre was lodged with the Board of Trade by 1897. However, it was not until 1972 that the metric system of measurement and coinage was introduced by law, and there is still considerable reluctance in certain trades to abandon Imperial linear measures, and Imperial scales and rules continue to be manufactured today.

In France pioneering work on engine-dividing machines for linear scales was done by the Duc de Chaulnes (1724–69) between 1765 and 1768; in Britain the ideas behind the engine-dividing machines developed by Jesse Ramsden *c.*1775 were not applied to drawing scales until the early nineteenth century. Imperial measures were confirmed by statute in 1824 and the needs of the expanding technical professions were met by such specialist scale makers as Charles Holtzapffel from 1846 and W. F. Stanley from 1856. These makers began to produce high-quality engine-divided Imperial scales in 6, 12 and 18 in versions to standard designs which remained in general use until metrification in 1972. Most British comprehensive sets of drawing instruments made between 1860 and 1960 had compartments with divisions to take a wide selection of these scales [156]. In addition, special large sets of scales, usually 12 inches long, were sold separately in mahogany cases fitted to contain a dozen or more. These were available to suit the specific needs of railway, civil or military engineers or for land-surveyors. For the latter, chain scales were provided, usually with 2 in offsets to match each scale, for taking measurements perpendicular to the main scale [IV].

Marquois scales were devised by a captain of that

[111] Engraved plate from Peter Nicholson's *Practical Builder* (1837 edn) which shows alternative scales.

112

[112] Comparative scale board of boxwood signed ELLIOTT 499 STRAND, LONDON, divided into inch scales for 16 different localities in Europe including England, the Rhineland, Austria, Italy, Amsterdam and Moscow, compared with lines (1/12) and centimetres. 14 in (360 mm). *c.*1850. *Museum of the History of Science, Oxford.*

name *c.*1780 for use with his system of surveying for military purposes. Equidistant parallel lines could be drawn with speed and accuracy using his special plain-edged scales together with a triangle. The triangle easily recognizable since it has two plain and one bevelled edge, is set with angles of $22\frac{1}{2}°$ and $67\frac{1}{2}°$ and has two sides marked with an index matrix. Sets of these special Marquois scales continued to be made throughout the nineteenth century.

In Britain, from 1840 onwards, the scales used for technical drawing were made in three main patterns. The first was a plain flat section with two bevelled edges, the second an oval section with four bevelled edges, and the third a triangular section with six fully divided scales. The latter was useful but not so easy to read dimensions off as the oval section, which was also superior in having an edge that could be easily placed against the line to be measured. These scales were produced with divisions to suit each individual profession. Chain scales were made for civil engineers, and land-surveyors and railway engineers, while architects and engineers required various divisions based on fractions of an inch scales.

The most common Imperial drawing scales and the most convenient to use were double scales, which included some of the following divisions: $\frac{1}{8}$, $\frac{1}{4}$, $\frac{3}{8}$, $\frac{1}{2}$, $\frac{5}{8}$, $\frac{3}{4}$, 1, $1\frac{1}{2}$ and 3 inches to one foot. In addition, scales for 1/500, 1/1250 and 1/2500 and 6 inches to one mile were introduced as standard scales for plotting site, road and land plans. These scales were generally made of boxwood but ivorine, a substitute for ivory, was employed from the 1890s as it proved hard wearing and could be clearly marked with divisions. (Natural ivory split and was easily damaged and was neither so stable nor so accurate.)

Several English firms became renowned as scale makers during the nineteenth century, notably Cary, Elliott, Holtzapffel, W.F. Stanley, Charles Baker and W.H. Harling. Of these, the last three continued to supply quality accurately-divided scales until the 1950s.

The materials for modern scales are mostly durable synthetics such as simulated boxwood or white plastic. The best are engine-divided and incised with the indices copper-plate engraved and then filled with black ink. The maker's name and any colour coding is screen-printed on later. These scales are made with either Imperial or metric divisions in a choice of patterns similar to nineteenth-century British designs [113]. Blundell Harling of Weymouth are the foremost manufacturers of quality scales in Britain. Several of the firms that make pencils, such as Staedtler and Faber-Castell, now include scales in their ranges of products, as do the Danish company Linex and Marabu of Germany. In addition, scales are included as part of the arms of the various drafting machines, in both the track and the parallel counterpoised drafting systems.

Measuring angles

The accurate measurement of angles in connection with drawing dates from the sixteenth century, when improved mathematical instruments became particularly necessary for the new techniques of land-surveying. These techniques were based on the triangulation method, which had been developed around 1530 by Gemma Frisius, a Flemish mathematician and cartographer, and improved by Sebastian Munster, a Swiss geometer, cartographer and military engineer. Similar work was done in England by Leonard Digges, who designed a number of instruments for surveying including his theodolite of 1558.

PROTRACTORS

The first protracting instruments were made of brass, either as a circle or a semi-circle with the arc graduated into 360° or 180° respectively. Some skilled instrument makers incorporated a circular protractor into their surveying instruments; there is one in the Augsburg case by Christoph Schissler of *c.*1599. In 1709 Nicolas Bion illustrated a plain semi-circular version for drawing purposes [114], and the German architect Johann Penther illustrated a similar design in 1723 [25]. From 1700 onwards this was the type most commonly included in small instrument cases. Variations on the plain circular and semi-circular protractor were made until the end of the nineteenth century, in brass, silver (later German silver or electrum), gun-metal and finally celluloid.

Larger protractors were also supplied separately in fitted cases and were sometimes provided with a radius or protracting arm [115]. From 1750 onwards there are numerous medium and large cased protractors by well-known makers such as Heath and Wing and the Adams workshop, which show improved divisions and engraving. A Vernier scale was often included on the protracting arm which enabled detailed measurement to be taken to the nearest minutes of arc [116]. Vernier scales were used on astronomical, surveying and mathematical instruments from *c.*1630. They were named after Paul Vernier (1580–1637) who introduced a short movable graduated scale attached to a mathematical scale for reading minute measurements, linear or angular.

During the eighteenth century it became customary to combine the divisions required for measuring angles

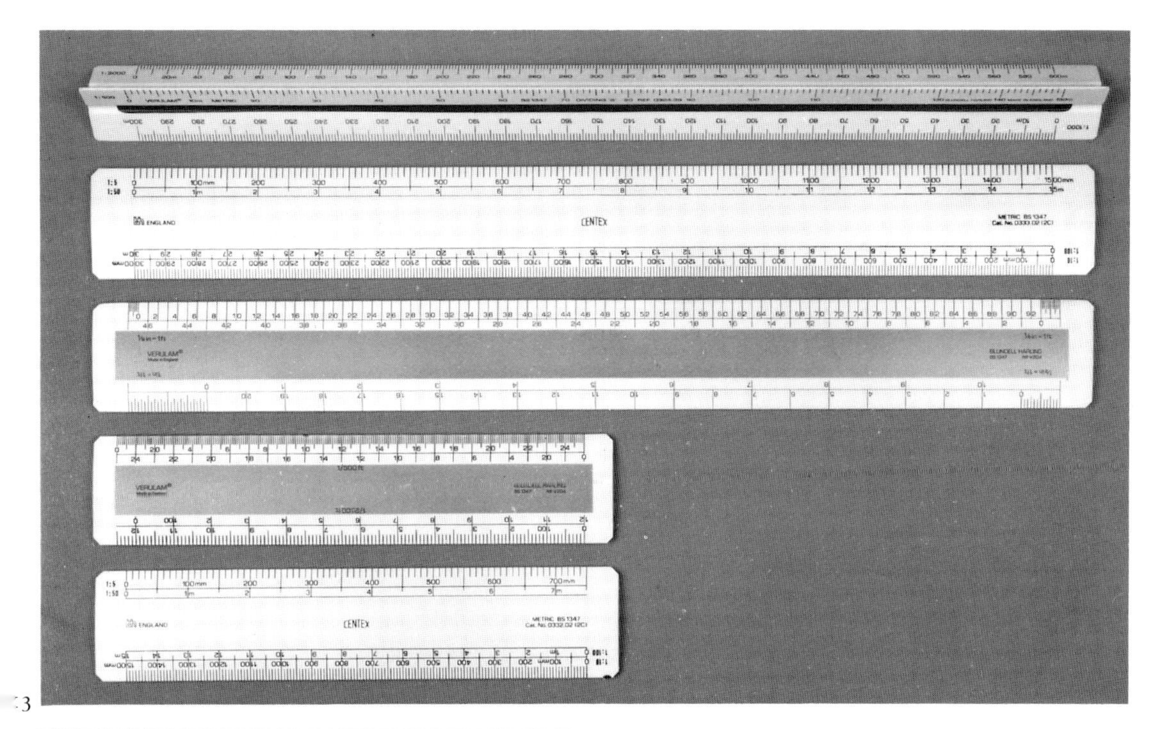

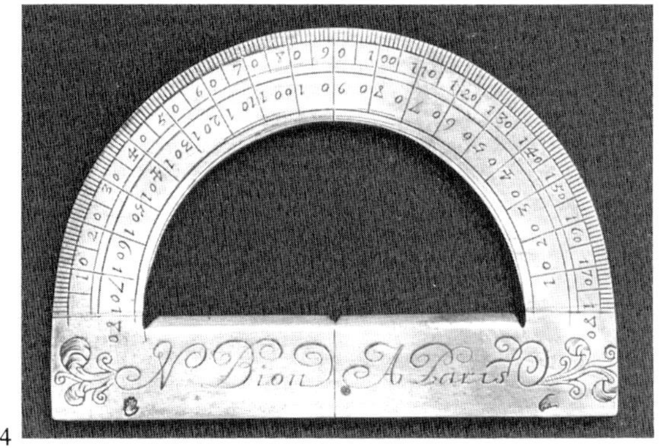

[113] Twentieth-century scales: scale with open divisions; single scale with single figuring flat section; single scale with two bevelled edges; triangular section with six scales. *Blundell Harling, Weymouth.*

[114] Semi-circular protractor in silver signed 'N Bion A Paris', graduated 0–180° and 180–0° with foliate decoration; from the small pocket case shown in [168]. $2\frac{1}{4}$ in (55 mm).

with a wide, plain scale rule in a rectangular form suitable for small fitted cases. These *combined scale protractors* varied from $4\frac{1}{2}$ to $6\frac{1}{2}$ in (115 to 165 mm) in length and were usually made of brass, silver, ivory or even boxwood in modest cases [XVII]. Protractors were also combined with plotting scales on 6 in (152 mm) parallel rules as in cases by Thomas Wright (*c.*1686–1748) [X] and Thomas Heath.

From 1600 the day-to-day needs of technical and architectural draughtsmen wanting to measure angles were met by *plain protractors*. During the nineteenth century 6 in. quality versions were made in electrum. Glass was tried as a material but required protection and cleaning. From its introduction in 1870 celluloid, combining the advantages of transparency and lightness, proved more popular. However, from 1900 to 1930 protractors were still made of brass and German silver (electrum), and rectangular versions were made of ivory, ivorine and boxwood. Acrylic sheet has replaced celluloid for present-day plain drawing protractors, and several manufacturers produce high-quality accurately divided versions in this material (not to be confused with stamped ones for school or student use). As previously mentioned, for some general drawing purposes the protractor has been superseded by the adjustable set square, which incorporates a protracting arc. For many purposes in mechanical engineering, cartography etc, where drawing machines are now normally used, an accurate circular protractor forms part of the hinge for the drafting arms fitted with scales.

FOLDING ARM PROTRACTORS

More accurate drawing protractors for use by surveyors and mechanical engineers were made from

1800 onwards by such makers as W. & S. Jones, Troughton (later Troughton & Simms) and W. F. Stanley among others. These drawing protractors were circular and designed with either one extending arm or a pair of hinged folding arms, usually with a Vernier scale attachment to each and sometimes improved by the provision of a magnifying glass. They were made in small versions which could be included in a magazine case or large versions which were supplied in a fitted case.

[115] Semi-circular protractor signed 'Heath & Wing in the Strand London', complete with radius arm with Vernier scale and shaped pointer. *c.*1775. Length of base line 12 in (305 mm). *Private collection.*

[116] Circular protractor of brass signed 'G Adams Matht Instrut. Maker to his MAJESTY Fleet Street London' with two radius arms and Vernier scales, graduated to 360°; shown in its lined octagonal fitted case. Diameter 12 in (308 mm). *Private collection.*

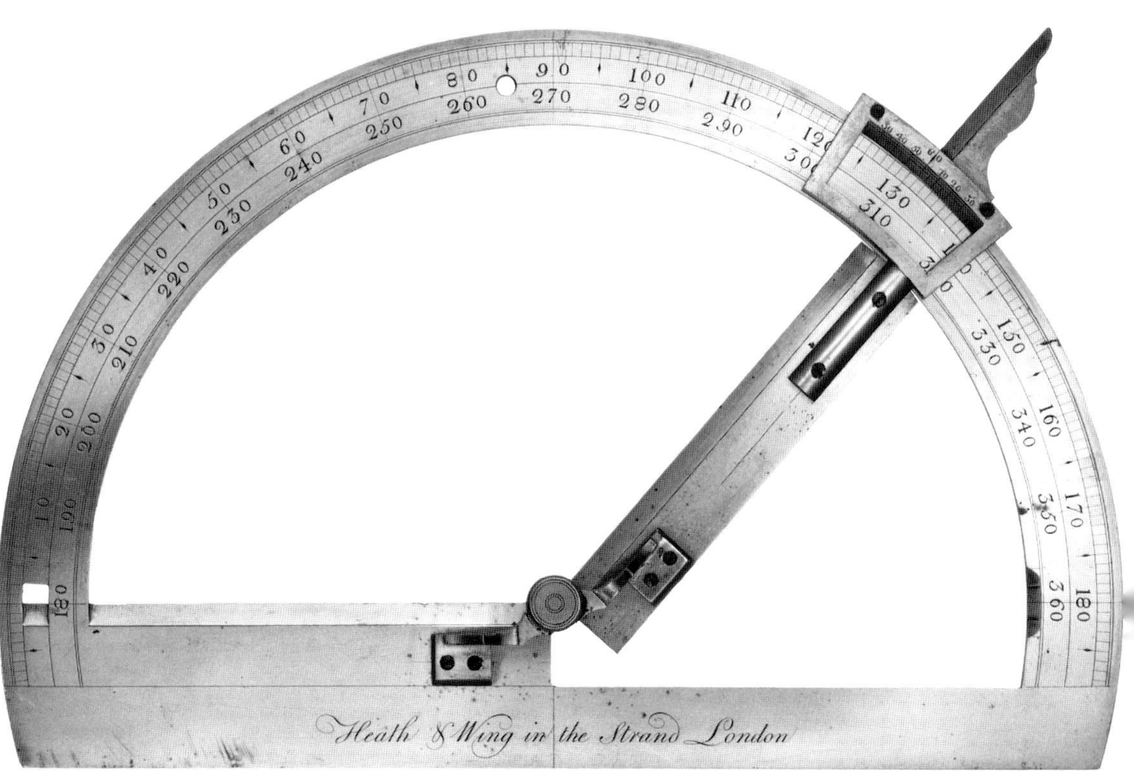

115

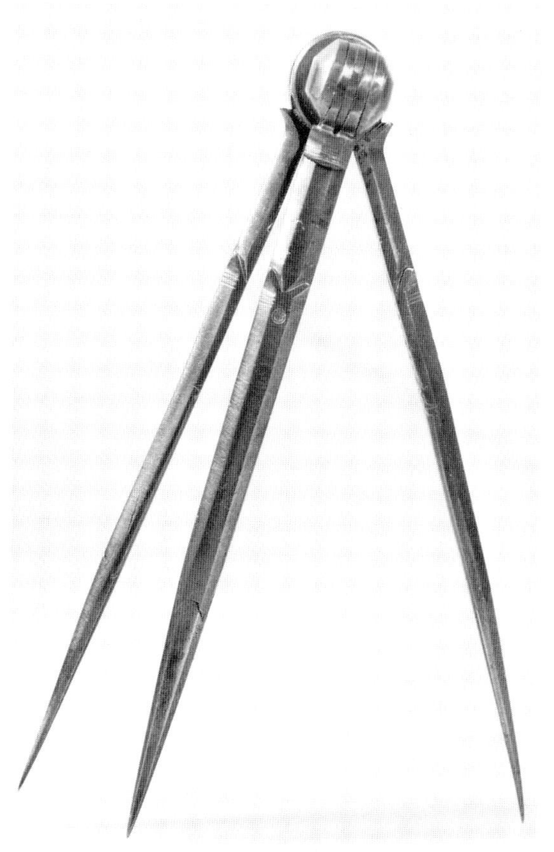

117A

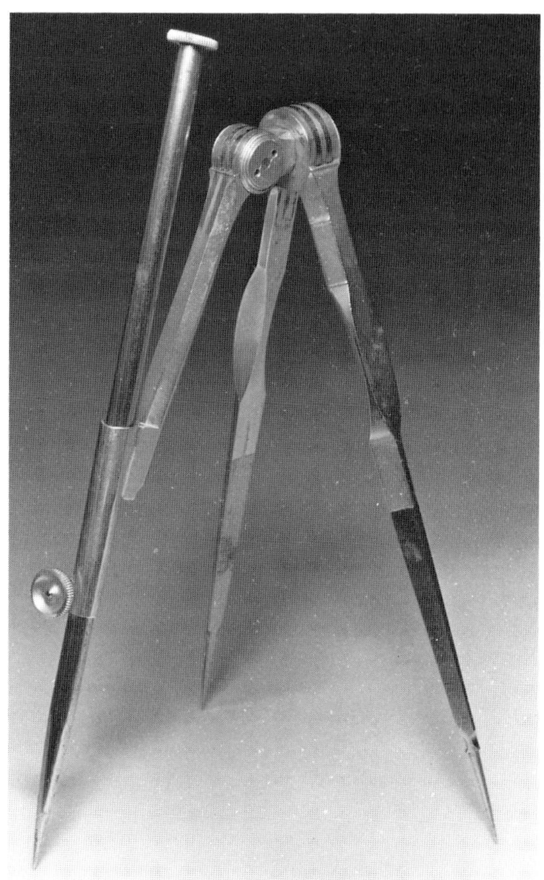

1:

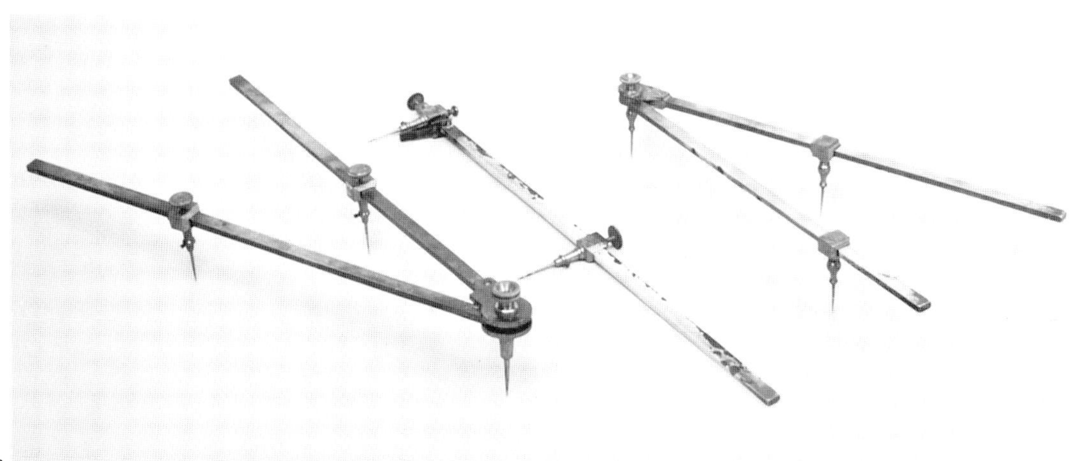

117B

[117A] Triangular compasses of cast brass with chiselled decoration and steel points. German. Late 17th century. *Germanisches Nationalmuseum, Nuremberg.*

[117B] German triangular beam compasses used for copying large drawings or maps, as made by G. F. Brander, the Augsburg instrument-maker. *c.*1770.

[118] Triangular compasses of nickel silver, the third leg a straight rod with the point adjustable by a fine screw. From the 1868 Archbutt magazine case in [154].

8

Copying, Enlarging and Reducing

Copying

One of the earliest methods for copying drawings or maps and charts was to take off each dimension separately with the points of a pair of dividers and transfer them one by one from the original to the new drawing, marking the vellum, parchment or paper with a prick. The prick marks were then connected up to form the copy. This was made easier if the paper was set out with a grid, as is normal practice with charts.

TRIANGULAR COMPASSES

Three-legged dividers – generally called triangular compasses although they will not delineate a circle – were introduced during the seventeenth century. They proved very useful for taking off the distances of three points simultaneously both for reading maps and charts and for copying drawings. A fine example dates to the late seventeenth century [117], and Nicolas Bion illustrated triangular compasses in his Plate of 1709 [22], shown with an octagonal ball joint. They were quite commonly included in larger sets of drawing instruments throughout the eighteenth century, sometimes provided with a removable third leg. During the nineteenth century triangular compasses were designed to new patterns, as in a version where the third leg is set at right angles to the main pair in the form of an extended post [118].

Triangular beam compasses were made from 1600 with the object of taking measures from widely separated points, and Georg F. Brander illustrated his version in 1767 for use in land-surveying [117B]. W. F. Stanley includes a similar beam compass in his treatise of 1866.

George Adams the Younger illustrated a flat three-legged instrument for transferring three widely spaced points, and this was also shown by John Farey, together with traditional triangular compasses, in his plate of 1811, in Rees's *Cyclopaedia* [31]. A similar design appeared, again in 1811, in a German work on mathematical instruments by Johann Gotthelf Studer, an engineer at the court in Dresden.

PRICKERS

By the end of the sixteenth century many Italian architects, including Palladio, had begun to use a needle-pointed instrument, later known in English as a 'pricker', to mark through the important angles or the main outlines of an original drawing onto a similar piece of paper below. This technique was originally used by Renaissance fresco painters to transfer drawings from paper to wall surface. Having pricked their designs through onto the wall from the original drawing they sprinkled coloured chalk through the small holes in the paper, giving emphasis in colour to the dots. This powder technique is sometimes called 'pouncing'. Examples of prickers are to be found in several sixteenth-century instrument cases, such as the Milanese set [147] and the Newsam case [145].

Joseph Moxon included the term 'protracting pin' in his *Mathematical Instruments* of 1701, and describes the instrument as a 'tapered piece of brass with a point of silver to draw lines on mathematical paper or to hold a needle to prick off any degree'; the term 'protracting pin' was used by several English eighteenth-century makers. Prickers or protracting pins were often incorporated in the turned handle of a brass or silver ruling pen or provided separately in a short form with a screw-on cap to protect the fine point [see 39B]. During the nineteenth century prickers with ivory handles to match those of the ruling pens were provided in cases of drawing instruments. W. F. Stanley introduced his improved 'patent needle holder' *c.*1866, using needles similar to fine sewing needles which could be easily replaced when worn or damaged. The spare needles were often contained in small ivory cases [119].

Pricking continued to be a popular means of copying until *c.*1840, but prickers were by tradition still provided in some cases until 1900. Copying large drawings by means of tracing paper was not established practice until the second half of the nineteenth century.

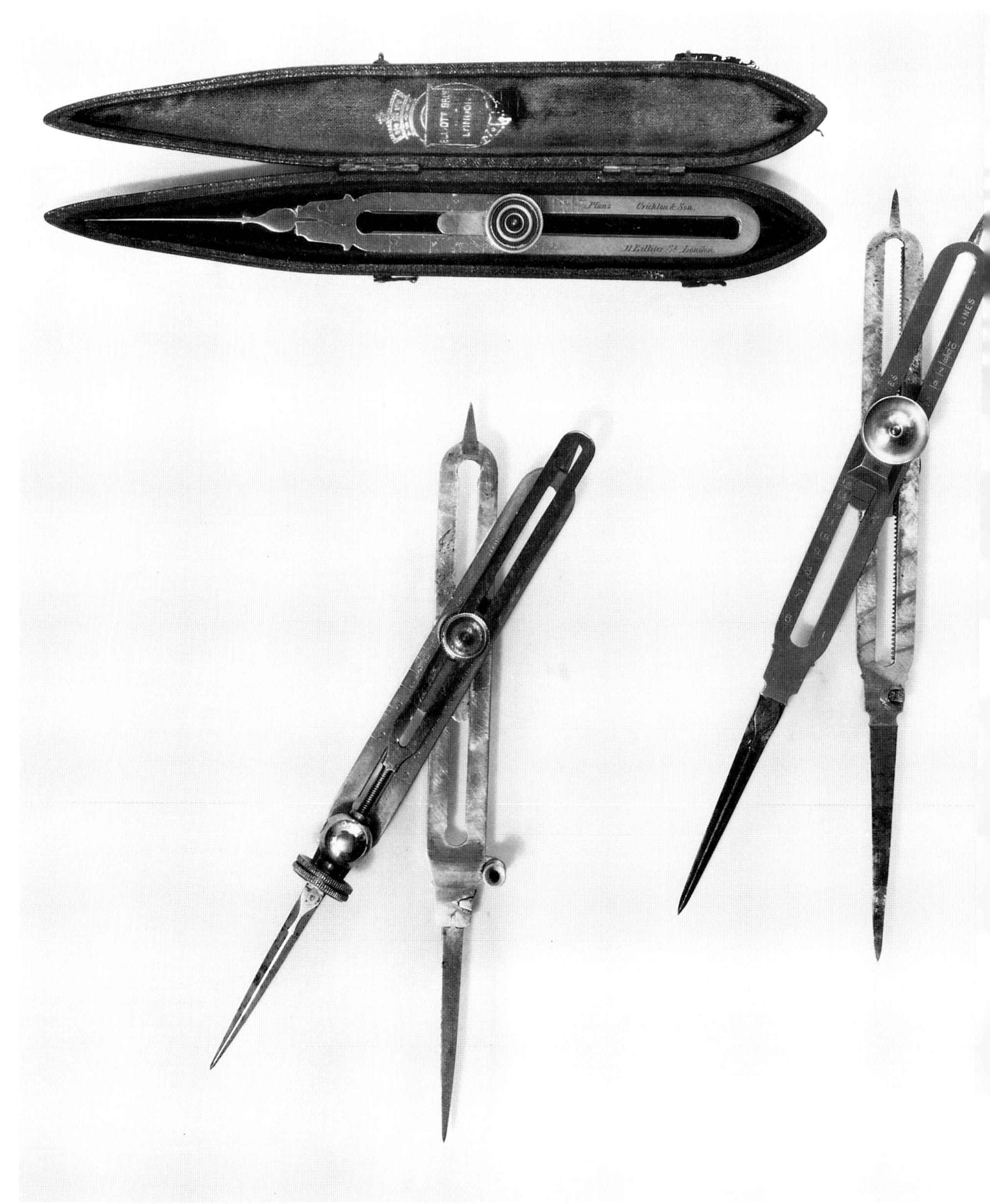

119

TRACERS

A tracer is a blunt tapered instrument for applying pressure to drawing paper without puncturing it. The earliest tracers were for use after blacklead was applied to the back of drawings to be copied; the outlines were then traced onto blank sheets of paper. Tracers were not necessarily used with tracing paper although various forms of transparent paper were commonly available in Europe from 1700 onwards, and one form is known to have been made in Italy in small quantities from the fifteenth century onwards. A tracer is shown in the plate which accompanies John Robertson's treatise on mathematical instruments [27] of 1747; similar instruments were included in several instrument cases, sometimes with a pricker at the reverse end.

By the mid-nineteenth century carbonated paper was manufactured large enough for technical drawings, and tracers were provided in cases of drawing instruments for use with it. In nineteenth-century instrument cases tracers were usually made of the same material as the compasses – nickel-silver, perhaps, or electrum – with ivory handles, to match the ruling pens. In 1866 Stanley recommended the use of agate for tracer heads since 'it is rounded and it is capable of considerable pressure without perforating the paper' [120].

In the *Edinburgh Encyclopaedia* of 1808–30 John Farey described drawing pencils set into mounts of silver or brass, specially shaped so that they could also be used as tracers [33]. The singular shape of these mounts is sometimes thought to be only for the easy extraction of the pencil from a vertical fitted pocket case.

The tracer became obsolete once tracing paper together with an ink or pencil line was accepted as the usual method of copying architectural and engineering drawings. Tracing paper was more widely used during the period from 1840 to 1870 for copying drawings, and its use increased once the blue-print method of reproducing drawings – a simple photo-process using daylight for which a transparent original was essential – was commercially established from 1880.

Enlarging and reducing

PROPORTIONAL COMPASSES

Proportional compasses can be used for calculations of dimensions when transferring drawings either when enlarging or when reducing. The first-century mathematician, Heron of Alexandria, whose writings deal with the practical application of mathematics, has

[119] Assorted proportional compasses made of nickel silver. (*Above*) Plain set in fitted case marked ELLIOTT BROS LONDON; (*below left*) pattern with bar and Vernier by W. F. Stanley; (*below right*) version with ratchet and pinion adjustment, also by Stanley. All late 19th century. *David Gray Collection, London.*

[120] Tracers, one with a steel head and one with an agate head, blunt but able to apply accurate pressure to paper. English. 19th century. *Michael Scott-Scott Collection, Dartmouth.*

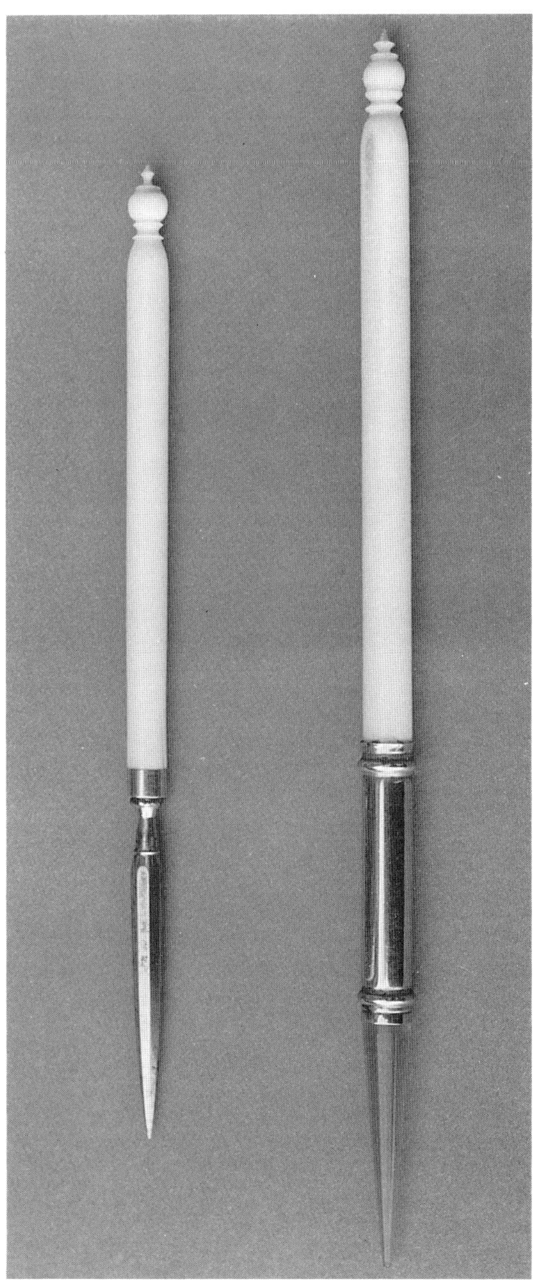

120

been credited with the invention of a device used for copying drawings by a set ratio – probably an early form of fixed proportional compasses. There is an example of a Roman fixed type of proportional compasses in the set of instruments found at Pompeii [10]. Leonardo da Vinci, in a sketch *c.*1495, shows both a fixed pair of proportional dividers and one with slit legs; sixty years later Jacques Besson, in his work *Theatrum instrumentorum* (1569), included his design for a slotted version of adjustable proportional compasses with the legs engraved with linear scales. Daniel Speckle, a German military engineer, illustrated six different fixed compasses with ratios from 1:2 to 1:7, in his work *Architectura* of 1589. Fixed versions were quite common, the most popular being 1:2 or 'wholes and halves' [121] and these were provided in several early instrument cases including the Milanese set with three fixed versions and the Newsam set [147 and 148].

It is Jost Bürgi (1552–1632), a Swiss-born instrument maker attached to the court at Cassel in Germany, who is credited with the invention *c.*1588, of variable proportional compasses bearing geometrical and trigonometrical scales [122]. These instruments are called *Reduktionzirkel* in German and *compas de réduction* in French, but whatever their name they are the same instrument. They are adjustable to a variety of ratios and can be used to enlarge or reduce any dimension. Bion illustrates both fixed and slotted versions in his Plate 8 of 1709 [22], while the English maker John Rowley (fl.1698–1728) made a version with a fitted case *c.*1720 [123]. A detailed drawing of proportional compasses fitted with a bar appears in John Robertson's treatise on mathematical instruments of 1747 [27], and Edmund Stone included a more complex version than Bion's in his revised edition of the Bion treatise of 1758. Further developments in the design of English proportional compasses can be seen by studying the plate by Barrow of 1792 [30] and W.&S. Jones's revised version of Adams's plate, dated 1823 [54]. These offered ratios for 'Lines' and 'Circles' for the purpose of calculating the reduction of both linear measures and diameters of circles. By contrast, proportional compasses in some late-eighteenth-century French instrument cases still resembled the earlier pattern, with a large wing-screw on a sliding cursor.

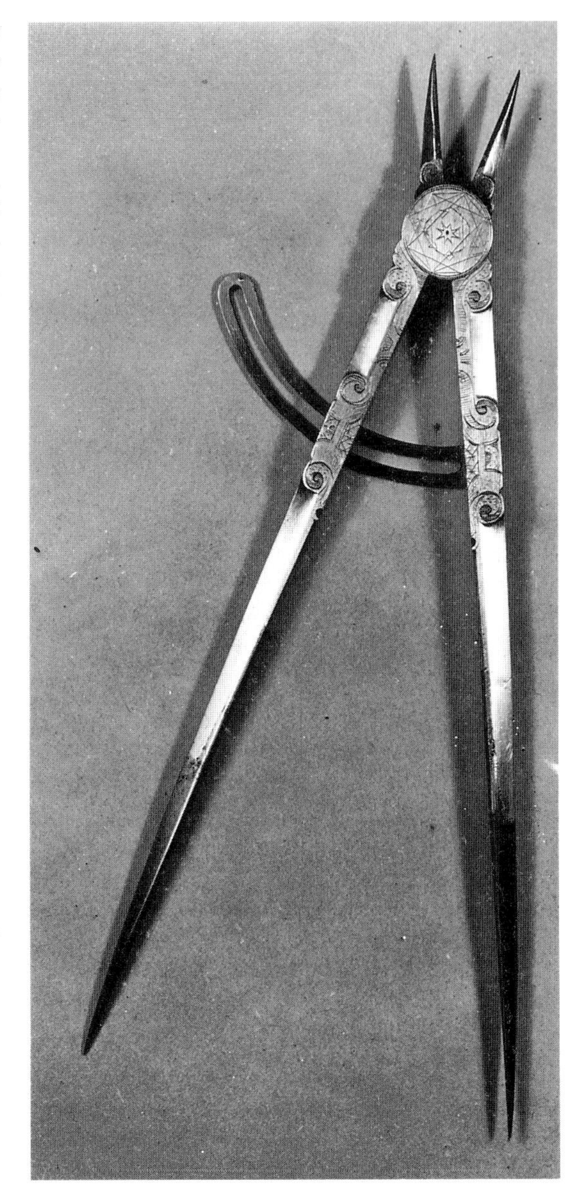

[121] Fixed proportional compasses, ratio 1:5, with wing arc of gilt-brass finely engraved, and steel points. German. Height 8 in (200 mm) *c.*1590. *Mathematisch-Physikalischer Salon, Zwinger, Dresden.*

The demand for this instrument increased during the nineteenth century, especially in Britain, for use by engineering draughtsmen, and high-quality versions were made by all the reputable makers there and in Europe. In 1866 W.F. Stanley offered simple 'wholes and halves' and several more complex versions which included four scales to calculate ratios for length, circles, area and volume. Others had a bar attachment or a ratchet and pinion as well as Vernier scale models – all to suit the varying demands of the engineering professions [119]. Many of these nineteenth-century proportional compasses were supplied in fitted

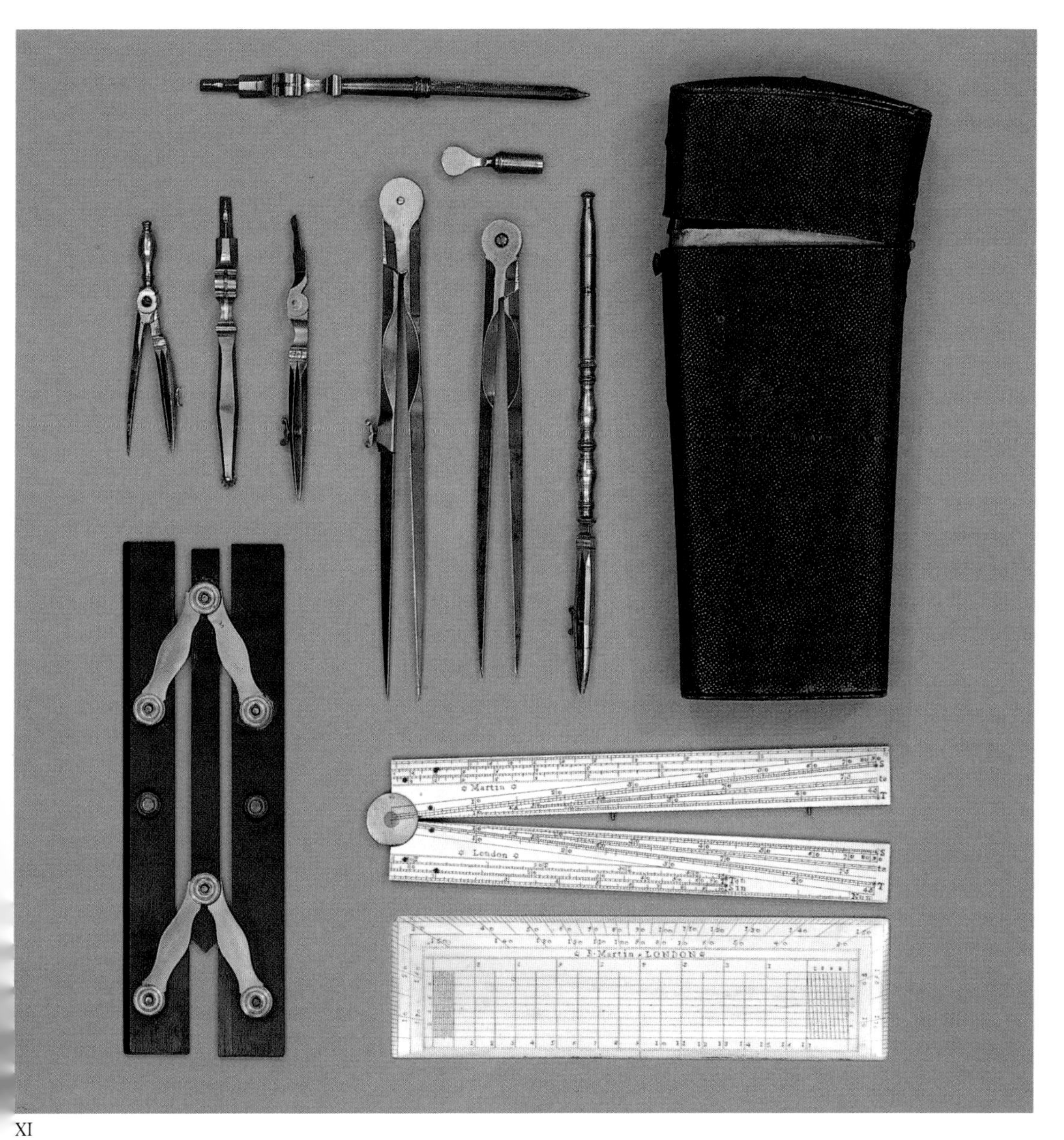

XI

[XI] Black fishskin-covered pocket case with ink signature within cover 'Capt Cotton 1784'; contains brass instruments together with ivory scale rule and sector, brass mounted, both signed 'B. Martin LONDON'. Note the double parallel rule in ebony with brass parallel links, seldom found in French or German sets. Benjamin Martin died in 1782 having gone bankrupt in 1780 but his stock was disposed of by his son. Size of case $6\frac{7}{8} \times 3$ in (175×75 mm).
Andrew Alpern Collection, New York.

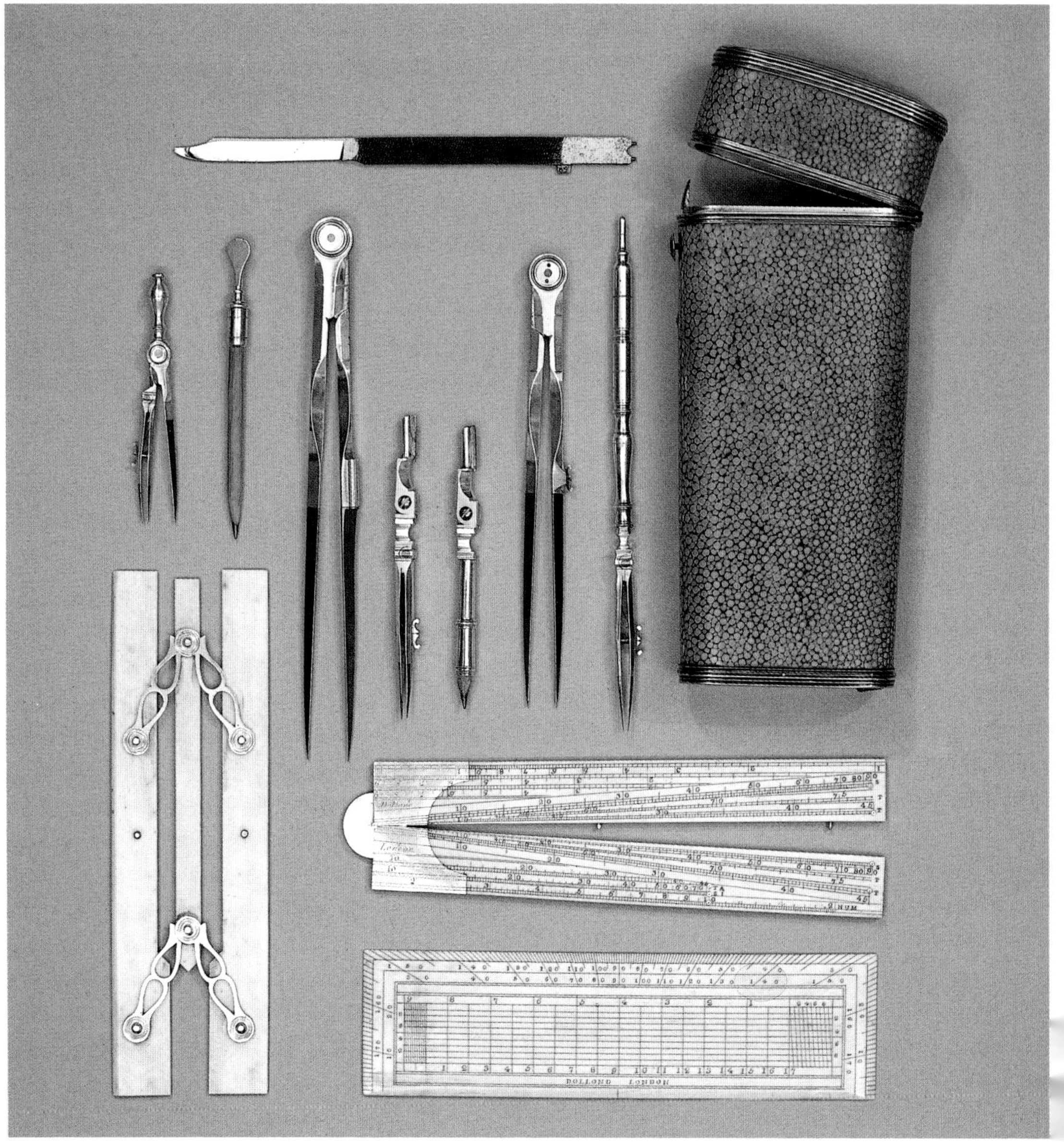

XII

[XII] Shagreen-covered pocket case with silver mounts containing complete set of silver instruments together with ivory double parallel rule, scale rule and protractor combined and silver arch-mounted sector. Note the penknife which doubles as an adjustment tool. Sector and scale are signed 'Dollond London'. Probably by Peter Dollond (1730–1820). Case: $6\frac{3}{4} \times 2\frac{3}{4} \times 1\frac{1}{4}$ in ($170 \times 70 \times 32$ mm). *Andrew Alpern Collection, New York.*

[122] Variable proportional compasses designed by Jost Bürgi in 1588; the original pair (*right*) contrasted with a modern replica (*left*). *Kunstsammlungen Hesse Landesmuseum, Cassel, West Germany.*

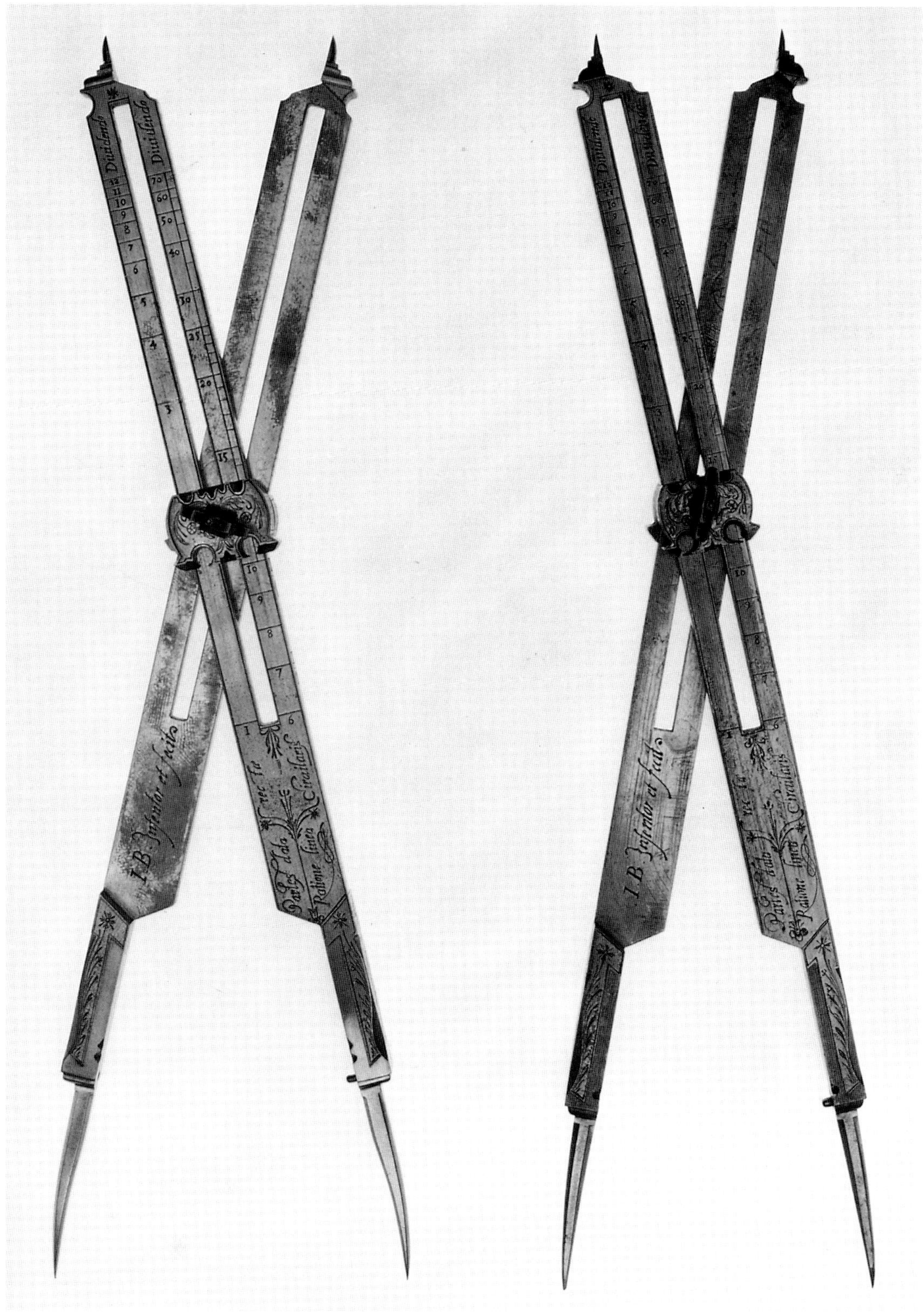

122

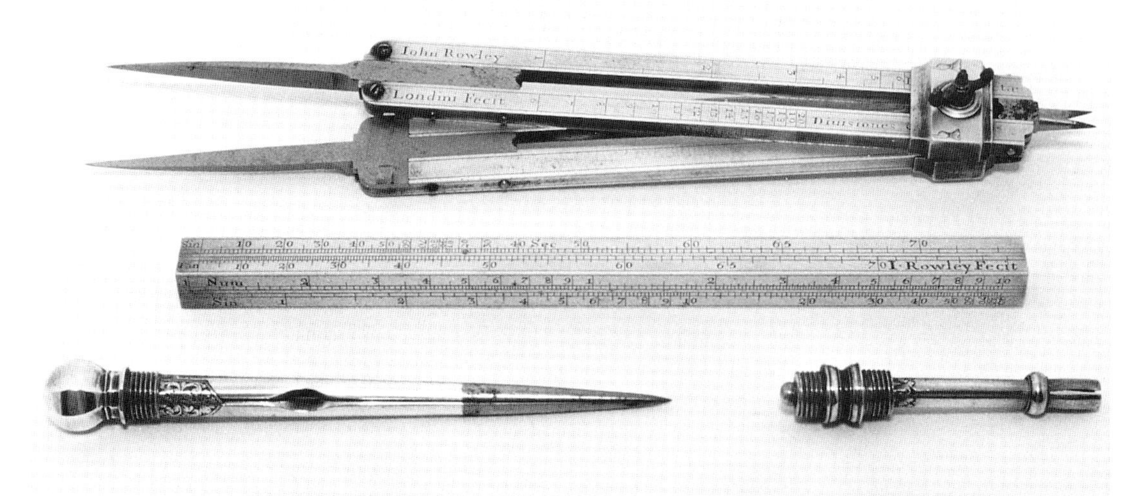

cases in a variety of sizes down to 6 in (152 mm) pocket models. They were made by such London makers as Elliott, Harris, R. B. Bate and Cary, and continued to be made by British quality instrument makers until 1960. Today high quality versions are made by a number of European instrument makers, including Haff, Riefler and Kern, for use by engineers and graphic specialists [124].

PANTOGRAPHS

The design of an apparatus for enlarging and reducing drawings of *c.*1603 – a pantograph – is credited to the Jesuit mathematician and astronomer Christoph Scheiner (1575–1650), who described its construction and its use in his work *Pantographice*, published in 1631. A wooden parallelogram, designed to enlarge and reduce to the ratio of 1 : 2, it consisted of six rods, two of which were double the length of the others, jointed like lazy tongs [125]. Samuel Pepys knew of this instrument; after a visit to the London instrument maker John Spong in December 1668, he wrote in his diary:

> I had most infinite pleasure, not in his ingenuity in general but in particular with his shewing me the use of the Parallelogram, by which he drew in a quarter of an hour before me, in little, from a great, a most neat map of England – that is, all the outline, which gives me infinite pleasure and foresight of pleasure. I shall have it; and therefore desire to have that which I have bespoke made.

In 1701 Moxon described this parallelogram as '5 rulers of brass or wood with sockets to slide or set any proportion to enlarge or diminish Draughts'; Bion illustrated his version, item K of Plate 9, in 1709. A fine illustration of the use of the pantograph is

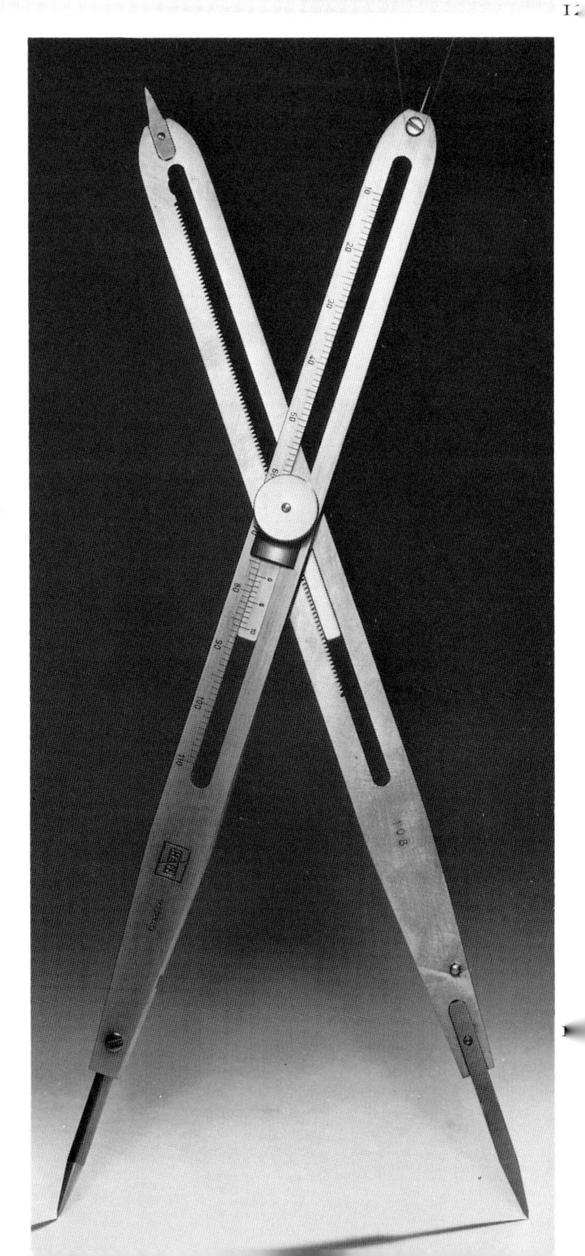

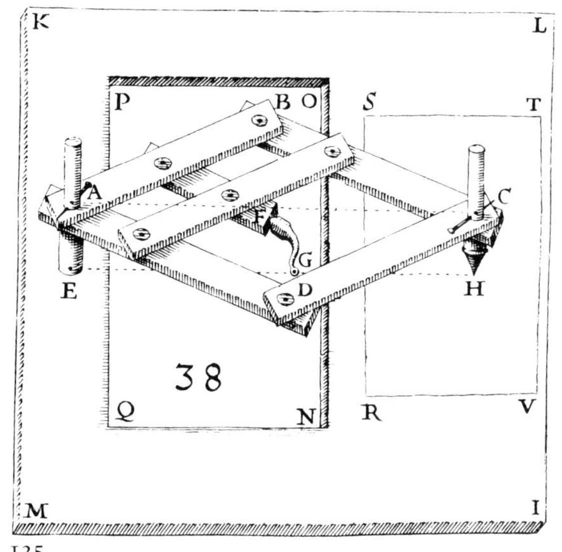

125

[123] Variable proportional compasses in silver signed 'John Rowley Londini Fecit', with divisions for lines and solids and wing-nut to adjustable slide and steel points; provided with fishskin-covered wooden case. Shown with square hollow scale rule with dividers and crayon-holder withdrawn. *c.*1700. *Museum of the History of Science, Oxford (Orrery Collection).*

[124] Precision proportional dividers by Haff; brass matt chrome-plated with engraved scales for lines and circles; available in 6 and 8 in (160 and 200 mm) versions, supplied in fitted case. *c.*1980.

[125] Pantograph as originally designed by Christoph Scheiner, which consisted of six wooden rods, arranged as a parallelogram, jointed like lazy tongs, as illustrated in Scheiner's *Pantographice* published in Rome in 1631.

[126] Pantograph shown in use, as illustrated in the *Dessein* section of the *Encyclopédie* of Diderot & d'Alembert, published in Paris in 1763.

126

included in the *Dessein* section of Diderot and d'Alembert's *Encyclopédie* in 1763 [126]. Surprisingly, it does not show the improved version introduced in 1743 by the talented French instrument maker Claude Langlois, who rearranged the mechanism so that his pantograph could easily be used for alternative ratios of reduction. This design was included in the published list of inventions meeting with the approval of the Paris Académie des Sciences, edited by M. Gallon (1735–77).

In England during the latter part of the eighteenth century improved pantographs were made by many of the principal makers including Heath & Wing, the Adams workshop and Benjamin Martin (1714–82), the last of whom issued a pamphlet with his improved design *c.*1770. These pantographs were made of brass or ebony with ivory scales, sometimes inset onto the arms, with ivory or china castors or wheels fitted to the articulated joints. A lead weight was provided at the fulcrum, and the pantograph was usually supplied with a fitted mahogany case [127]. George Adams the Younger included his version of what he called a 'pentograph' in the plate to his *Geometrical and Graphical Essays* (1791), a term also used by John Farey in

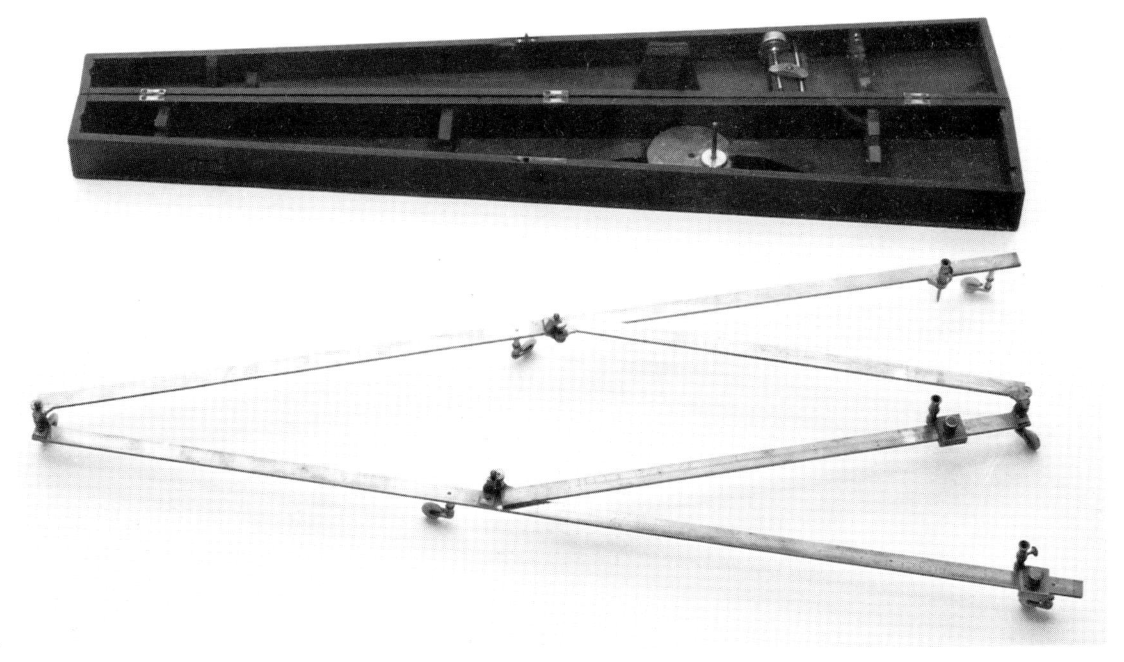

127

[127] Brass pantograph by W. & S. Jones of Holborn, London, provided with mahogany fitted case, china castors, lead weight and sliding drawing points; typical of those produced during the 19th century. 37-inch (940 mm) large model. *Private collection.*

[128] Eidograph made by W. F. Stanley and formerly owned by Professor Willis of Cambridge, shown in use for site plans. *c.*1900. *Science Museum, London.*

1830 in his plate for the *Edinburgh Encyclopaedia* [33].

During the early nineteenth century the main London makers supplied pantographs in a variety of sizes from 10–12 in (250–300 mm) to 24–36 in (600–920 mm), responding to an increased demand, probably for use by land-surveyors and railway engineers. From 1866 W. F. Stanley produced his improved version made in brass which incorporated ideas contributed by J. D. C. Gavard of Paris. Stanley describes the method of its use in both the 'erect or reverse' manner, 'erect' being the same way up as the original drawing as its name implies. Today simple timber pantographs are still included in ranges of aids supplied to graphics and joinery draughtsmen for enlarging and reducing designs and patterns. Keuffel & Esser market a precision version made of lightweight alloy which can be set to ratios of between full size and 1 : 10.

EIDOGRAPHS

By the beginning of the nineteenth century one of the most important applications for the pantograph was in making copies accurately 1 : 1 for engravings. It was with these requirements in mind that William Wallace (1768–1843), Professor of Mathematics in Edinburgh, designed his eidograph in 1821. Edinburgh had an outstanding reputation for fine engraving at this time, and plates for several encyclopaedias were prepared and printed there. Bartholomew's, the map-makers, were also based in Edinburgh. Wallace's eidograph was both more accurate and easier to use than the pantograph, since its feet and joints did not obscure the drawing surface as was the case with the pantograph. In a paper given in 1831 (later published in the *Transactions of the Royal Society of Edinburgh* and other works), Wallace described the origins of the pantograph at length and gave details of his design for the eidograph; an illustration of it appeared when the paper was printed [128].

The first examples were made by R. B. Bate (w1808–47) of 17 Poultry in London and his successor J. D. Potter (w1851–1880). Both these makers made eidographs to the same design where the main cross-rail was of a hardwood with a triangular cross section. Other versions were made, presumably to Wallace's commission, by the Edinburgh family firm of Alexander Adie (fl.1837–81). These were usually made with a square section cross-rail in brass. Adie's young-

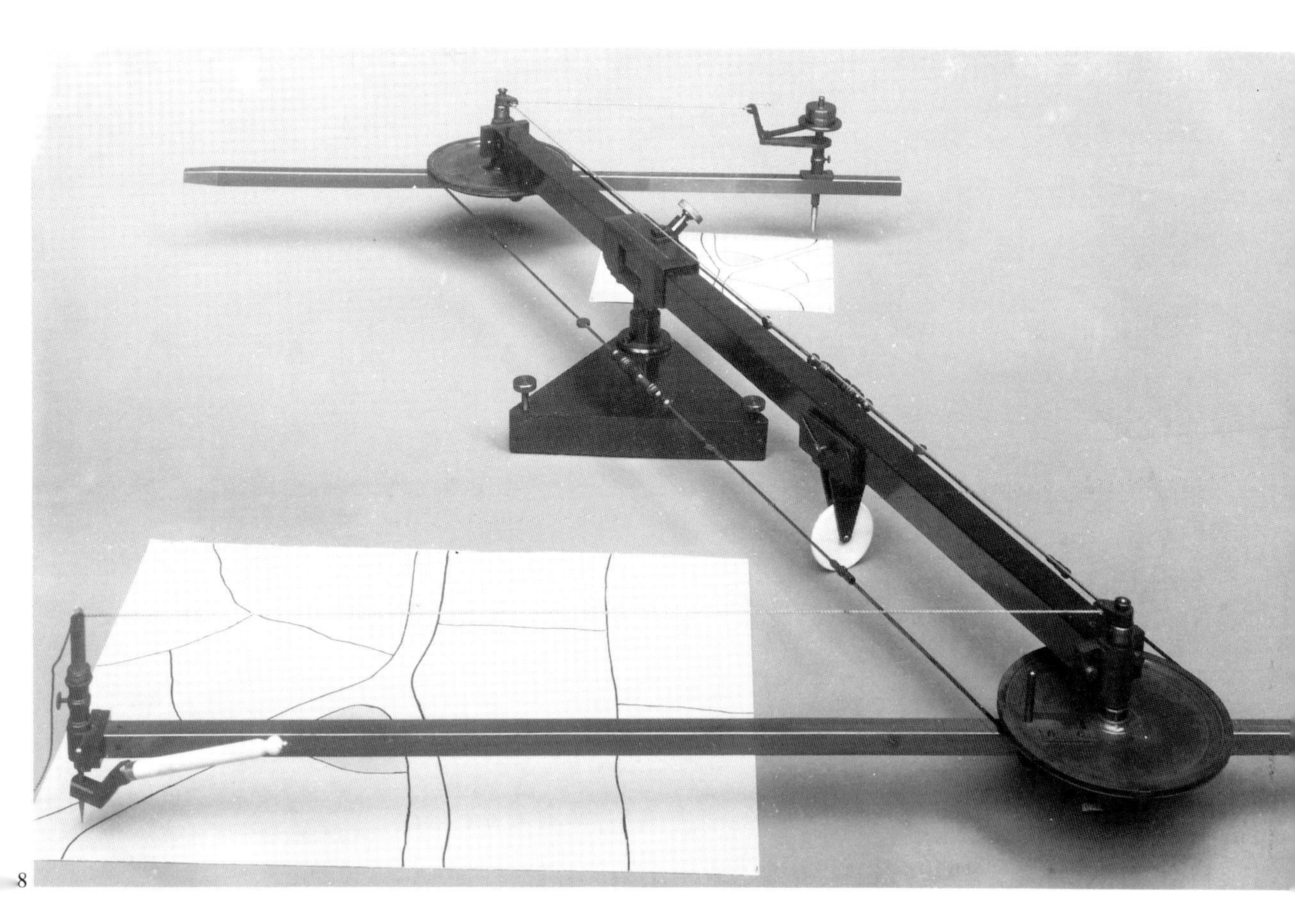

8

est son, Patrick, who set up in London *c.*1840 at premises in the Strand, also specialized in eidographs. W. F. Stanley, who found this copying device superior to the pantograph although it was more expensive, produced his own version. Stanley stated in the first edition of his treatise in 1866 that it was strange that the eidograph did not achieve a wider use and that this was probably due to inadequate promotion. W. F. Stanley eventually took over Adie's London firm and continued to make, or at least to advertise, the supply of eidographs, judging from their 1960 catalogue. Examples by Stanley appear in the sale-room and sometimes the cross-rail is of gun-metal instead of brass.

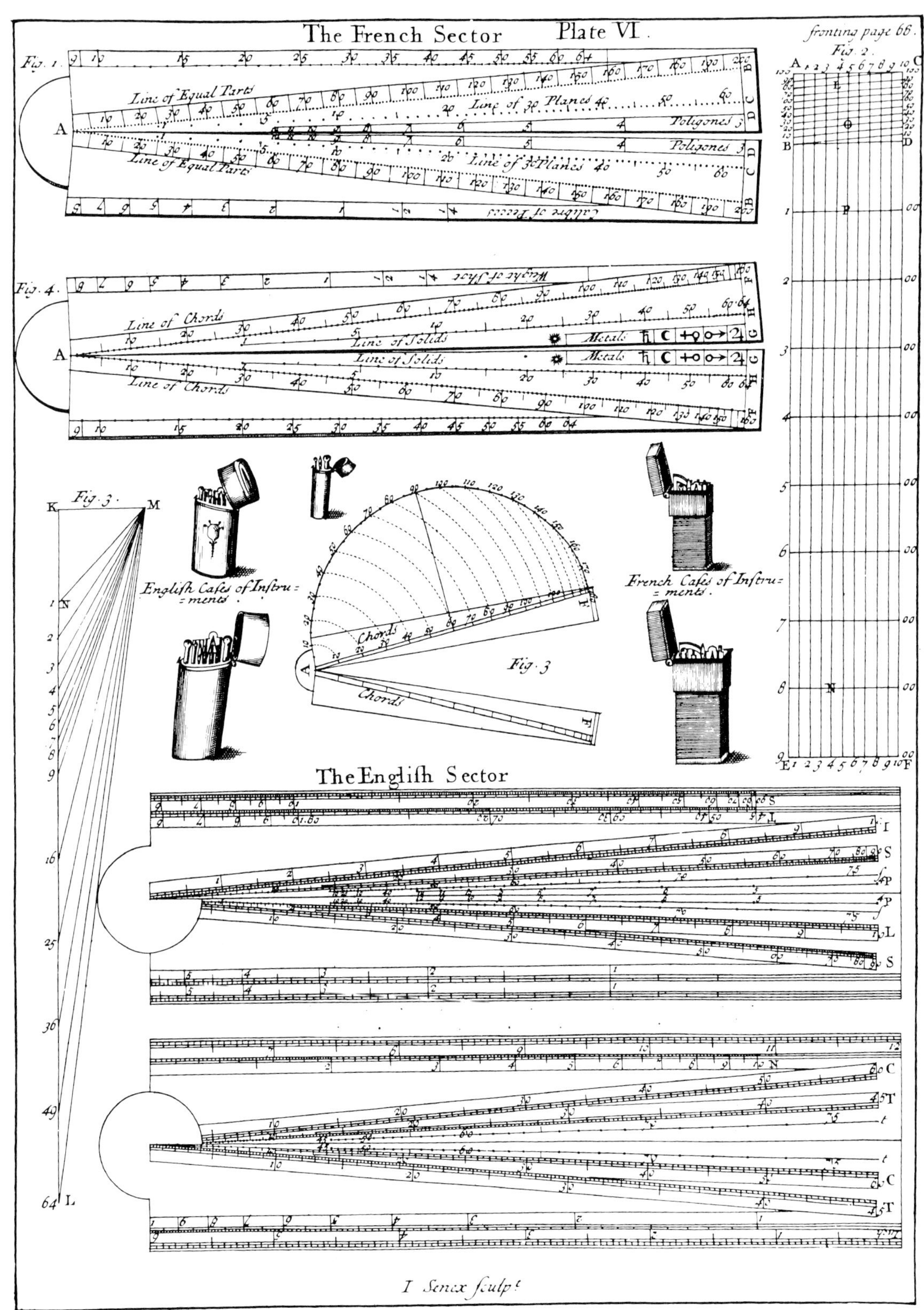
The French Sector
Plate VI.
fronting page 66.
Fig. 1.
Fig. 2.
Line of Equal Parts
Line of 30 Planes
Poligones
Calibre of Pieces
Fig. 4.
Weight of Shot
Line of Chords
Line of Solids
Metals
Fig. 3.
English Cases of Instru=
=ments.
French Cases of Instru=
=ments.
Chords
Fig. 3
The English Sector
I Senex sculp.

9

Proportion and Ratio

Sectors

Proportion became important in the design of buildings in the Renaissance, and several functions of mathematics were related by ratio. The sector was devised as an instrument to perform various calculations involving ratios, based on the properties of the sides and angles of triangles. The first sectors were in use from 1600 and were made of brass or silver in the form of a hinged rule; later versions were made of ivory and boxwood.

Thomas Hood published his *The Making and Use of the Geometrical Instrument called a Sector* in England in 1598. His instrument was developed for gunnery, and a graduated arc was an essential part of the design. This may have determined the name he gave it, which has been used ever since in England. The two arms carried scales of proportion based on the principle of similar triangles. These scales were read using a pair of dividers, which are a necessary accompanying instrument with every type of sector.

The sector developed in Italy by Galileo Galilei between 1597 and 1599 was a more complex instrument intended for use as a general purpose calculator and for military use. He described it in his treatise *Le operazioni del compasso geometrico e militare*, published in 1606. (The sector is known in Italian as a *compasso di proporzione* not to be confused with proportional compasses which in Italian are called *compasso di riduzione*. In German it is known as a *Kreissektor* and in French as a *compas de proportion*, both of which can cause confusion.)

In England the sector was further developed by Edmund Gunter (1581–1626), who also developed the land-surveyors' chain of one hundred links in 1620. Gunter described his sector in 1624 in *Description and Use of the Sector*; his major contribution was to incorporate a logarithmic scale on the arms.

From the early part of the seventeenth century sectors were made in various countries to carry out different calculating functions in connection with navigation, gunnery, civil engineering and land-surveying. The German treatise *Theatrum arithmetico geometricum* by Jacob Leupold, first published in 1727, lists twenty functions which could be performed with various sectors. A clear description of the use of both the English and French sector can be found in the 1758 edition of Bion's *The Construction and Principal Uses of Mathematical Instruments* translated by Edmund Stone [129]. For drawing purposes the sector performed calculations graphically, the results being measured with dividers. A considerable variety of seventeenth- and eighteenth-century sectors still survive [130 and 131].

In Italy as many as four or five sectors, each with specific scale divisions required for calculations serving different purposes, might be included in a set of instruments [132]. The French sector was intended for gunnery whereas in England sectors were essentially a draughtsman's aid. English sectors were made for three centuries in a variety of sizes – from 6 in (150 mm) pocket versions to 12 in (300 mm) and even 18 in (460 mm) giant models – and in a variety of materials: silver, brass, ivory and boxwood. Sometimes the hinge of the sector was designed so that it could also be used as a set square, with a small brace to hold it rigid. The hinge, called a 'sector hinge', was usually round, but in the late eighteenth century arched brass or silver hinges were introduced. Some sectors were made with either a ledge on one of the arms or a third friction leaf to hold the limbs at a set angle [133].

Sectors continued to be used as calculating instruments until the mid-nineteenth century when logarithmic tables came into general use; after 1880

[129] The design and divisions of both an English and a French sector as shown by Edmund Stone in *Construction and Principal Uses of Mathematical Instruments by M. Bion* (1758).

[130] Sector of brass inscribed 'Butter Field A Paris' with a hinge and stay to hold arms open at 90°. French. Length 6 in (152 mm). *c.*1700. *Private collection.*

[131] German sector signed 'Peter Rahne Fecit: Zu Berlin', of brass, finely engraved and variously divided for lines, circles, cubic, logarithmic and military measures, with a circular hinge. Length when folded 11¼ in (285 mm). *c.*1740. *Gustav and Margarete Thorban, West Germany.*

[132] Italian sectors of brass, each engraved with different scales to suit the calculations necessary in different occupations, and provided with fine decorative burnished steel points for setting the sector up accurately; shown as one tier of a comprehensive case arranged as a bound leather book. 6–11 in (152–280 mm). 18th century. *Museo di Storia della Scienza, Florence.*

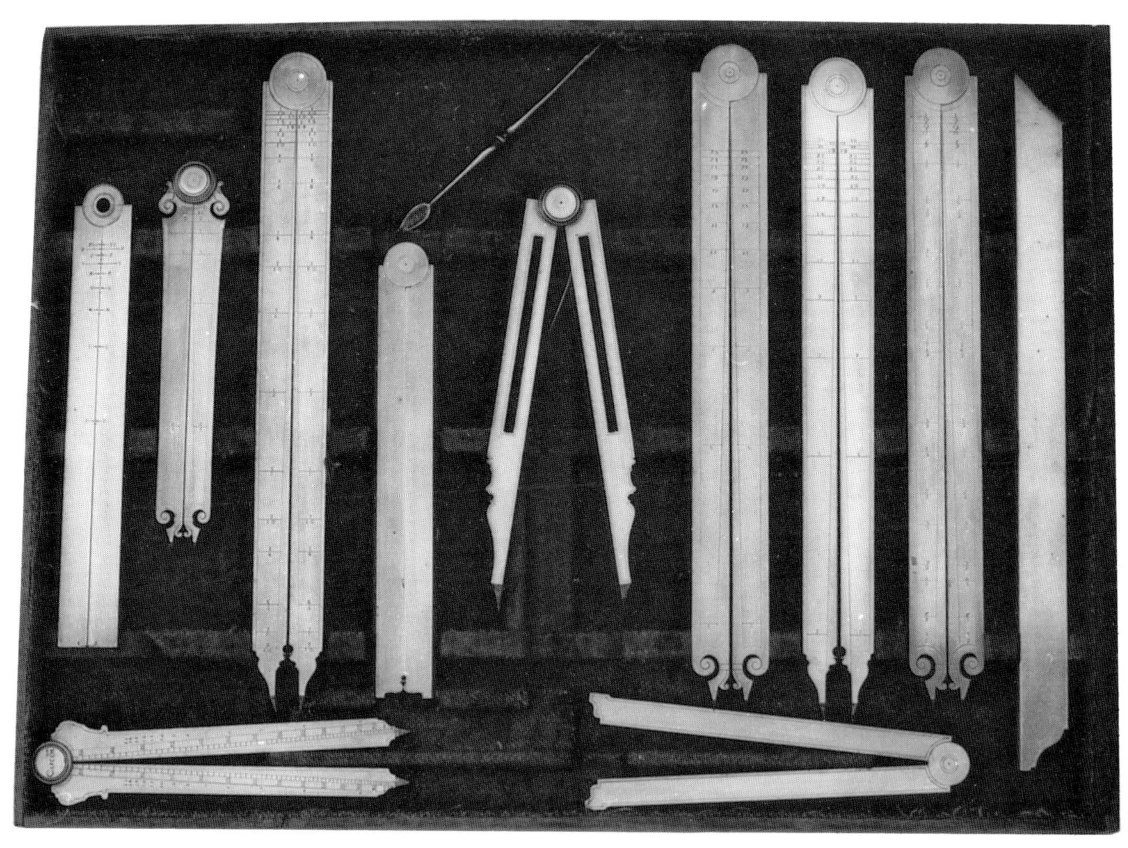

132

the availability of engineers' slide-rules further eroded their value. (Some slide-rules were, in fact, introduced in England as early as 1700, but these early boxwood and ivory slide-rules were designed to carry out only the calculations necessary for a particular trade or material, such as fluid measures for Customs & Excise, timber measures or compound interest). From 1850 onwards a sector continued to be provided in cases of instruments as a symbolic or traditional calculating instrument, but it ceased to be used after 1900 [167].

ARCHITECTONIC SECTORS

During the seventeenth century an exceptional interpretation of the sector was developed out of the then current interest of many architects in the refinements of proportion. As early as 1627 an Italian dilettante architect, Revisi Bruti, published a treatise in Vicenza entitled *Archiesto per formar con facilità li cinque ordini d'architettura*. In this he explained a method of calculating the proportions of the five Classical orders of architecture and he described the proposed instrument for doing it. The book included an engraved plate showing the design of this special sector together with the two sides of its architectonic arc with details of the divisions and inscriptions which were required. There were, however, no practical annotations on the method of setting the instrument up. The work was translated into English by Thomas Malie in 1737.

Before this, 1723, Thomas Carwitham, an English architect, published his *Description and Use of an Architectonic Sector and also Architectonic Sliding Plates* in association with Thomas Heath, the instrument maker. It included descriptions of 'the Sliding Plates whereby Scales of all Sizes are most readily and Universally obtained for fluting pilasters & columns, Drawing Geometrical Planes & Uprights in any of the Five Orders according to the given diameter of a Column'. Unfortunately, Carwitham did not illustrate the instrument itself, but a brass architectonic sector, possibly based on this treatise, can be seen at the Museum of the History of Science in Oxford [134].

A somewhat different version of the Architectonic Sector was made by George Adams the Elder (1704–73), examples of which are extant dating to *c.*1760. These instruments were described and fully illustrated in Joshua Kirby's *Description of the Correct Use of an Architectonic Sector*, which was published with a front-

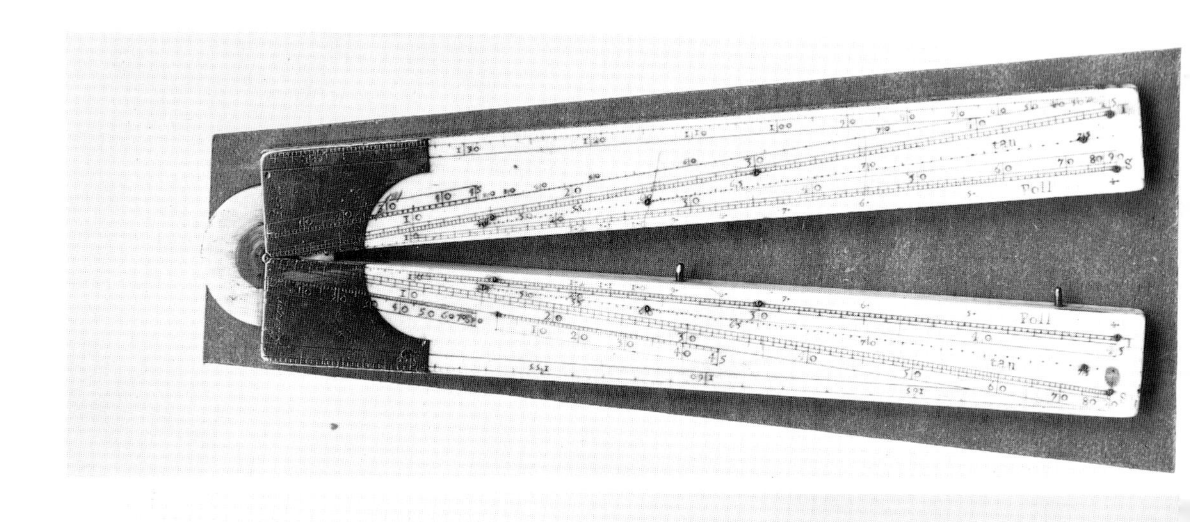

133

134

[133] Three English sectors: (*above*) ivory with silver arched hinge, signed 'Carver Fecit'; (*below*) both of brass finely engraved and provided with a third hinged arm, the left hand version signed 'Berge', the right 'Culpeper fecit'. Length 6 in (152 mm). Mid-18th century. *Science Museum, London.*

[134] Architectonic sector in brass, possibly based on a design described by Revisi Bruti of Vicenza in his treatise of 1627; arranged as a hinged sector with sliding architectonic plates or arcs, the latter finely engraved with scales for calculating all the elements which make up the five Classical orders of architecture. Maker Culpeper? Length $11\frac{1}{2}$ in (290 mm); diam $6\frac{1}{2}$ in (165 mm). *c.*1730. *Museum of the History of Science, Oxford.*

ispiece by William Hogarth in 1761 and dedicated to George III. Kirby, who had been drawing master to the King when Prince of Wales, praises the instrument through which, correctly used, 'any part of Architecture may be drawn with facility and exactness; it can be used to set up the Orders of Civil Architecture according to the principles given by Palladio'. It appears that the use of this instrument was very time-consuming and that most architects could calculate the proportions of the various architectural elements by much simpler methods [134 and 135].

One excellent example of Adams' version of this

135

[135] Architectonic sector of silver inscribed 'Made by Geo: ADAMS Math Instru Maker to His Royal Highness the PRINCE of WALES Fleet Street LONDON' and consisting of a 12-inch sector with wide plate in the form of an arc; both finely engraved on each face, with decorated screws to locate the arc and a steel stay at the base of the instrument. The letters T,D,I,C and R on the arms of the sector refer to the five orders of architecture. *c.*1761. *RIBA Collection, London.*

[136] Engraving from Batty Langley's *The City and Country Builder's and Workman's Treasury of Designs* (1740), which shows the proportions of Ionic order with its capital, base, and pedestal and column, set out in relation to the diameter of the column.

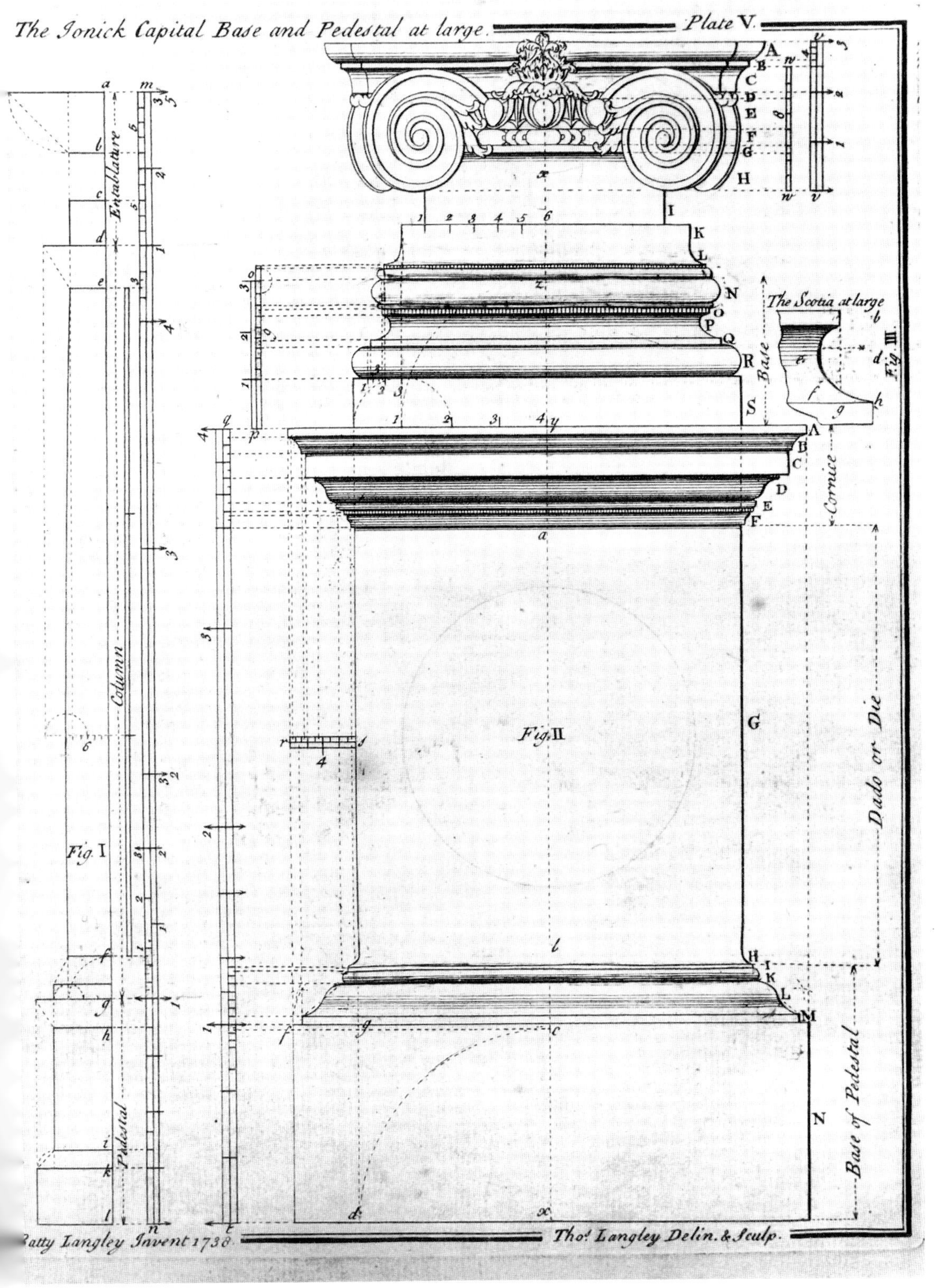
The Ionick Capital Base and Pedestal at large.
Plate V.
Entablature
Column
Pedestal
Fig. I
Fig. II
The Scotia at large
Fig. III
Base
Cornice
Dado or Die
Base of Pedestal
Batty Langley Invent 1738.
Thoˢ Langley Delin. & Sculp.

136

instrument was made in silver with both the faces of the plates engraved according to Kirby's treatise [136]. In another example Adams used ivory for the sector and arc and silver for the hinge and indices.

ARCHITECTURAL PROPORTIONAL RODS

Another instrument designed for calculating the proportions of the Classical orders also had its origins in the seventeenth century. A design for some architectural proportional rods first appeared in a treatise published in Latin and German in Leyden in 1662 by Nicholas Goldmann (1611–66), a professor of mathematics and architecture. Entitled *Tractatus de stylometris sive instrumentis quibus quinque ordines architecturae*, it shows six triangular rods incorporated in the design of the title page [138]. A complete set of rods based on this design exists with a fitted cylindrical case. These rods must be included amongst the interesting examples of specialist drawing instruments which were never adopted into common use [137].

During the eighteenth century one finds further attempts at designing an instrument to carry out calculations when dealing with architectural proportions. In his small work *Magnum in parvo* of 1728, William Halfpenny includes an illustration of Thomas Heath's protractor arc for calculating the five orders. William Pain included a design for a rule for calculating the proportions of the orders in his patternbook *The Builder's Companion and Workman's Assistant*, published in 1762. The attention given to these aids had diminished by 1800, since by then architects and builders could call on the more accurate measured drawings of Classical remains made by such architects as James Stuart and Robert Adam in the second half of the eighteenth century. No subsequent changes in the handling of the proportions of the Classical orders have required the development of new instruments.

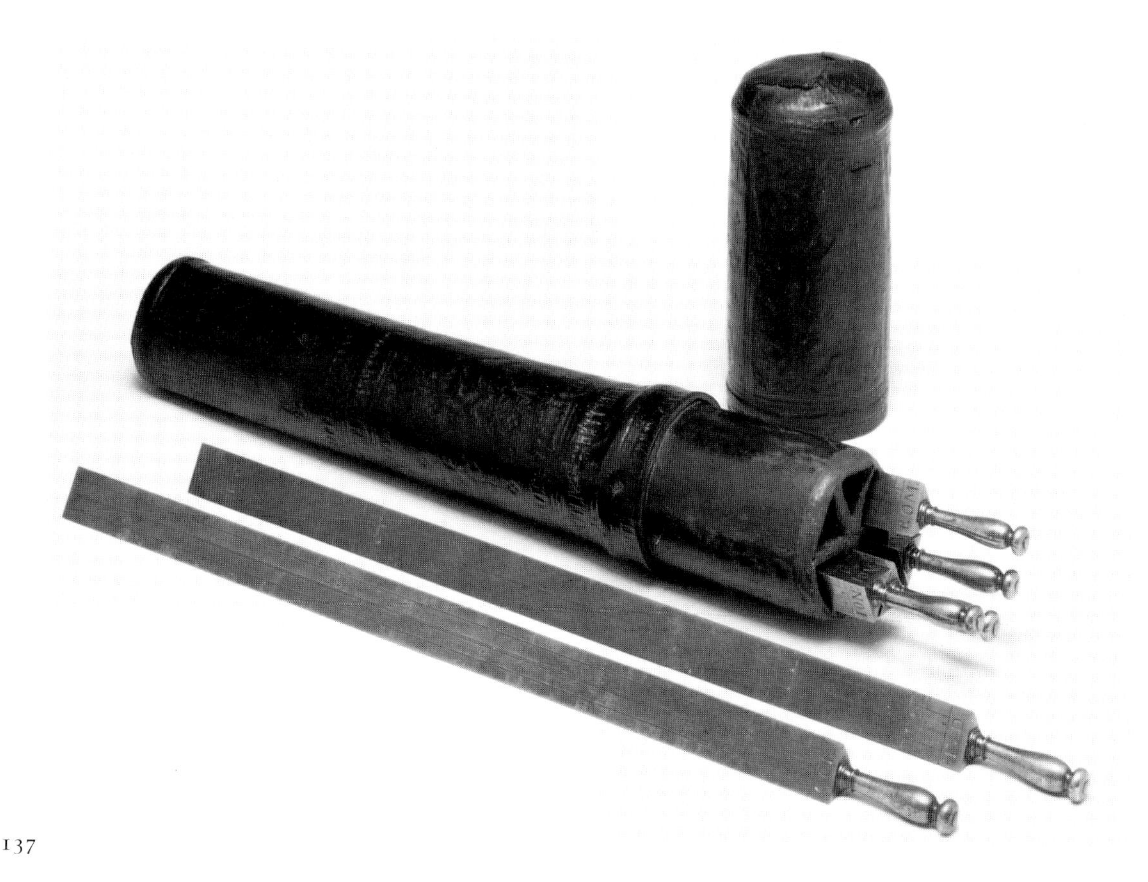

137

[137] A set of five triangular brass architectural rods which fit inside a leather-covered cylindrical case with a slip top. Length of rods $10\frac{3}{8}$ in (262 mm). *c.*1660. *Whipple Museum of the History of Science, Cambridge.*

[138] Engraved title page of Nicholas Goldmann's *Tractatus de stylometris sive instrumentis quibus quinque ordines Architecturae*, published in Leyden in 1662; the design includes a set of triangular proportional rods graduated with scales to calculate the elements of five architectural orders. *British Architectural Library, London.*

TRACTATVS
DE
STYLOMETRIS.
ſive
INSTRVMENTIS.
quibus
Quinque Ordines
ARCHITECTVRÆ
Methodo quâ facilior inveniri nequit,
expeditius et accuratius longè quam ullo Proportiona:
torio in modicâ et majuſcula forma deſignantur.
Inventore
Nicolao Goldmanno Vratiſl: Sileſ:

Gebrauch
Dehr Bauſtäbe
durch dehrer hülffe
Die Fünf Ordnungen der Baukunſt
aufs aller leichteſte, ja behänder
und genauer als mit einigem
Ebenpaßer in großer und
kleiner Form abgebildet
werden.

LVGDVNI BATAVORVM,
Apud Autorem.
M D C L X II.
DEO SOLI OMNIS GLORIA.

Jan. Mathysz. sculp. Amstelod.

138

10

Perspective Aids

Perspectographs

The subject of geometrical perspective and the drawing apparatus devised as aids for it warrants a separate book. It has obsessed various artists and architects since the early Renaissance when Brunelleschi first established his principles of perspective in early fifteenth-century Florence. From 1420 onwards his theories were generally adopted. Most particularly realized by Piero della Francesca in the second half of the fifteenth century, they involved working from plans and elevations drawn to scale and the use of vanishing points.

The contribution to the subject of geometrical perspective by Piero's contemporary Leon Battista Alberti was contained in *Della pittura* (1436). Alberti was known to have used a perspective apparatus which consisted of a frame divided into squares by wires; the drawing paper was also squared up and the outline of the image viewed through the screen was transferred to the equivalent square on the paper. Working at the end of the century, Leonardo da Vinci substituted a sheet of glass with squared divisions for the frame with wires, and this was used in the same way. Early in the sixteenth century, Albrecht Dürer published his influential book on measurement, *Unterweysungen der Messung* (1525), which contained illustrations of two types of perspective apparatus. Most of the early perspective apparatuses were designed to assist in drawing accurately from a fixed point and to deal with the problems of foreshortening and central perspective. Dürer's work was followed by a spate of similar treatises such as those of Serlio (1537), J.A. du Cerceau (1570), Vredeman de Vries (1605), Jean F. Niceron (1646); Abraham Bosse (1659) and Sebastian le Clerc (1669).

Several attempts to develop various perspective aids were made in the seventeenth century, some based on Alberti's and Dürer's simple squared-up grid frames. Jost Bürgi invented his table model perspective device in Cassel in 1604 and made one for presentation to the Emperor Rudolf in Prague. His son-in-law Benjamin Bramer, the mathematician and architect, also designed a perspective apparatus (*c.*1630). This was another table-mounted instrument, but provided with two sighting pin-holes. An engraving illustrating Bramer's version was included in the German edition of Bion, published as *Mathematische Werkschule* in 1717 [139]. This plate also included a perspective apparatus designed by the French mathematician and optician Jean F. Niceron, who had written a treatise on optics and perspective, *Thaumaturgis opticus*, in 1646.

In 1669 Sir Christopher Wren presented his design for a 'perspectograph' to the Royal Society in London. This incorporated a parallel drawing straight edge operated by cords, rather similar to a modern parallel motion, attached to a board placed vertically behind a stand to which is bracketed the single pinhole viewing device. A drawing of Wren's device was included in *Mathematische Werkschule* [140].

Variations of these table-mounted devices recur during the eighteenth century. One example is the far more complicated apparatus designed by George Adams the Younger, which is illustrated in his *Geometrical and Graphical Essays* (Plate 32) of 1795 and incorporates a drawing machine on rollers [141].

Perspectographs continued to be made in the nineteenth century and there are examples in British museums by the French inventor J. D. C. Gavard designed around 1840; one by him was exhibited in the Great Exhibition in London in 1851. He had earlier published his design for another perspective apparatus which he called *Le Diagraphe* in 1833.

Other variations of perspective apparatus are those designed with easel or tripod types of support. Of these the most interesting is the one designed by James Watt in 1765 during his early period in Glasgow as an instrument maker and land-surveyor. This is an ingenious device made to be easily transportable for use when preparing exterior perspectives [142]. Watt never patented his design, made in conjunction with

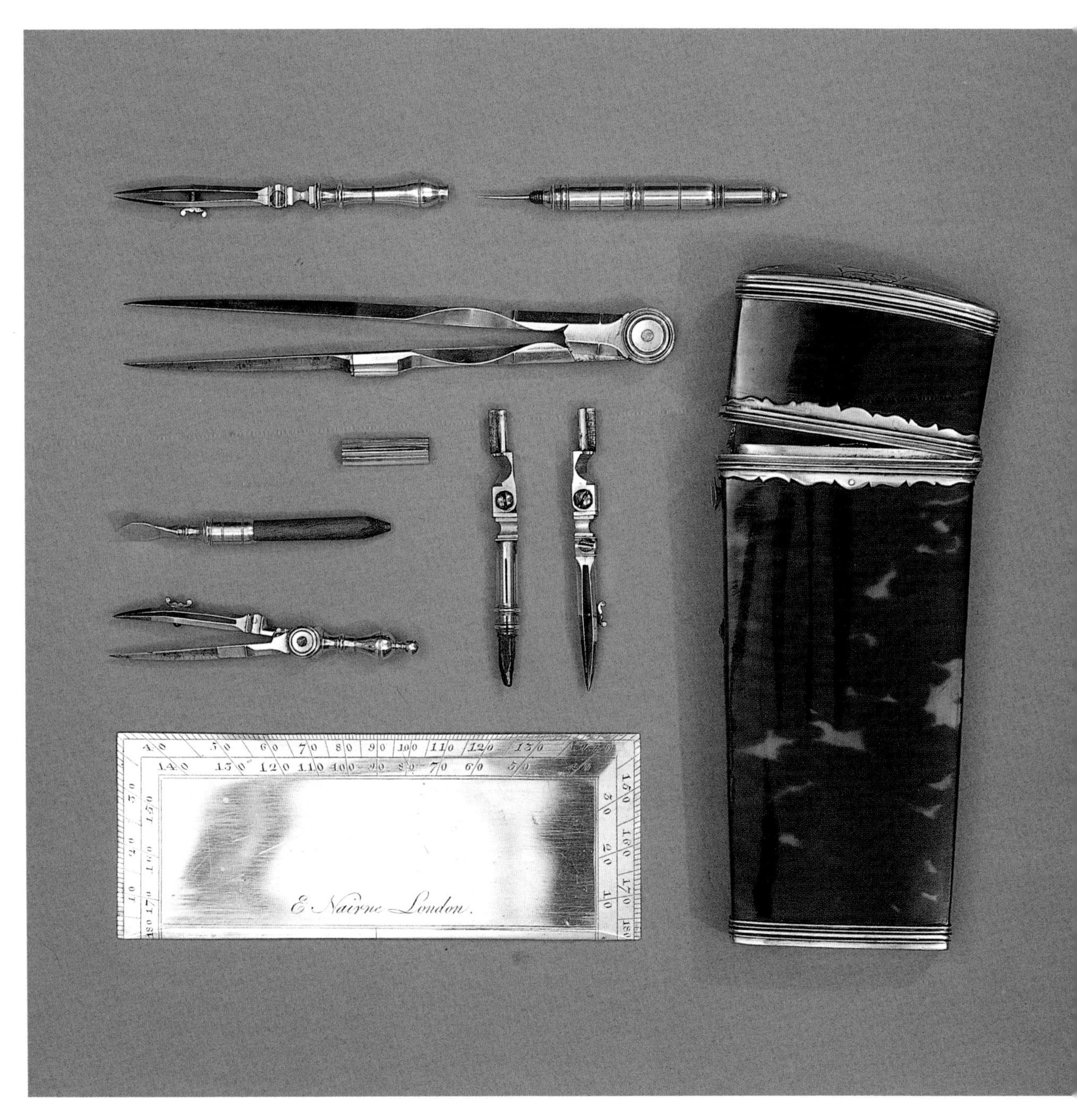

[XIII] Tortoise-shell-covered small pocket case with decorative silver mounts which contains silver instruments; the $4\frac{1}{2}$-inch protractor is signed '*E. Nairne London*'. This small set includes a pair of large compasses with inserts for pencil and ink (note the link piece for their storage), a pair of small bows for ink, a ruling pen with turned handle with the protracting pin shown exposed and a silver mounted pencil. Case: 5 in (127 mm) long. *c.*1770. *Andrew Alpern Collection, New York.*

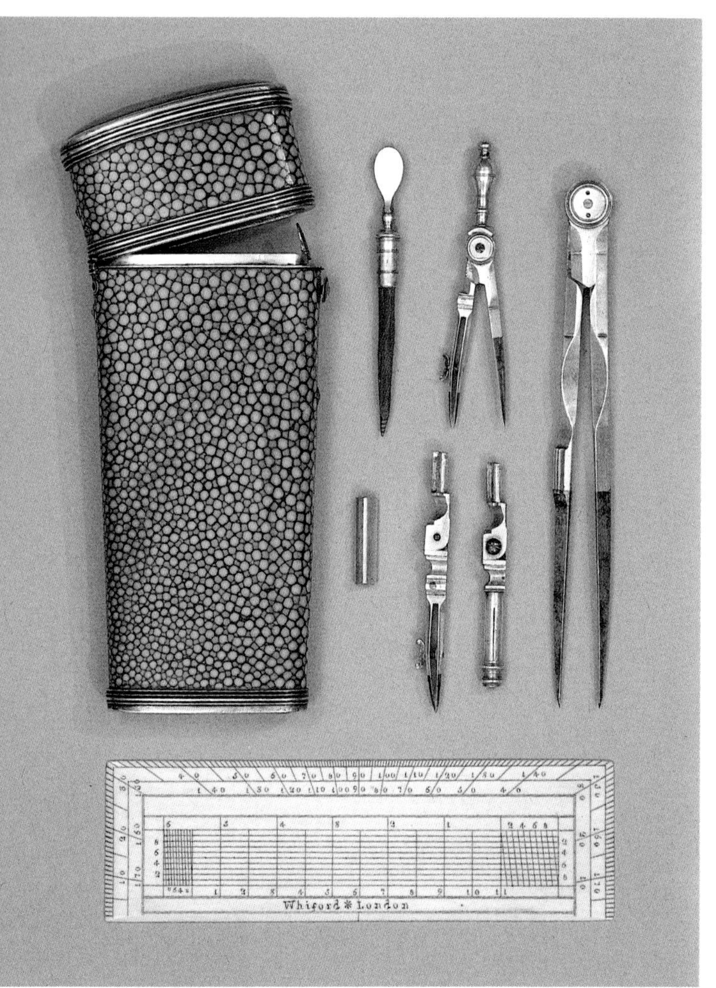

XIV

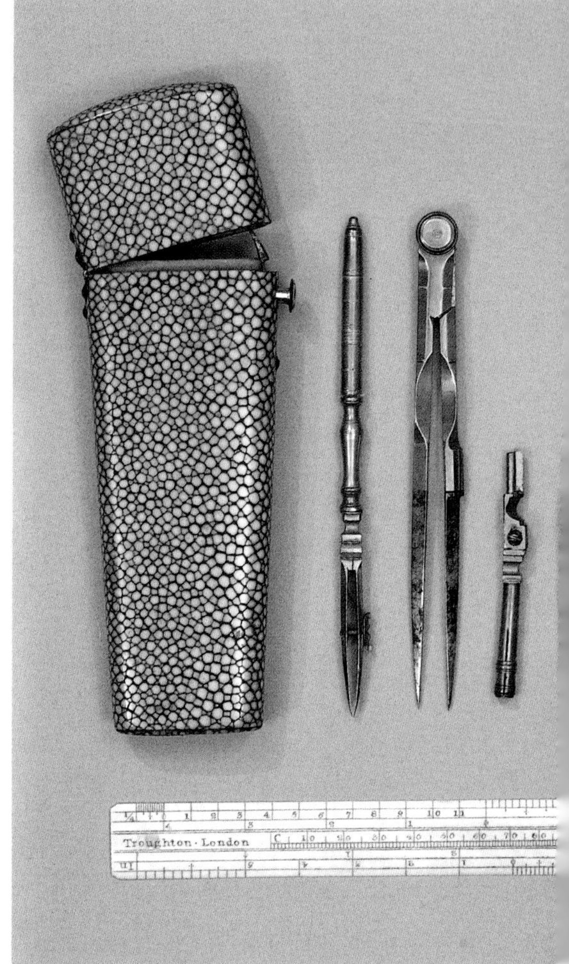

XV

[XIV] A small shagreen-covered pocket case with silver mounts containing a large pair of compasses with insert for ink and pencil and their connector, a small pair of ink bow compasses, a silver-mounted pencil with end shaped for use as tracer and an ivory scale combined with protractor signed 'Whiford London'. Late 18th century. Case: $5 \times 2 \times \frac{3}{4}$ in ($127 \times 52 \times 20$ mm). *Andrew Alpern Collection, New York.*

[XV] A simple shagreen-covered pocket case with a small set of brass instruments, a ruling pen with hand-cut wing-nut, a pair of compasses with inserts for pencil and ink and a drawing scale graduated for inch divisions and a small centimeter scale centrally placed, and signed 'Troughton London'. Case: $5\frac{1}{2}$ in (140 mm) long. Late 18th century. *Andrew Alpern Collection, New York.*

James Lind the medical explorer, and George Adams the Elder is believed to have brought out a similar instrument based on Watt's design soon afterwards.

Considerably later, in 1819, John Farey illustrated 'Mr Peacock's Delineator', a similar but more cumbersome apparatus with a framed drawing board and easel stand and with a viewing pin-hole to an adjustable arm [143].

Delineators

Many of the instruments already described in this chapter fall into the category of aids to artists in drawing in perspective; they would not have been used for the preparation of technical or architectural presentation drawings. Delineators were devised from 1800 onwards to deal with the specific problems of drawing lines in perspective to an inaccessible vanishing point or points, and they were of use to technical and architectural draughtsmen as well as artists. Peter Nicholson, the expert draughtsman and mathematician, is credited with the invention, in 1814, of an instrument which he called a 'centrolinead'. He was awarded a silver medal by the Society of Arts in 1815 when he presented his improved version of the centrolinead together with a paper on its use [144]. John Farey, who won a prize for his ellipsograph in 1813, illustrated his own design for a similar device in his plate on drawing instruments for the *Edinburgh Encyclopaedia* in 1830. Towards the end of his life Farey claimed that he had designed his 'delineator' in 1807, and there are strong reasons to believe that Nicholson modified his design to include details from Farey's design.

The centrolinead was included by Stanley in his treatise, and it continued to be used through the nineteenth century as it was particularly suited to oversize drawings. Patrick Adie made several examples of this instrument and another, more complicated version called a 'bi-centrolinead'. All such devices were used to set up the large and complex perspectives fashionable in the nineteenth century. The centrolinead was still being used during the first half of the twentieth century by the few artists and architects who carried out similar large perspective drawings during the 1930s, among them Cyril Arthur Farey, E. W. English and Edward D. Lyons.

OVERLEAF

[139] Engraving from Bion's *Mathematische Werkschule* which illustrates (fig. 1) Benjamin Bramer's table apparatus, of *c.* 1630, with two sighting pin-holes at (A) and (B) and a timber drawing frame (D–G and E–F). Fig. 3 shows the apparatus designed by Jean F. Niceron, a French mathematician and optician. *c.* 1640.

[140] Engraving from *Mathematische Werkschule* (a German version of Bion), which illustrates (fig. 1) the perspectograph designed by Sir Christopher Wren in 1669. Fig. 5 shows another apparatus which has two viewing points and operates with a horizontal drawing parallel motion.

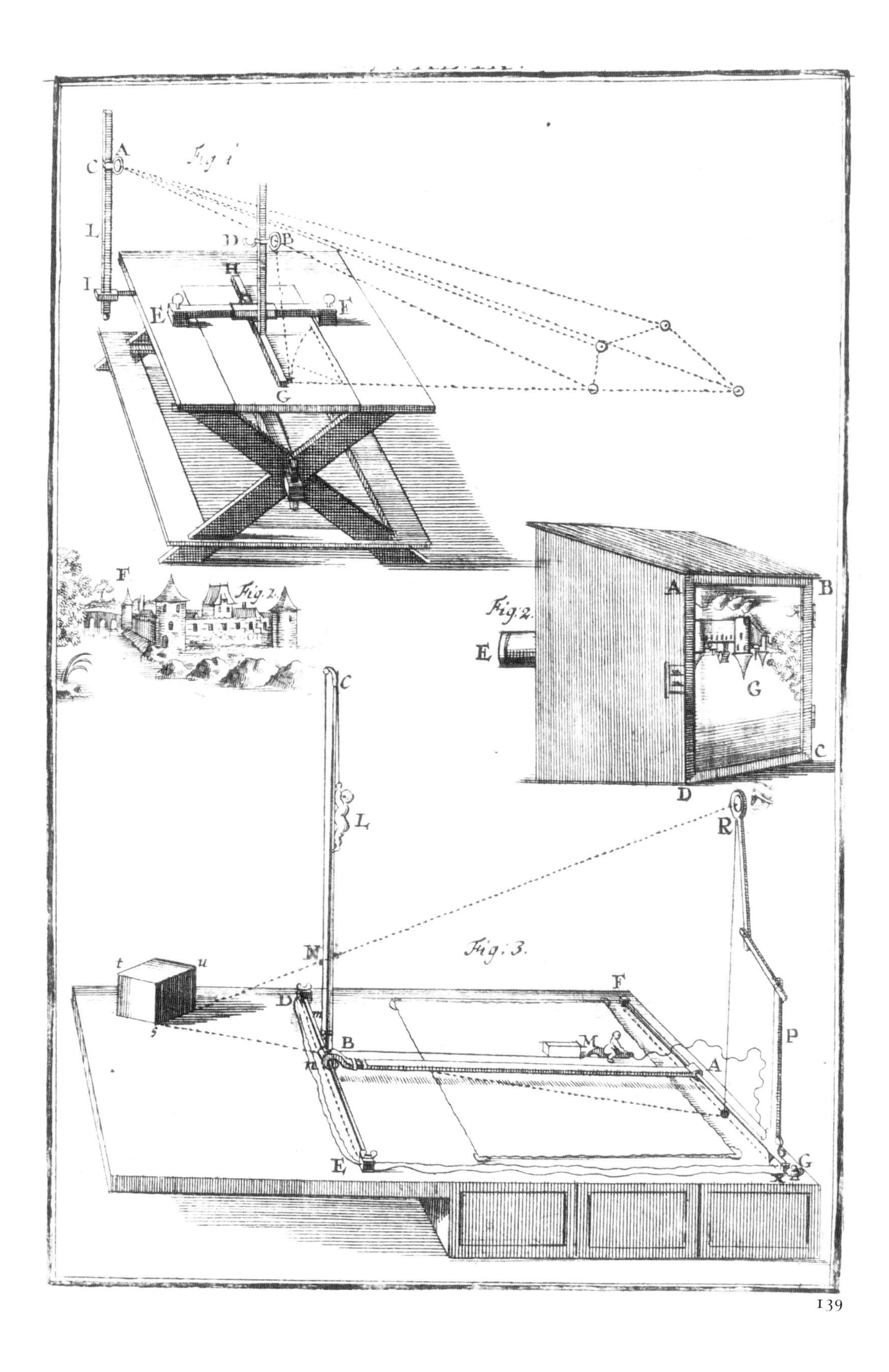
Fig. 1
Fig. 2.
Fig. 2.
Fig. 3.
139

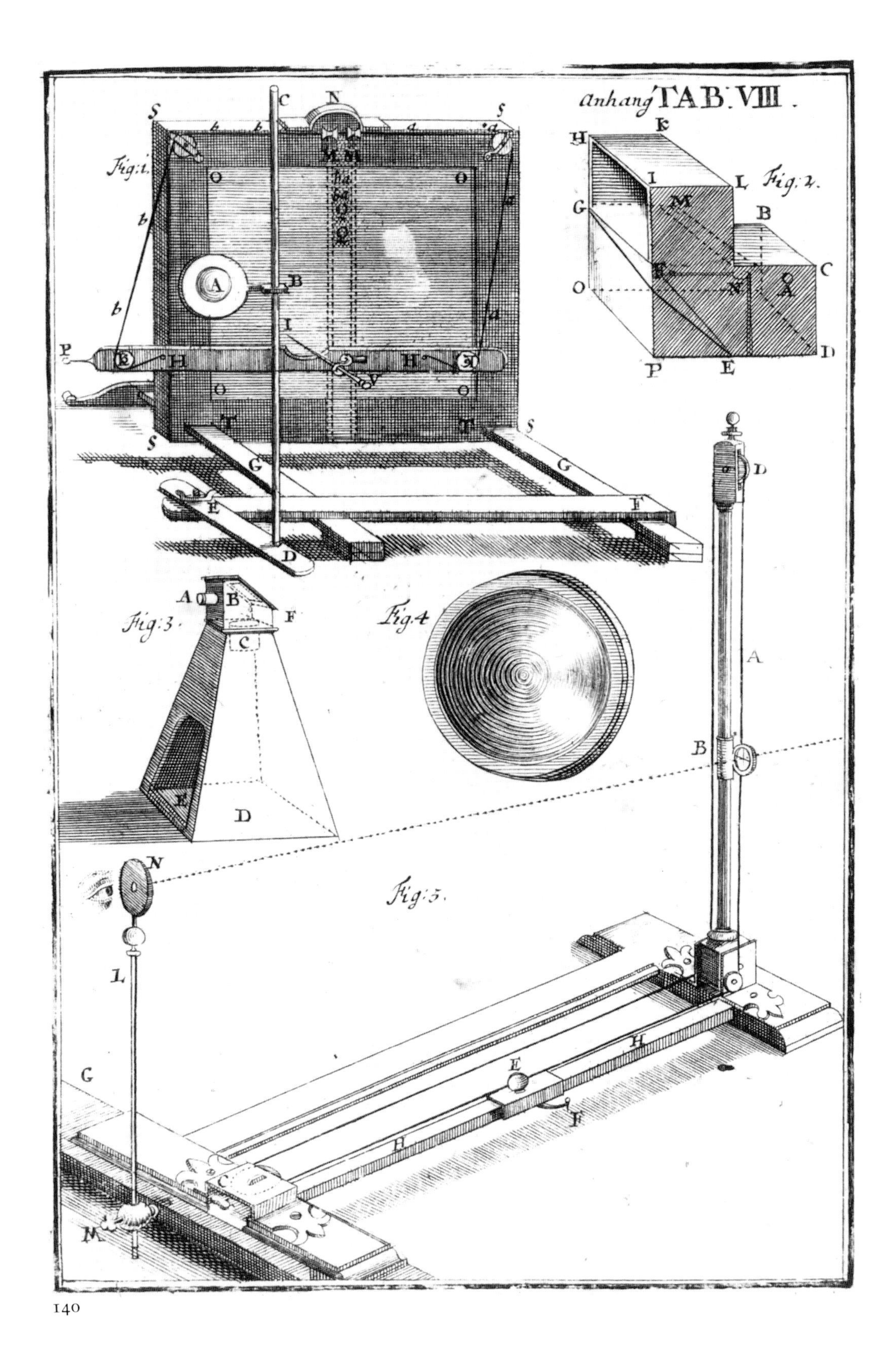

140

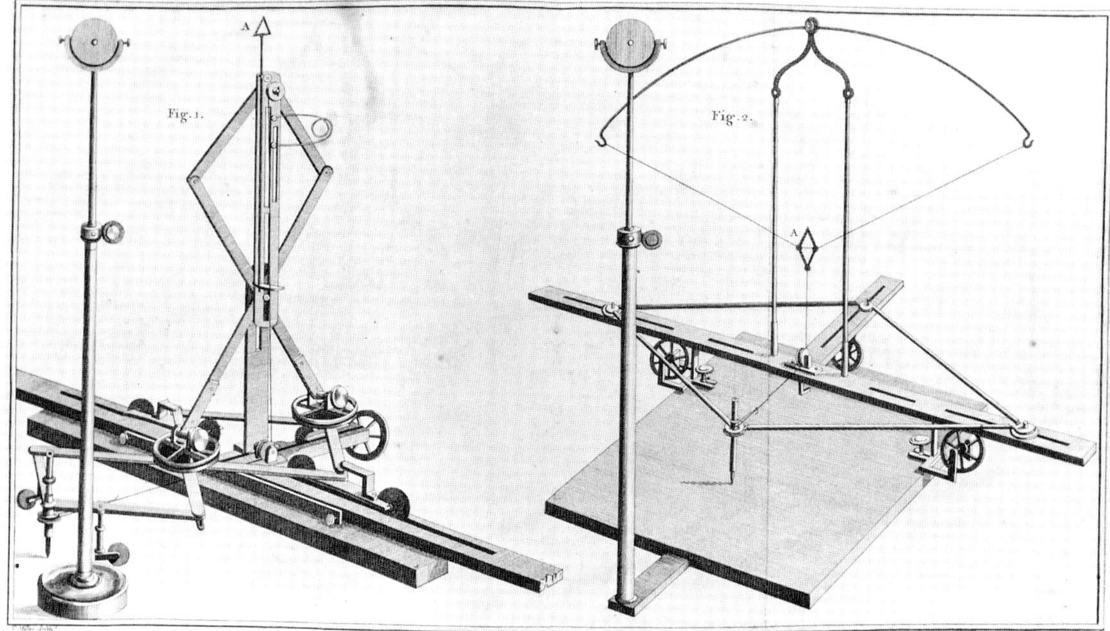

141

[141] Engraving from George Adams the Younger's *Geometrical and Graphical Essays* dated December 1796; Fig. 2 shows Adams' perspective apparatus, a complex device which incorporates three rollers to operate the drawing point suspended by wires from a counter-balanced metal frame.

[142] Perspective apparatus designed by the engineer James Watt and made by him in Glasgow in 1765. This is an ingenious device, easily transportable, for use in external perspectives. The apparatus folds away into a fitted hardwood case, which also forms the drawing board; its stand fits together to form a walking stick. *Science Museum, London.*

[143] John Farey's plate illustrating Delineators from Dr Abraham Rees' *Cyclopaedia* (1819).

OVERLEAF
[144] Engraving by M. A. Nicholson, dated 1836, which illustrates a Centrolinead, originally invented by his father, Peter Nicholson, in 1814, together with details of the construction of the hinged triple joint. From Peter Nicholson's *New Practical Builder or Workman's Companion.*

142

Plate I.

DRAWING INSTRUMENTS.

DELINEATORS.

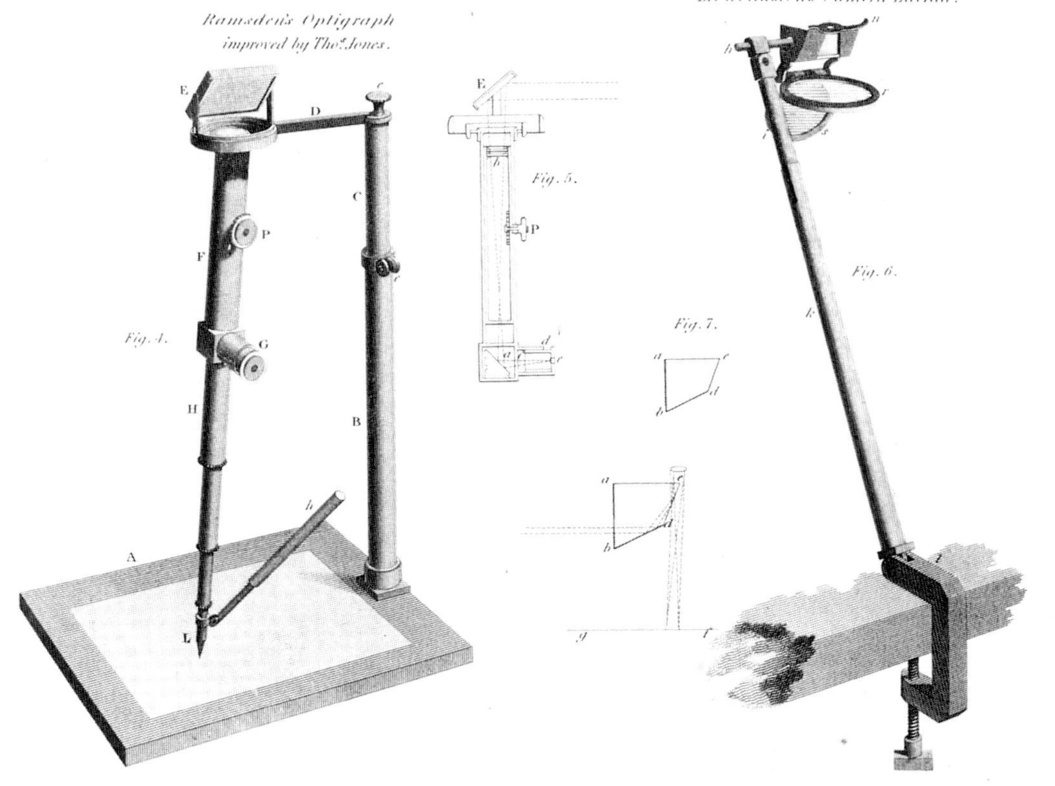

Published as the Act directs, 1812, by Longman, Hurst, Rees, Orme and Brown, Paternoster Row, London.

Engraved by W. Lowry.

143

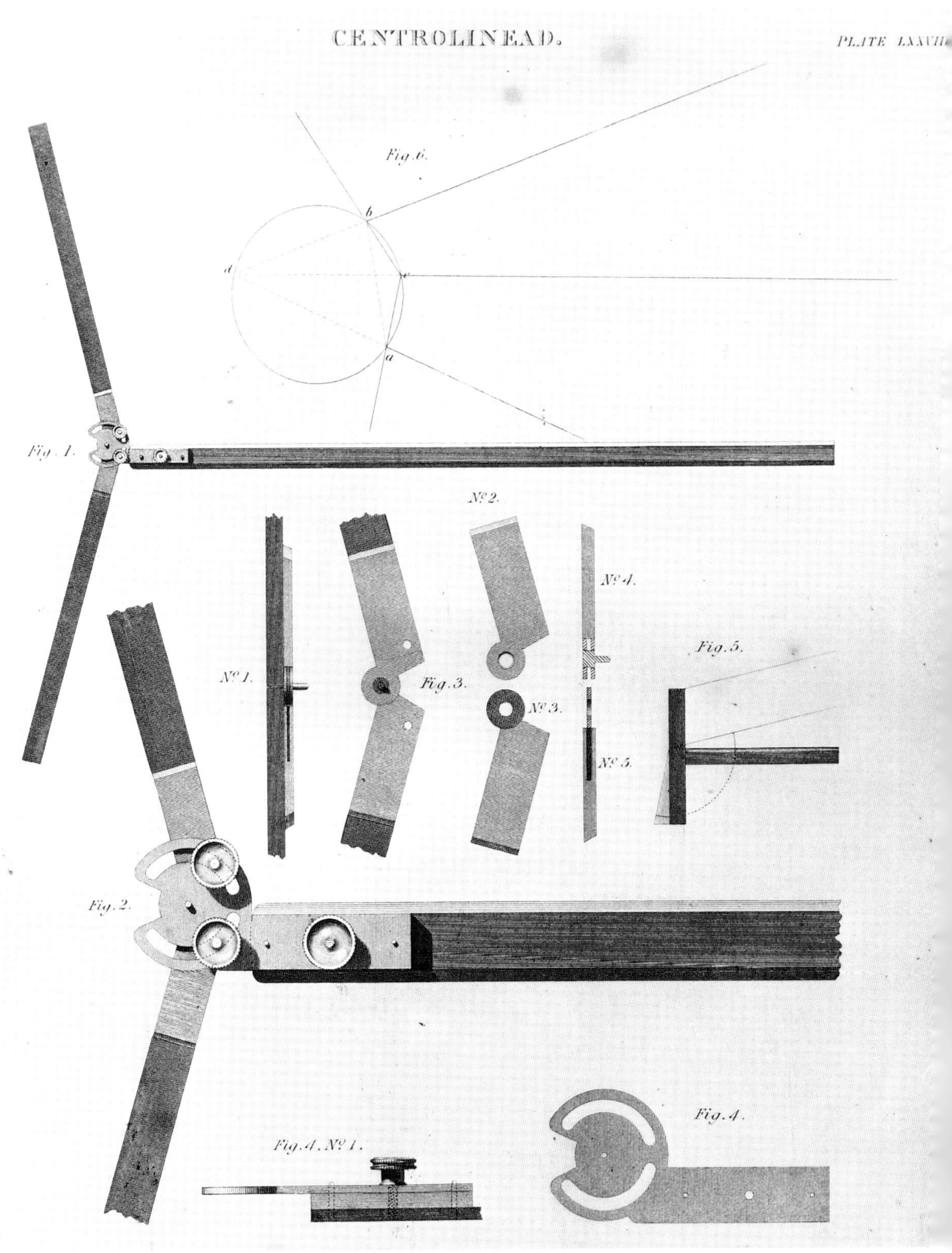
CENTROLINEAD.
PLATE LXXVII
Fig. 6.
b
d
c
a
Fig. 1.
Nº 2.
Nº 4.
Fig. 5.
Nº 1.
Fig. 3.
Nº 3.
Nº 5.
Fig. 2.
Fig. 4.
Fig. 4. Nº 1.

144

Cases of Drawing Instruments

[145] Compendium case of drawing instruments in the form of a tall square gilt brass case with all four sides engraved. The top is hinged and on the bottom is the maker's name: *Barthelomewe Newsum* (a London clockmaker). The gilded instruments are of brass, arranged in vertical slots and comprise: a folding set square, a folding rule, a pair of compasses with one leg with split end for use for scoring, a beam compass, large and small dividers, a pen with fixed nib, a crayon-holder, a pricker, a pair of scissors, two knives and a sharpening hone, and fixed proportional compasses (1:3). The brass is finely chased with bulbous tops to turned holders. Case: 193 × 83 mm square. *c.*1570. *British Museum, London.*

Introduction

From the sixteenth century onwards cases were provided for the protection and easy transportation of drawing instruments, usually combined with other mathematical instruments. Initially the demand for these cased sets of instruments was varied and included formal presentation collections ordered by heads of state or presented to them by others as tokens of esteem, as well as everyday sets for regular use.

There was considerable variety in both the form and design of the early cases. Many presentation cases were elaborately engraved and decorated 'compendia' of silver or brass gilt; their drawing instruments were sometimes stored vertically together with scissors, tweezers and other useful articles. An unusually pious version exists in the form of a crucifix case of gilt brass [146]. However, mathematical instruments were usually set into wooden panels arranged in compartments or tiers within a hinged flat case of polished or inlaid wood. In Italy and Germany flat cases were often covered in plain or tooled leather, sometimes with gilt decoration, and by 1700 examples can be found where the case is disguised as a book. Flat cases together with some squat boxes continued to be made in all sizes until 1900, the contents often being related to the specialist needs of the owner.

In the seventeenth century vertical cases became common for small sets of instruments, first as leather pouches, later with the core made of wood with slots to take each instrument vertically (like some medical instrument cases). This system continued to be used until the mid-nineteenth century, with the largest cases holding a full set of up to a dozen drawing instruments, the smaller four to six and the smallest only three or four items. In addition miniature versions were made of all designs as mementoes, and drawing instruments were also incorporated in 'virtuoso' containers. The choice of materials determined the cost; only in rare instances did purchasers order cases in expensive materials like sterling silver.

Strangely enough there are no detailed illustrations of instrument cases in either the large eighteenth-century reference works that include engravings of drawing instruments or in the small treatises that describe in detail what cases should contain. Some trade cards show a small sketch of a pocket case but none exists of the larger cases offered [26].

Drawing instrument cases do not reflect the dec-

[146] Crucifix dial in gilt brass containing drawing instruments, some signed H + D + F 1618. The crucifix is engraved to combine various calendrical and astronomical functions. The set of instruments of gilt brass, silver and steel, which fits inside the hollow cross, comprises: a pair of scissors; a pair of compasses with removable point; a pounce-pot; a sector; a writing pen with a crayon-holder at the reverse end; a scissored parallel rule engraved with various foot measures; a ruling pen with a stylus at the reverse end; a penknife; an inkpot; a folding square which can be used as dividers; the back plate of the case, also engraved with foot measures. German. Case: 6 in (152 mm) high. *Museum of the History of Science, Oxford.*

orative style of their period unlike other storage articles such as nécessaires and boxes. There is little evidence, except in elaborate presentation cases, of the influence of rococo or neo-classical design, for example, which is to be found on contemporary silverware and cutlery, and most drawing instrument cases were treated simply as protective containers. Small cases dating from 1700 to 1850 are seldom decorated; those covered in black fishskin are the most austere. When more expensive materials, such as shagreen or tortoise-shell, were used the design of the cases was still restrained and usually confined to the silver mounts and the name-plate. In France, by contrast, some eighteenth-century leather cases exist with embossed gilt emblems, and during the nineteenth century polished hardwood was used for both medium and larger cases with elaborate inlay in the form of a cartouche design in brass and mother-of-pearl [VIII].

Apart from a few caskets and cases of exceptional design, practicality was the prime consideration, and from the eighteenth century the greatest demand was for everyday cases. By 1700 many instrument cases were covered in ordinary fishskin. Later rayskin and sharkskin were also used since, like fishskin, these materials handled well and were waterproof. Shagreen became a very popular finish in England and was used for covering all manner of boxes, étuis, cases for scientific instruments such as telescopes, domestic objects such as spectacle cases, sewing sets and even tea-caddies. The material used for shagreen was either natural sharkskin, rayskin or leather treated to simulate the singular texture of sharkskin, usually dyed green for drawing instrument cases (white, blue and pink shagreen being used for other objects).

The dating of instrument cases is best done from a study of the design of the contents, noting the pattern of the ruling pens and compasses and other items provided, and the detail of the pen blades and screws or the compass joints, etc. It should be remembered that some instrument cases are composite, that is, they were either made to contain various instruments assembled over an often considerable period of time, or they contain odd instruments added as replacements for lost items. Certain national characteristics emerge in the details of design, materials and colours in the cases. In both Germany and Italy there was frequent use of rust or natural coloured suede (or chamois) for lining cases. During the eighteenth century the lids of flat cases from other countries were lined with satin or silk damask while the instrument trays were lined in hand-cut silk velvet or felt. Olive green and dark red were popular colours in England whereas in Germany and France emerald green velvet with gold braid trimming was regularly used. By the mid-nineteenth century the new aniline dyes made possible the dark blues and purples used extensively for both the velvet (now usually machine-made velour) for the tray lining and the satin or grosgrain for the lid lining. These colours became particularly associated with English cases for the next one hundred years.

As described in Chapter 1, most drawing instrument cases were provided as bespoke items by European makers until the early nineteenth century. However, in London by the mid-eighteenth century the regular demand for certain items was sufficient to warrant certain established makers providing a few 'off-the-peg' instruments in sets. This tendency increased throughout the following one hundred years and it appears that makers such as the Adams workshop, Dollond, Elliott, Troughton and Cary provided this facility. However, when one examines pocket cases dating to the period 1750–1830 there is still considerable variation in both the actual size and the contents of the individual cases as well as the patterns and materials used for the pieces which they contain. The user whether naval, military or civil engineer, architect or land-surveyor, often still determined the contents. Neither pocket cases nor boxes were made as standard items at this time.

By the latter part of the nineteenth century there were firms specializing in the manufacture of drawing instruments. In Britain the most important offered a standard range of hinged cases in a variety of sizes to suit the purse of the purchaser. The finest were of decorative veneered or solid hardwoods such as burled walnut, rosewood, maple, mahogany or oak with brass or electrum-bound corners, locks and sometimes name-plates. Even the smaller cases conformed to the tier design, with the top tier usually a velvet-lined removable tray to take all the metal instruments. The instruments were made of brass or, from 1860 onwards, German silver or electrum which handle better than brass and do not tarnish. An ivory or boxwood sector, a protractor and sometimes several scales to suit the professional needs of the user were provided in the lower compartment. In the most comprehensive sets of instruments – 'magazine cases' as they were called – extra tiers provided storage for other drawing accessories, such as curves and large circle dividers, and the lowest drawer might be fitted with a set of water-colours together with palettes, paint-brushes and sticks of Chinese ink.

Some comprehensive magazine cases were especially equipped for engineers, particularly railway or military engineers. For the former the cases were

[147] A field set of instruments in a black-japanned steel case with a brass nameplate on the lid which reads R.A.E. CHARD. Some instruments are signed CARY, LONDON. The nickel silver drawing instruments in the lift-out tray include two ruling pens, a pair of turn-about compasses. The lower section includes a Marquois triangle, a 12-inch long rule and a military plotting scale. Case: $13\frac{1}{2} \times 4\frac{1}{2} \times 1\frac{1}{2}$ in (340 × 115 × 38 mm). *c.*1900. *Andrew Alpern Collection, New York.*

fitted with sets of railway curves and scales; for the latter with Marquois scales and triangles (see page 120). The best were made of mahogany, from 14 to 24 in (355 to 610 mm) long, but as an alternative field cases were also made of black japanned steel by such makers as Cary [147] and Elliott. The latter would have been suitable for those working in tropical countries or for those carrying out surveys in exposed conditions.

During the latter part of the nineteenth century the large comprehensive tiered case was unusual in Europe. From 1840 onwards specialist firms such as Haff and Riefler in Germany and Kern in Switzerland began producing plain black leather covered flat cases of various standard sizes which were the forerunners of those made until the 1970s. By 1900 in Britain the principal instrument manufacturers, such as W.F. Stanley and W.H. Harling of London and Thornton of Manchester, supplied most of the high quality instruments although several factors or retailers advertised cases in their own names, and this accounts for the similarity of the pattern of the contents. This situation continued until the 1960s when all these British firms ceased manufacture.

During the past twenty years the considerably reduced demand for cases of quality instruments has been met world-wide by the main European firms such as Kern, Haff and Riefler. All these European makers produced flat cases of hardwood covered with black leather until the 1970s when they were replaced by black plastic boxes with neat long hinges and chrome clip fasteners. More recently the purchase of a complete set of drawing instruments has become less usual since draughtsmen have concentrated on acquiring large sets of technical pens and need only a small range of precision compasses with their attachments. The latter are now sold in small cases with clear acrylic lids – the ultimate in functional design.

Presentation cases

The most magnificent examples of early instrument makers' skills are found among the various presentation cases. Many of the instruments were made of valuable materials such as silver or brass gilt and were often elaborately decorated, displaying the maker's aesthetic sense, engraving skills and technical virtuosity. The earliest example of a presentation case included here dates from the sixteenth century and is possibly of Milanese origin [148]. This set of drawing instruments is exceptional in that it consists of a wide range of beautifully damascened instruments together with a small decorated box containing ink and pounce (a chalky powder used to prepare drawing paper). The design of these early Italian compasses, dividers and proportional compasses is of considerable interest and is similar to that in a splendid English compendium case of brass gilt *c.*1570, made by a London clock maker, Bartholomew Newsam [145]. Similar compendia were made in central Europe by such makers as Erasmus Habermel (1538–1606) and Heinrich Stolle, both of Prague, *c.*1600.

An example of a large early German presentation case of the same period is one by the famous Augsburg maker Christoph Schissler (1530–1609), which contains a wide range of mathematical instruments but few specifically for drawing [149]. The Italian instrument makers Jacobus and Domenicus Lusuerg continued the tradition started by Schissler of including in their cases elaborate examples of every instrument known at the time. There are several fine presentation cases made by the Lusuergs between 1680 and 1717 to be seen in museum collections in London, Cambridge, Vienna and Florence (see Gazetteer). A large case by Domenicus Lusuerg dated around 1701 contains twenty-five items several of which are intended for drawing purposes, while others are intended for surveying [VI]. A French presentation case, made *c.*1763 by Canivet (fl.1751–74) for Louis XV to give to the renowned mathematician Leonard Euler, can be seen in the Science Museum in London. All the instruments in this small case are made of silver, some with mother-of-pearl handles. In England, a remarkable four-tier case was made for Sir Roger North [150].

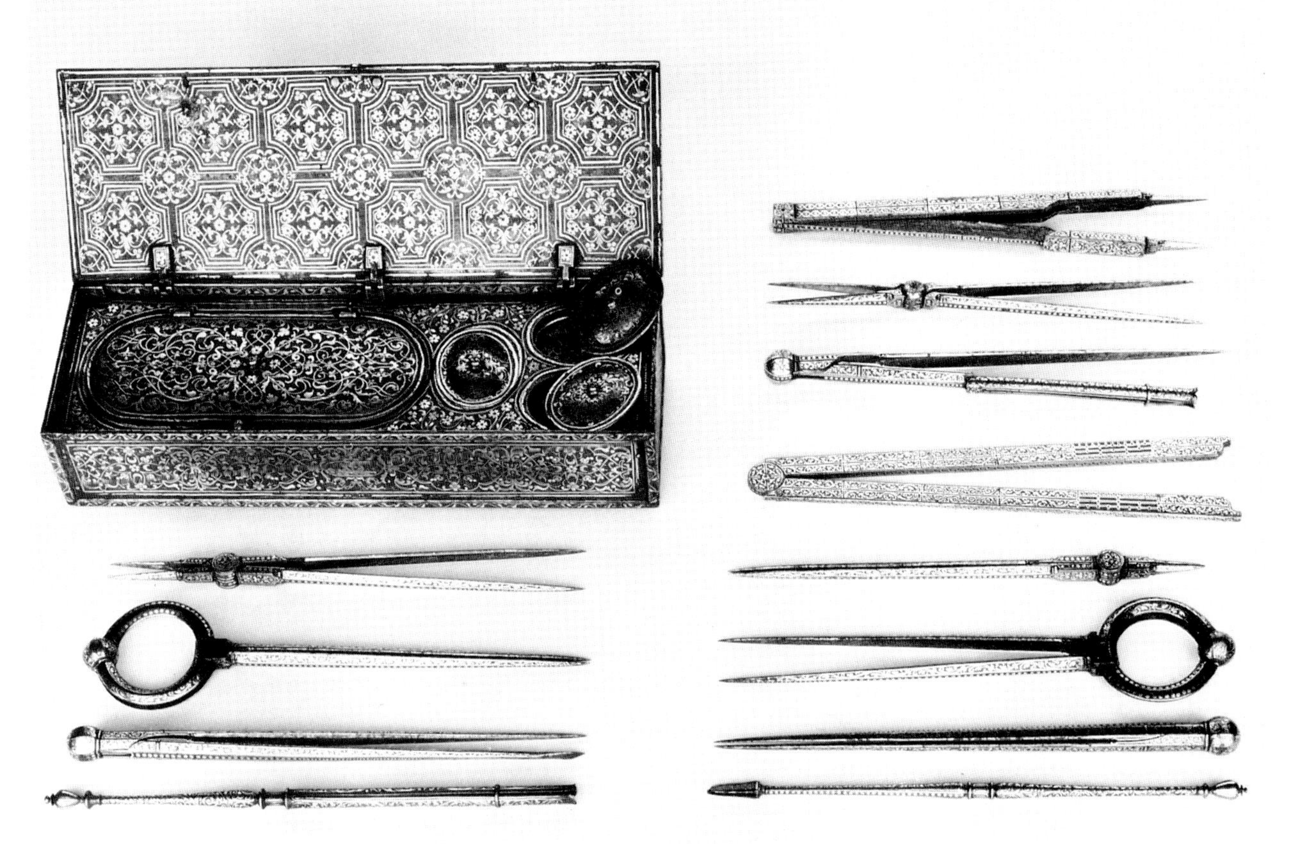

[148] Presentation set of drawing instruments, probably Milanese work, in steel damascened with gold and silver; the inner surfaces are gilt. The set includes a small casket containing ink-wells and a pounce-box. In addition there are a pair of tenoned dividers, three fixed proportional compasses, a pair of compasses with a crayon-holder to one leg, a folding graduated rule, two pairs of single-handed dividers, a pair of compasses with one leg split for scoring, a pair of dividers with ball joint, a crayon-holder and a ruling pen. Italian. Instruments: 6 in (158 mm). Early 16th century. *Museum of the History of Science, Oxford.*

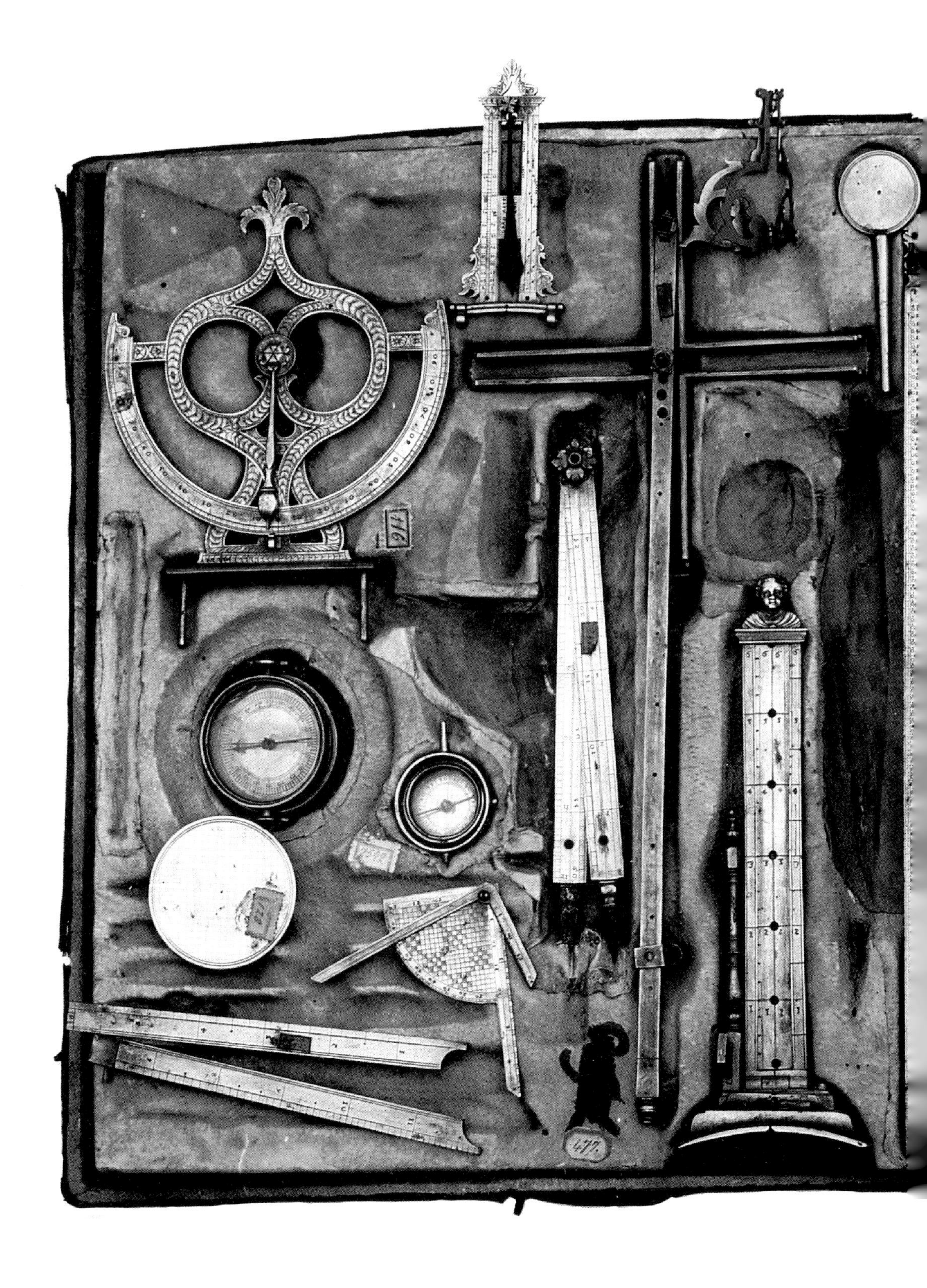

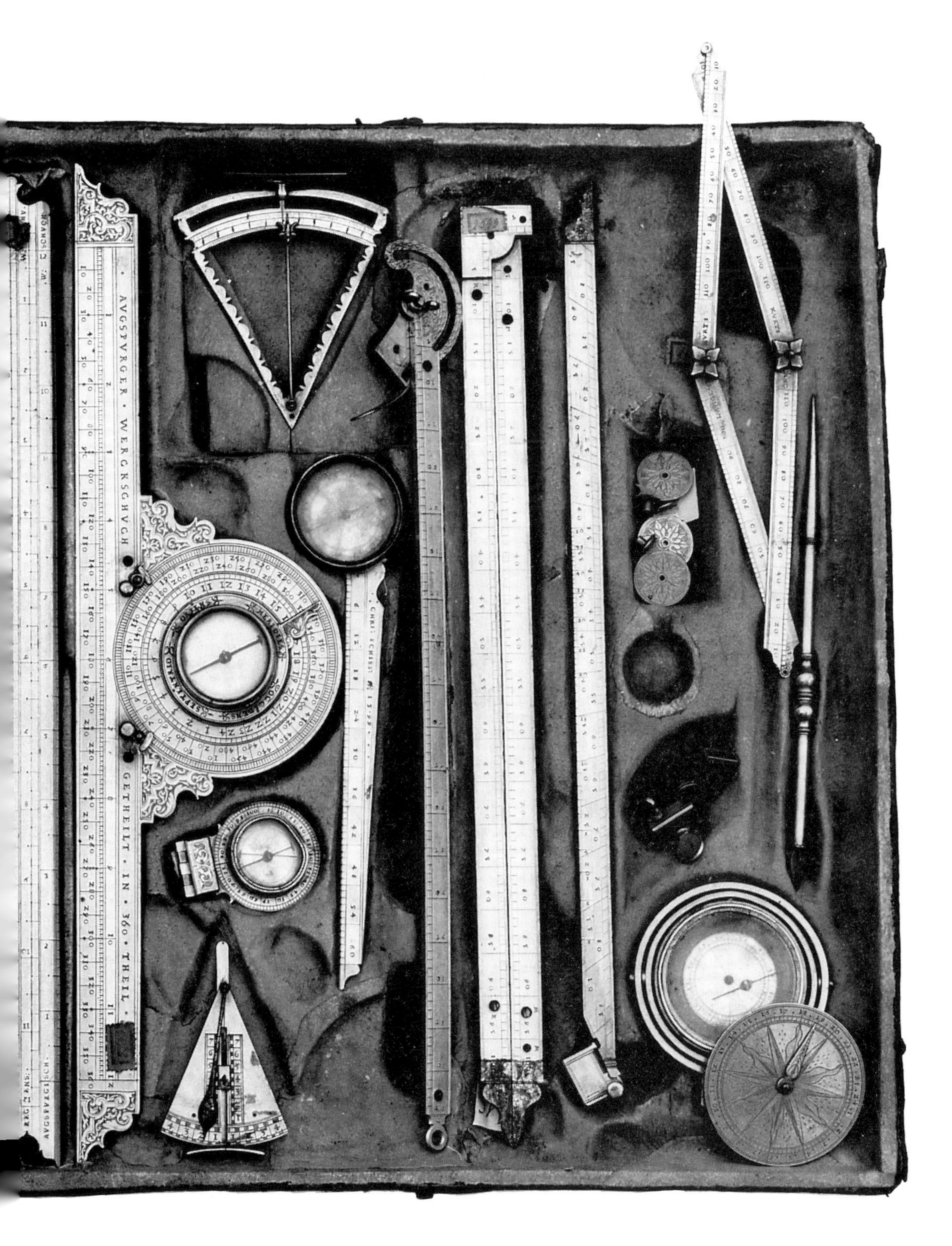

[149] Presentation case of mathematical instruments by Christoph Schissler of wood covered in leather, arranged as two tiers containing instruments for use by surveyors and military engineers for measuring lengths, heights and angles, taking bearings and gunnery levels. The drawing instruments include a large semi-elliptical trammel, a triangular beam compass and a ruling pen with spade-shaped blades and a stylus at the reverse end; all of brass, gilded and engraved. German. *c.*1599. *Museo di Storia della Scienza, Florence.*

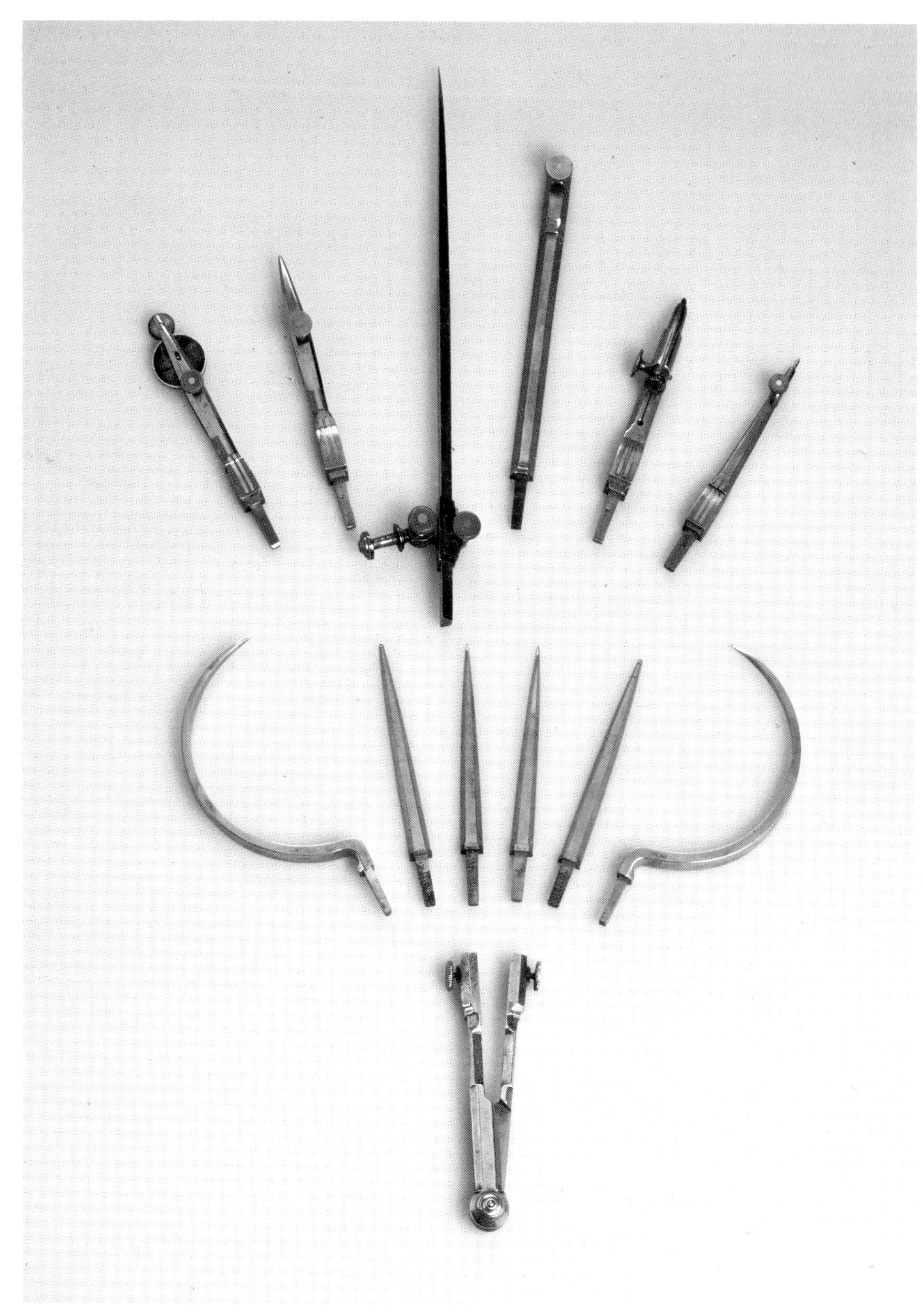

149A

Magazine cases

By the mid-eighteenth century established English instrument makers were offering bespoke cases which they called 'magazine cases', described by John Robertson in 1747 as 'the most complete collection [which] contains whatever can be of use in the practice of drawing' – in fact, a comprehensive selection of drawing instruments. The magazine case in many instances supplanted the presentation case as it was often made up using more valuable materials with highly decorated finishes. A typical example from the latter half of the eighteenth century is a magazine case by Jesse Ramsden (1735–1800) which is arranged in three tiers, with silver instruments in the top lift-out tray, a sector and scales in the middle tray and water-colours, paint palettes and brushes fitted into the lowest compartment. This design is the forerunner of many nineteenth-century cases arranged in a similar manner. It is now part of the National Maritime Museum Collection at Greenwich. A smaller magazine case, by George Adams the Elder (1709–72), consists of a Sheraton-style mahogany box lined with green velvet with brass instruments fitted to both the lid and the base [152].

From the late eighteenth century onwards magazine cases arranged in several tiers were also made in Germany. There is an example of a comprehensive set of drawing instruments in an elaborate three-tier case with compartments for water-colour bottles and paint palettes in the Deutsches Museum in Munich. These German cases were usually leather covered with gilt decoration and lined with velvet, with gold braid trimming around the edges [151].

In Britain magazine cases became more numerous during the nineteenth century and reflect the prosperity of those professions involved in drawing. One case which dates to *c.*1840 is arranged with four lift-out trays to provide metal instruments, scales, rolling rules and water-colours above two large paint palettes in the lowest level [153]. Another case, of figured walnut with brass-bound corners, lock and name-plate, is dated 1868 and was made by J. & W. E. Archbutt of Lambeth [154]. The inscription states it was given to an architect by his client. In this the water-colours are set into a drawer at the base of the case. At this time it was normal practice to render even working drawings in colour washes, and this accounts for the frequent provision made for paint and palettes. A four-tier case made by W. H. Harling of Moorgate, *c.*1900, which is unusual in having a purpose-made hide leather travelling case complete with shoulder strap for easier transportation, is now owned by Blundell Harling of Weymouth. Many varied examples can be found dating from the period 1850–1950. Some magazine cases contain as many as 35 metal instruments in the top tray, and by 1900 there are some unusual exceptions which do not conform to those designs advertised in the catalogues issued by Stanley, Harling, Thornton and Halden, such as the four-tier cabinet in the form of a small chest of drawers by W. F. Stanley [155]. In 1888 this firm advertised a case simulating a medieval chest complete with wrought iron strap hinges. Cases intended for specialist users were quite common, such as one made by Elliott Brothers equipped for a railway engineer, which contains 93 railway curves in addition to the usual drawing instruments and a full set of water-colours [156].

During the nineteenth century large elaborate cases were also made by European makers. The case of rosewood in [VIII] is a fine French example. It is inlaid with a design in German silver, the same metal used for the twenty-eight instruments. An Italian case dated *c.*1850 is similar in size to an English magazine case, but large calliper blades are included in the tray of metal instruments, and the base contains both metal and hardwood set squares but only one brass drawing scale [VII]. By the end of the century, however, comprehensive selections of the best instruments were usually arranged in large simple flat cases, as can be seen in an example by Kern of Switzerland dated *c.*1900 [IX]. This can be compared with a recent case made by Haff of Bavaria [157], the modern equivalent of the traditional magazine case. Similar cases are made now by both Kern and Riefler, but all are without provision for scales, drawing curves, etc.

[149A] Main pair of compasses from Milan case (VII) shown with its twelve inserts which include a pair of calliper blades, four divider points, ink and wheel pen points, and extension arm. *Alessandro Ubertazzi Collection, Milan.*

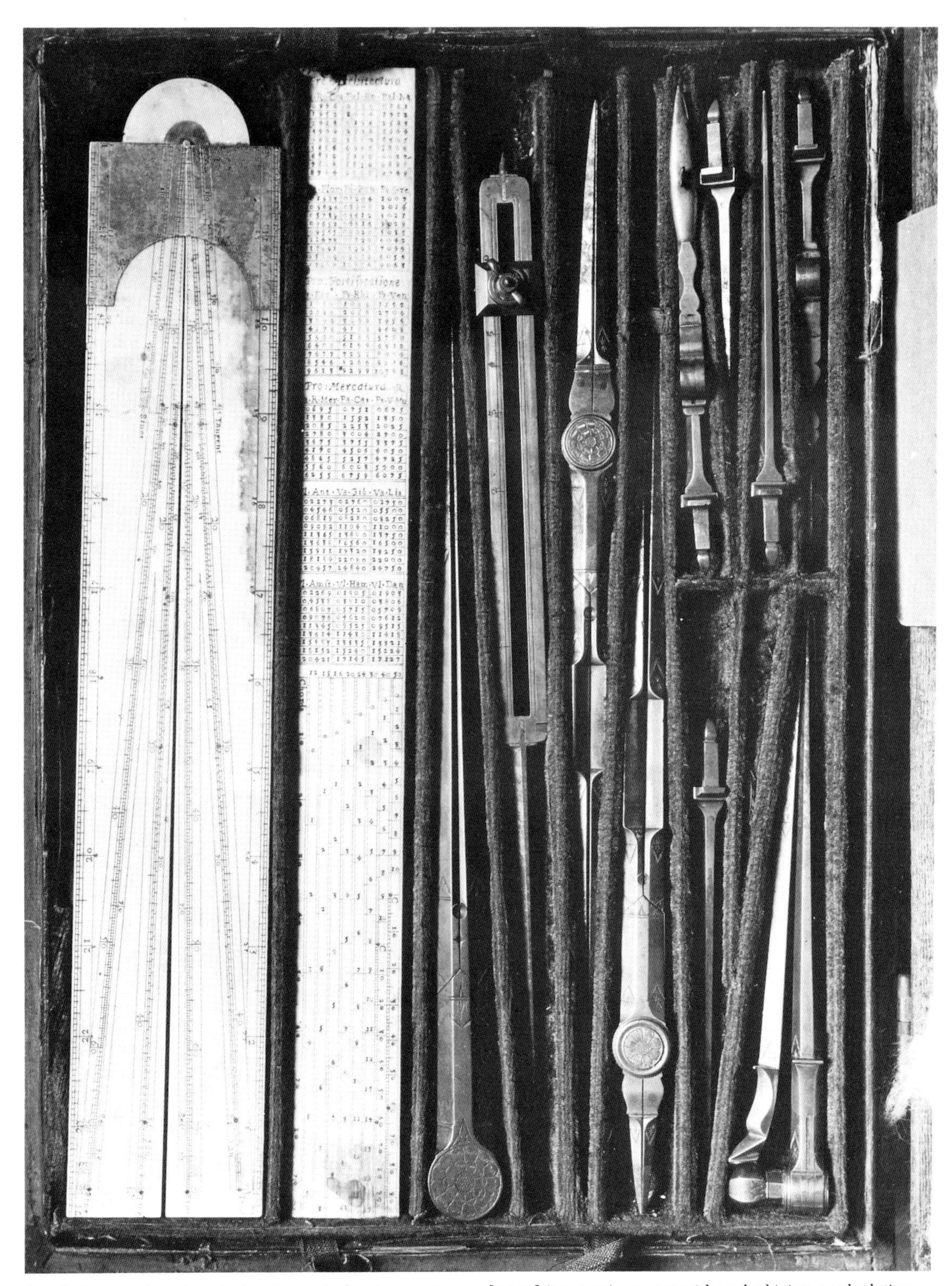

[150] A comprehensive set of mathematical instruments arranged in four tiers in a hardwood case, made for Sir Roger North, lawyer, historian and amateur architect. The four tiers are shown at [150A, A, C and D]. Case $15\frac{1}{4} \times 10\frac{1}{4} \times 4\frac{1}{2}$ in (360 × 260 × 115 mm). *c.*1680. *Jesus College, Cambridge.*

[150A] (top tray) a sector with arched joint, a calculating rule for military purposes, a large pair of compasses, a pair of variable proportional compasses, and a pair of triangular compasses and several ink inserts for the large compasses.

[150B] (second tray) a boxwood sliding rule, a calculating rule, a square slate framed in boxwood, an angle set square, a pair of pincers, various compasses and a ruling pen and crayon-holder.

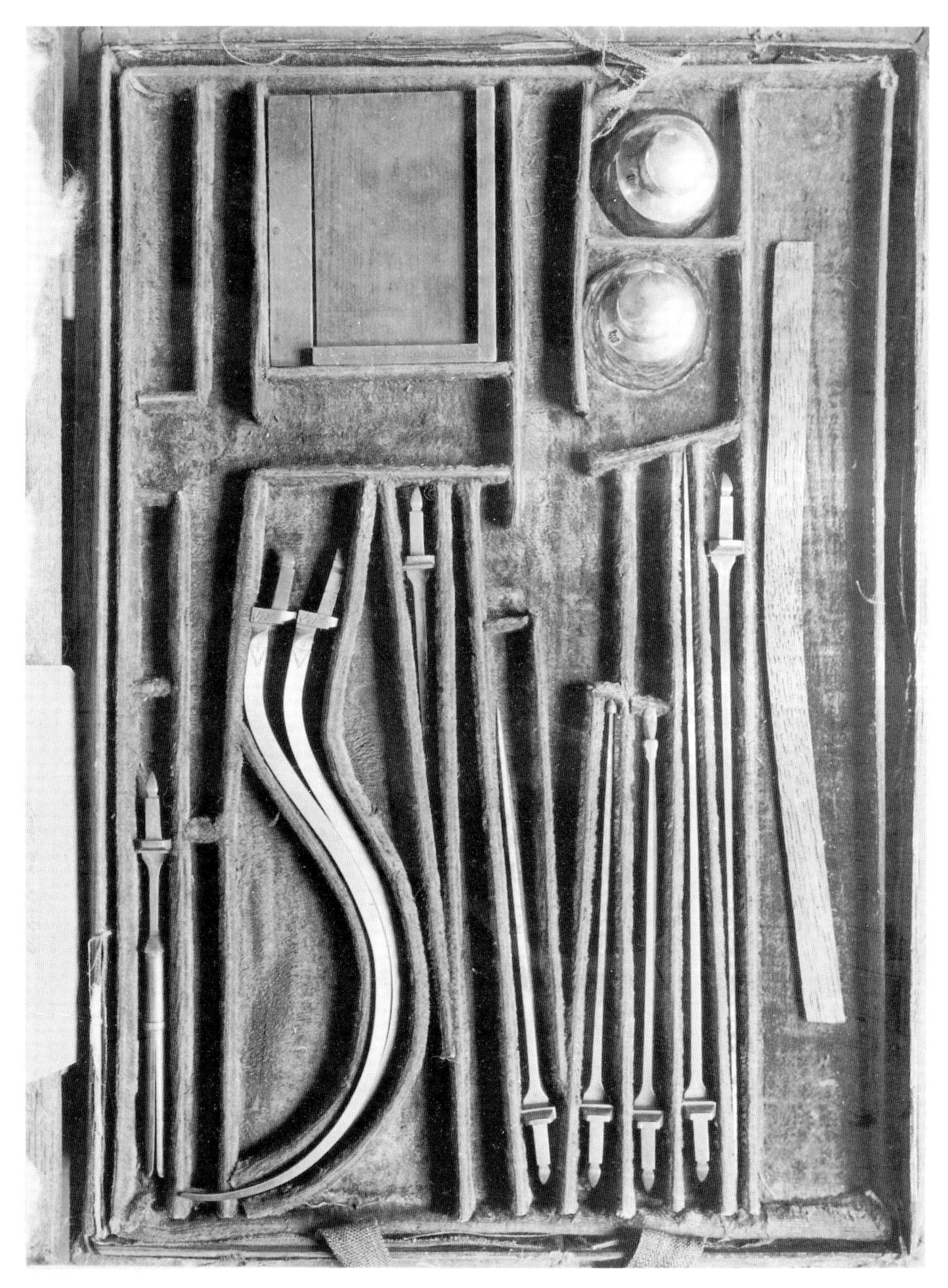

[150c] (third tray) various inserts for the largest compasses together with a pair of calliper blades, a pair of ink-wells, a whetstone for sharpening the steel points and a boxwood segmental drawing curve.

[150D] (fourth tray) a quadrant engraved with Roman numerals, a triangular 60° set square, a Universal dial, a pounce pot and plumb-bob and some cord.

[151] A three-tier German mahogany magazine case lined with velvet, containing a comprehensive set of 40 silver instruments including a large sector (152 mm), a large scale rule, a rolling parallel rule, an angle set square and a wooden triangle all fitted to the lid (shown at bottom). A full range of compasses and their fittings together with several ruling pens are provided in the middle tray, and the lowest compartment is fitted with paint pots, a palette, space for brushes, etc and four bottles for ink and water (shown at top). Some instruments are signed 'Georg Drechsler, Hannover, 1775'. Size of case $11\frac{1}{2} \times 10 \times 3$ in ($290 \times 205 \times 76$ mm). *Deutsches Museum, Munich.*

[152] A small magazine case of drawing instruments made by George Adams the Elder. The Sheraton-style case is of oak and mahogany lined with green velvet with the brass instruments fitted to the lid and to the base. This set includes a semi-elliptical trammel and drawing arm, proportional compasses, 6-inch pair of compasses and a 9-inch protractor combined with scales, medium dividers, small bows, and three sizes of ruling pens. There is a 9-inch sector, 6-inch callipers and a 6-inch parallel rule to the lid (not shown). The gunners' callipers and the protractor are signed and the sector is fully signed 'Improved & Made by GEORGE ADAMS at Tycho Brahes' Head in Fleet Street, LONDON', which dates the case *c.*1760. *Science Museum, London.*

152

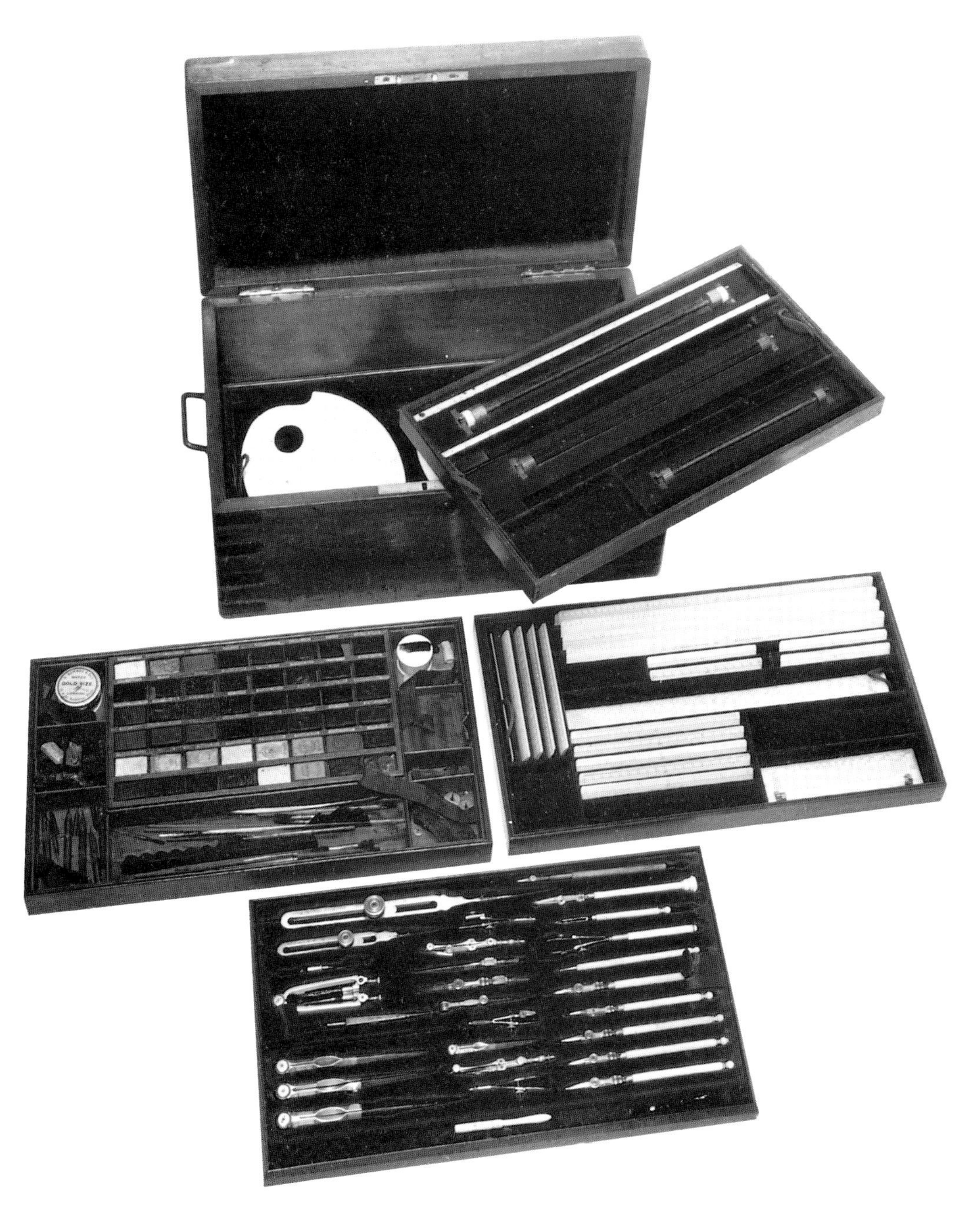

[153] A magazine case of drawing instruments of mahogany with recessed brass handles for carrying and the lid inlaid with a cartouche engraved 'Mr Philpott'. Inside are five fitted tiers lined with purple velvet which contain scales and proportional compasses signed 'Edwd. Wrench, 6 Gray's Inn Terrace, London'. The top tray contains 29 items: seven ruling pens, compasses, pillar folding compasses, two proportional compasses and bow compasses. The second tray contains three parallel rulers, one with ivory scales to both edges. In the middle tray there are several sets of ivory scales and a protractor combined with a rolling rule. A set of 48 cakes of water-colours embossed 'Ackermann, Strand' fit into the fourth tray along with wide bristle paint-brushes, some camel-hair brushes, a pot of gold size, quills and pen nibs, drawing pins and Chinese ink cakes. In the cloth-lined base compartment are two paint palettes marked 'Ackermann, 96 Strand'. Some paint cakes are marked 'Newman, Soho Square' with the Royal coat of arms of the House of Hanover, which dates them to *c.*1835. Case: 8$\frac{3}{4}$ × 17 × 10$\frac{1}{4}$ in (220 × 430 × 260 mm) *Private collection.*

[154] Magazine case by J. & W.E. Archbutt of Westminster Bridge Road, Lambeth with a brass plate on the lid inscribed 'Presented to Mr George Redfern by the Standing Committee and Sisters of the Devon House of Mercy AD 1868'. The case is of figured walnut with brass-bound corners and is arranged in three tiers with nickel silver or electrum instruments in the top, dark blue velvet-lined tray: 6½-in main compasses, 5½-in dividers, 5½-in triangular compasses, border, road, fine line and wheel pens, a tubular beam compass and fittings, four spring bows, a pricker, a tracer and an opisometer (the last three with ivory turned handles). There is a 12-in ebony rolling parallel ruler, a 6-in diameter electrum protractor and a 6-in parallel rule with electrum links in the middle lift-out tray. The compartment below, divided to take various drawing scales, is empty. There is a spring-released drawer in the base which has divisions to take 15 cakes of water-colours. Those remaining are all embossed with the maker's name, 'Roberson, Long Acre'. A ceramic paint palette remains and spaces for the water or ink bottles but these, the paint brushes and blocks of Chinese ink, are now missing. Case: 14½ × 9½ × 7¼ in (368 × 240 × 184 mm). *RIBA Collection, London.*

[155] Four-tier magazine case of drawing instruments by W. F. Stanley, Great Turnstile, Holborn, London with the unusual arrangement of four drawers behind hinged doors. The lid opens to reveal a tray fitted with electrum instruments, compasses, dividers and a range of ruling pens. The drawers below contain hardwood drawing curves, stencils and timber triangles, paints and palettes. *c.*1875. *Private collection.*

[156] An exceptionally large and comprehensive set of drawing instruments for the use of a railway engineer, contained in a multi-tiered mahogany case. Some are signed 'Elliott Bros., 449 Strand, London'. In addition to the usual pairs of dividers and range of compasses and specialist drawing pens, the set includes full sets of engineers' scales with off-sets, two parallel rolling rulers, architects' scales, pearwood French curves, a set of water-colours and 93 parallel railway curves. Case $23 \times 9 \times 7\frac{1}{2}$ in. ($584 \times 228 \times 190$ mm). Late 19th century. *Andrew Alpern Collection, New York.*

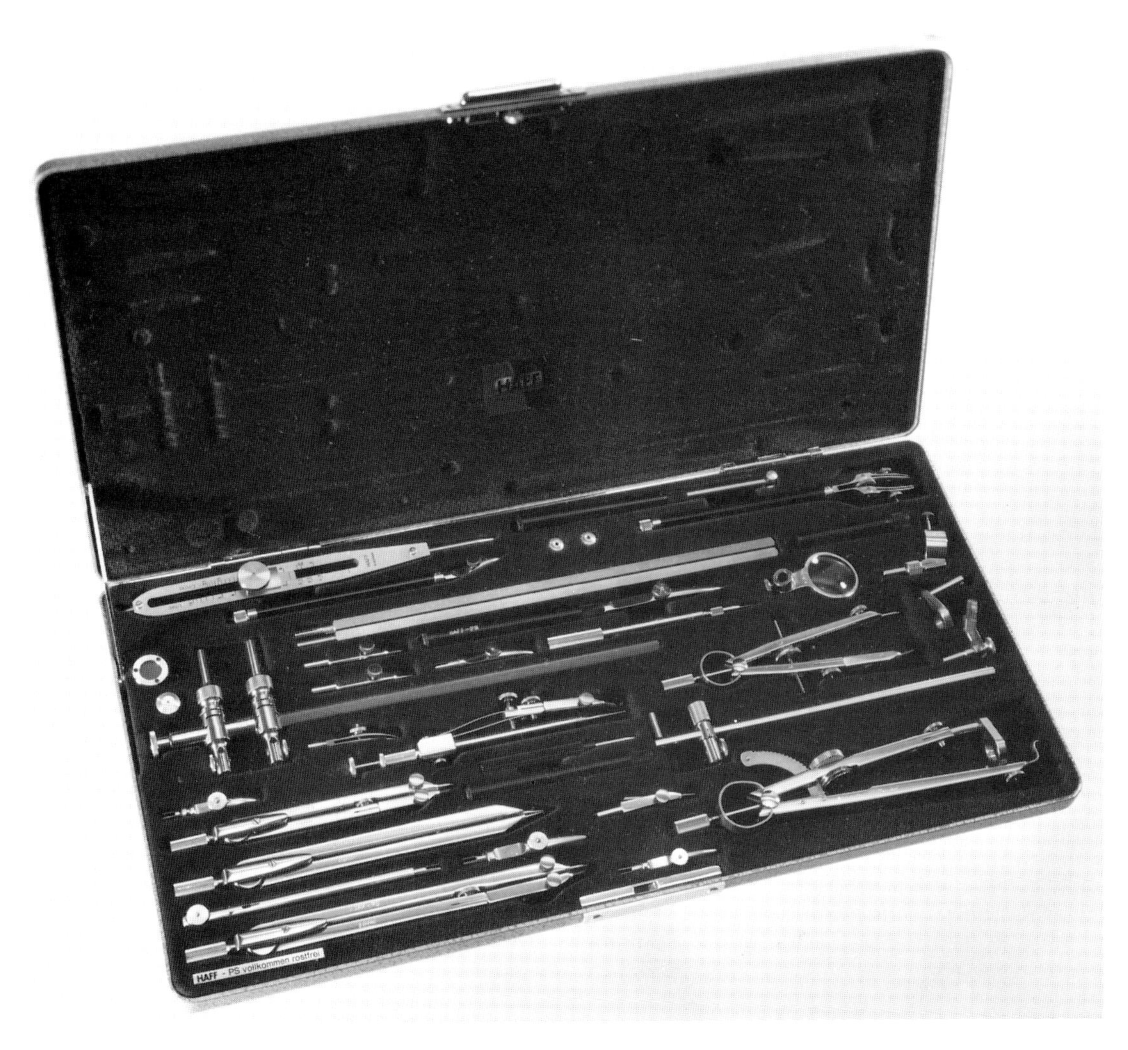

[157] An elegant modern magazine case of drawing instruments by Haff of Bavaria of black plastic with a hinged spring lock, containing a comprehensive set of instruments in chrome-plated brass. All the steel parts, such as blades to pens and points to compasses, are of bright stainless steel. This set includes a wheel pen, a curved pen and a double curve pen as well as beam compass fittings and proportional compasses, a small bow compass and a pump compass, all of which resemble their earlier prototypes. *c.*1980.

Medium-sized cases

Cases that contained a limited but useful range of drawing instruments were made from 1600 onwards. They were often assembled to suit the occupation of the purchaser, the size being dictated by the number of items which they contained or the price limit. A wide variety of instruments is provided in some of the early cases since many were intended for land-surveyors, military engineers or what in Europe were termed 'geometricians' (those who practised mathematical drawing). The early cases were usually rectangular polished hardwood boxes or flat leather-covered wooden cases fitted internally with recesses to the shape of each individual instrument, and often lined with suede or silk velvet [158]. The early-seventeenth-century Italian case in [159] is in red leather with all the instruments fitted vertically. Another Italian case of the same period is flat and leather-covered, and it contains sixteen items mainly for use in drawing [160].

During the eighteenth century many of the best English instrument makers produced practical medium-sized cases. One *c.*1730 by Richard Glynne (fl. 1705–30) is covered in black fishskin; the complete set of drawing instruments, in a tray lined in green cloth, includes two brass triangle set squares, a sector and a parallel rule in the lower level.

A smaller case, by George Hearne of Fleet Street (fl. 1725–41), has embossed paper instead of the more usual damask cloth lining the lid compartment [161A] and separate large compasses are provided for ink and for pencil. Similar cases were made late in the century by such makers as Edward Nairne (1726–1806) and Jesse Ramsden, usually with metal drawing instruments [161B] and sometimes proportional compasses in the lift-out tray.

By the mid-eighteenth century, in France, instrument makers had introduced flat leather-covered cases with rounded corners which were to become characteristic. At first these were fitted with clasp fasteners; later, makers used discreet rod/bolt fastenings which became a distinguishing feature of late-nineteenth-century European cases. A green leather-covered case to this pattern by Claude Langlois (fl.1730–56) can be seen in the Museum of the History of Science, Oxford. An example by a French provincial maker is that by Pigeon of Lyons [162]. Hardwood cases with lift-out trays were also made by French makers such as Lennel, Baradelle and Quillet *c.*1780; sometimes large calliper blades were provided. An early-nineteenth-century case by Etienne Lenoir (1744–1832) together with its contents, which include a folding square and a separate triangular ruler, can be seen in [163]. A plain late-nineteenth-century case by the maker Baraban illustrates the use of the rod/bolt fastener and the typically French design of the milled handles [164].

From the eighteenth century onwards German instrument cases develop their own national characteristics. Many were provided with ebony or other hardwood parallel rules, scales and triangle set squares, and often large calliper blades were included as inserts to the large compasses. As with magazine cases, emerald green velvet was a popular material for the lining, or in simpler cases natural suede was used with gold braid edging [XVI]. This style continued in use in Germany until *c.*1900 and appeared also in designs by Swiss makers such as Kern [165]. Clemens Riefler, who founded his firm in Bavaria in 1841, immediately commenced making elegant cases of a much simpler design. His son Sigmund introduced an advanced cylindrical design for the Riefler instruments in 1877, and the continued development of this can be seen in the firm's recent medium-sized case [166].

During the nineteenth century several English firms produced large numbers of high-quality medium sized cases to satisfy the considerable demand, such as Elliott Brothers, Archbutt of Lambeth and the larger suppliers; W. F. Stanley and his apprentice, W. H. Harling of London, and A. G. Thornton of Manchester. An excellent example is one by W. H. Harling [167]; similar cases continued to be made until after the Second World War.

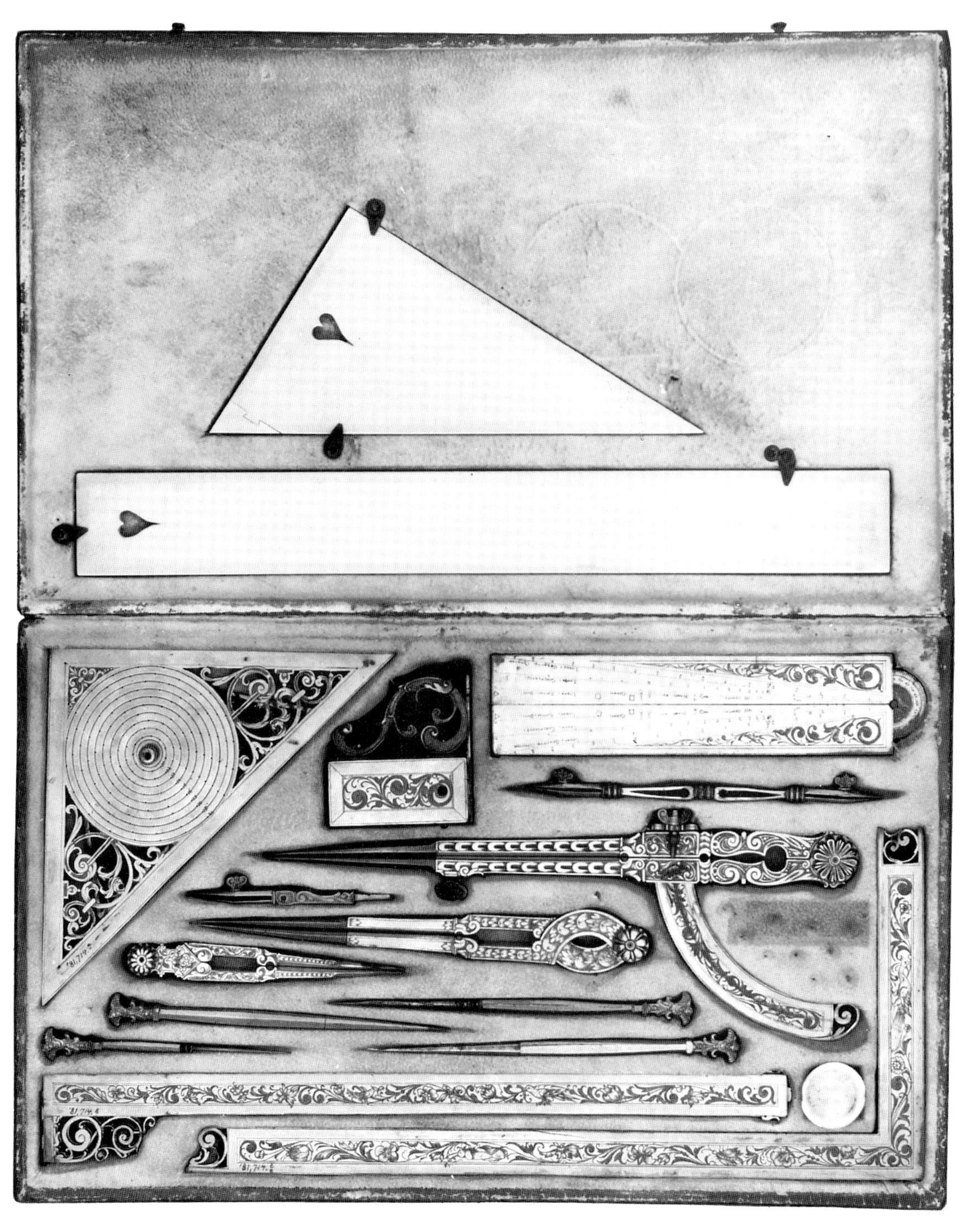

[158] Leather-covered wooden case of drawing instruments of gilt brass and steel, engraved with rich foliate designs, some incorporating birds and insects. This full set includes a 45° set square with circle dividing scales 11–20, a gradiant gauge, a sector, a double ended ruling pen, large wing compasses, with an ink insert, a pair of single-handed dividers, a pair of smaller dividers, No 4 styli with decorated heads, a folding rule with various lineal scales and a right angle rule. An ivory set square, 30/60° is provided in the lid. The folding rule is signed 'CTDEM 1619' so the case can be ascribed to Christoph Trechsler, 1619, the Dresden maker. Case size 8 × 5 in (200 × 120 mm).
Kunstgewerbemuseum, Berlin.

[159] Vertical case of drawing instruments covered in red leather with gilt decoration stamped on. The case contains a large sector and folding rule, a pair of tweezers, a pricker, a cross elliptical trammel with its bar and drawing point, a crayon-holder, a knife and a blunt tool (tracer?), a double-ended crayon-holder, a plumb-bob and finally a ruling pen with tapered grooves. Italian. 17th century. *Museo di Storia della Scienza, Florence.*

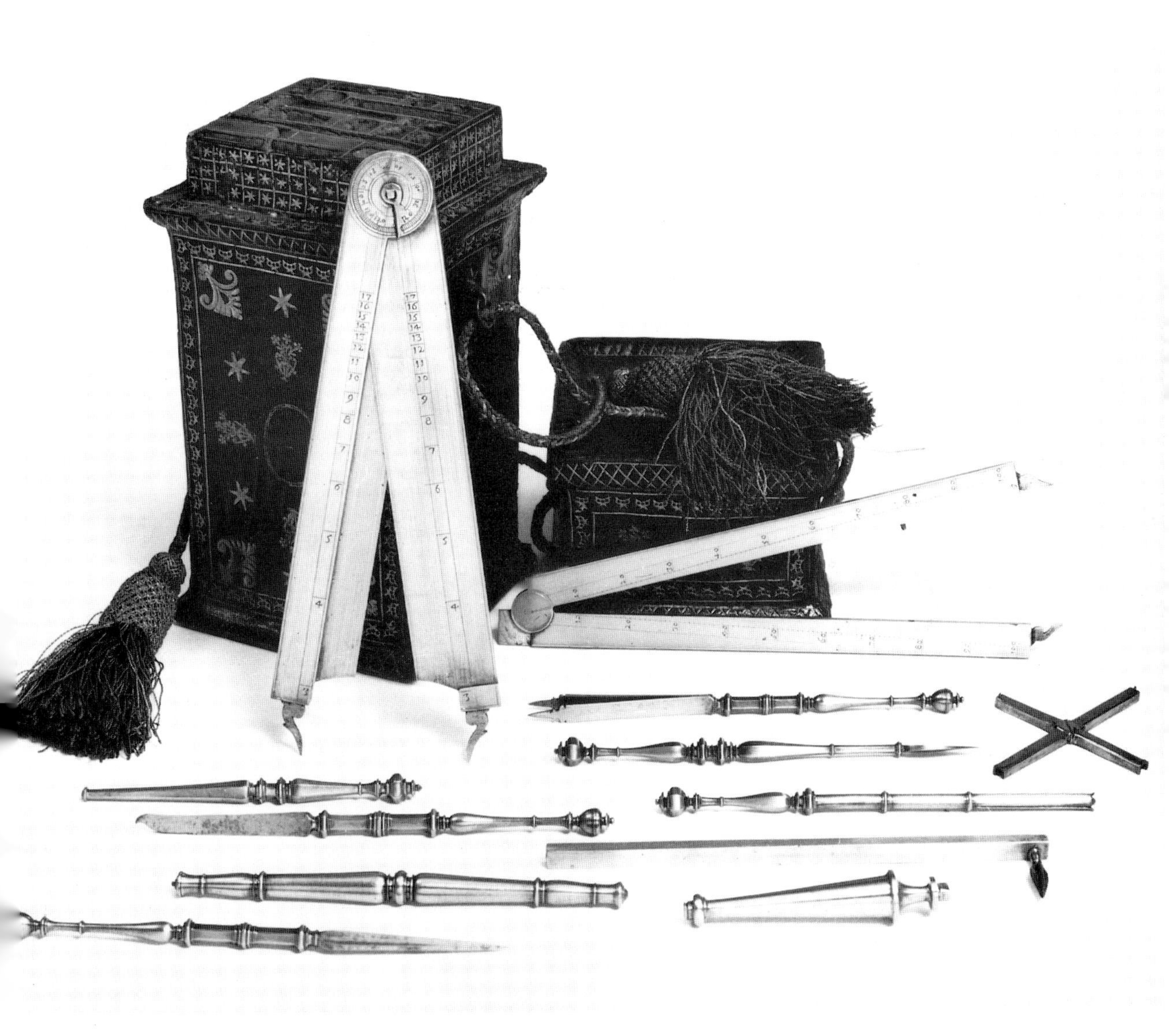

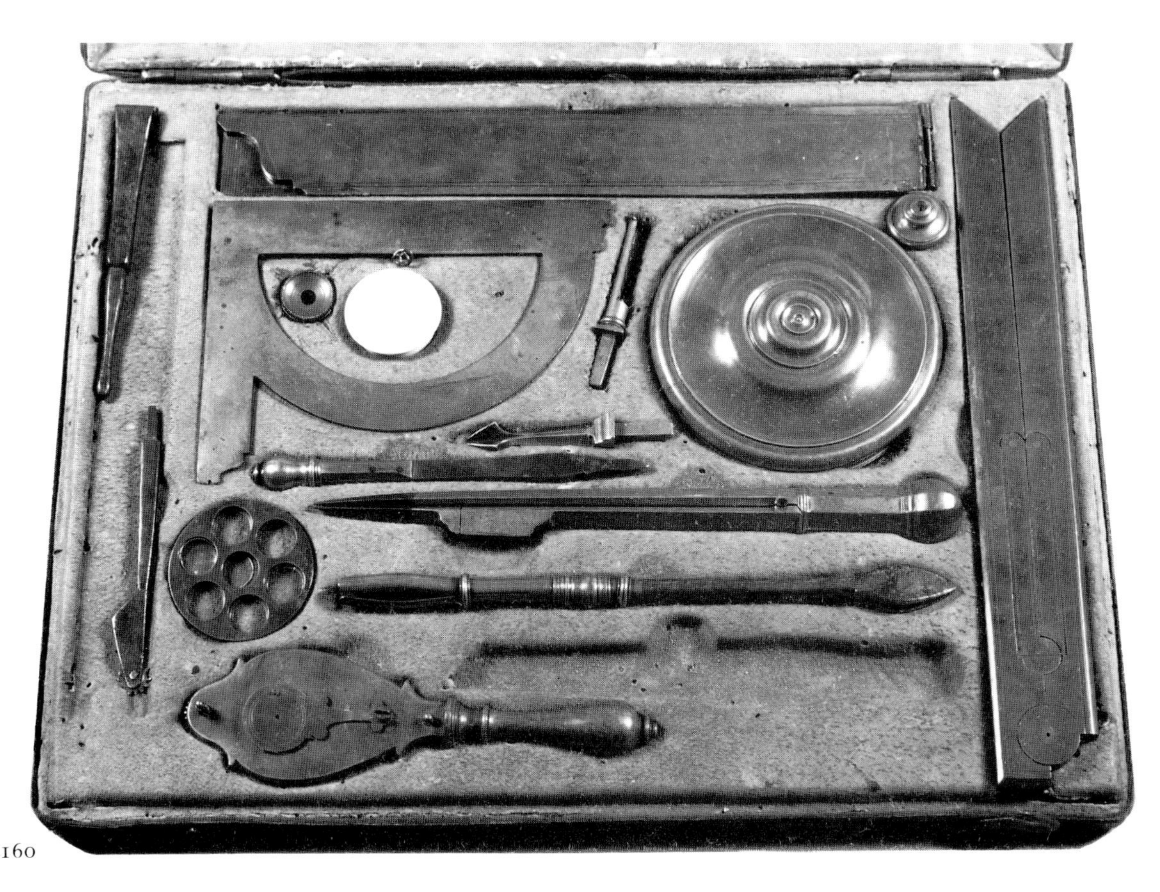

160

[160] Flat case of drawing instruments, leather covered with stamped gilt decoration. The brass instruments comprise: a folding square, a folding rule with unusual braced hinge, a semi-circular protractor and angle square combined, a plumb-bob and an ink-well, tweezers, a large pair of compasses with point, inserts for crayon-holder and for ink, a goat's foot pen, a dotting-wheel, a paper clip, a ruling pen with a crayon-holder at the reverse end, and a dotting-wheel instrument for copying charts or long outlines (one compass missing). Some instruments are signed 'Petrus Gallard fecit, Romae'. French or Italian. Case: 10 × $7\frac{3}{4}$-in (254 × 197 mm). Late 17th century. *Victoria & Albert Museum, London.*

[161A] Small set of brass drawing instruments in fishskin-covered case, silk-velvet lined interior with embossed coloured paper to lid. The brass drawing instruments comprise: (in the lid) a sector signed 'Georg Hearne fecit' with a foliate design to the hinge, and a rectangular protractor with divisions for 1–180° and 180–1° and with plotting scales to the reverse side; (in the tray) three pairs of dividers – large, medium and small – a pair of compasses with ink point, a pair of compasses with a pencil point, a ruling pen with a hand-cut screw and a crayon-holder at the reverse end, a pricker, and a tool/spanner. English. Case: $7\frac{1}{2}$ × $4\frac{1}{2}$ in (190 × 115 mm). *c.*1730. *Royal Museum of Scotland, Edinburgh.*

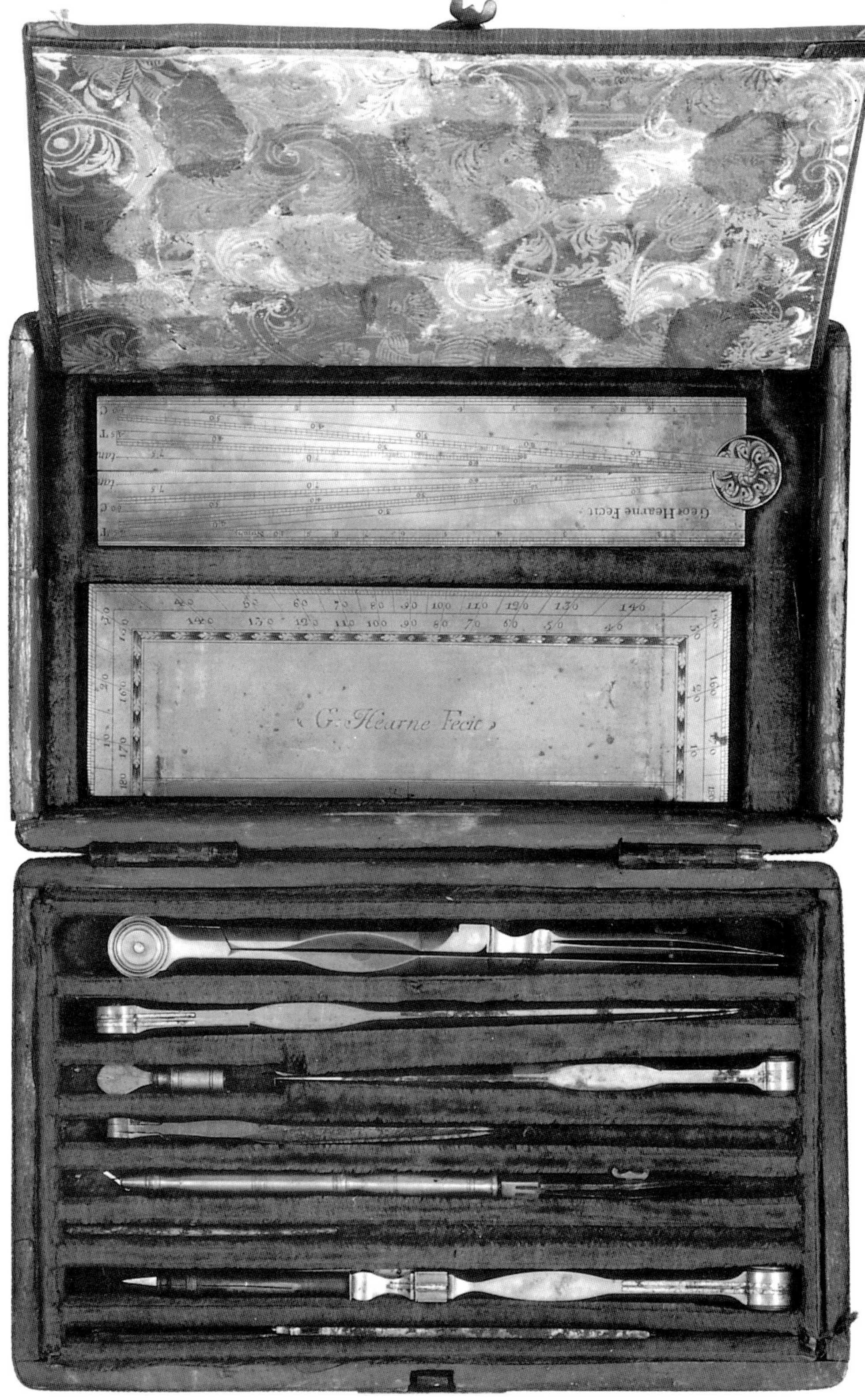

161A

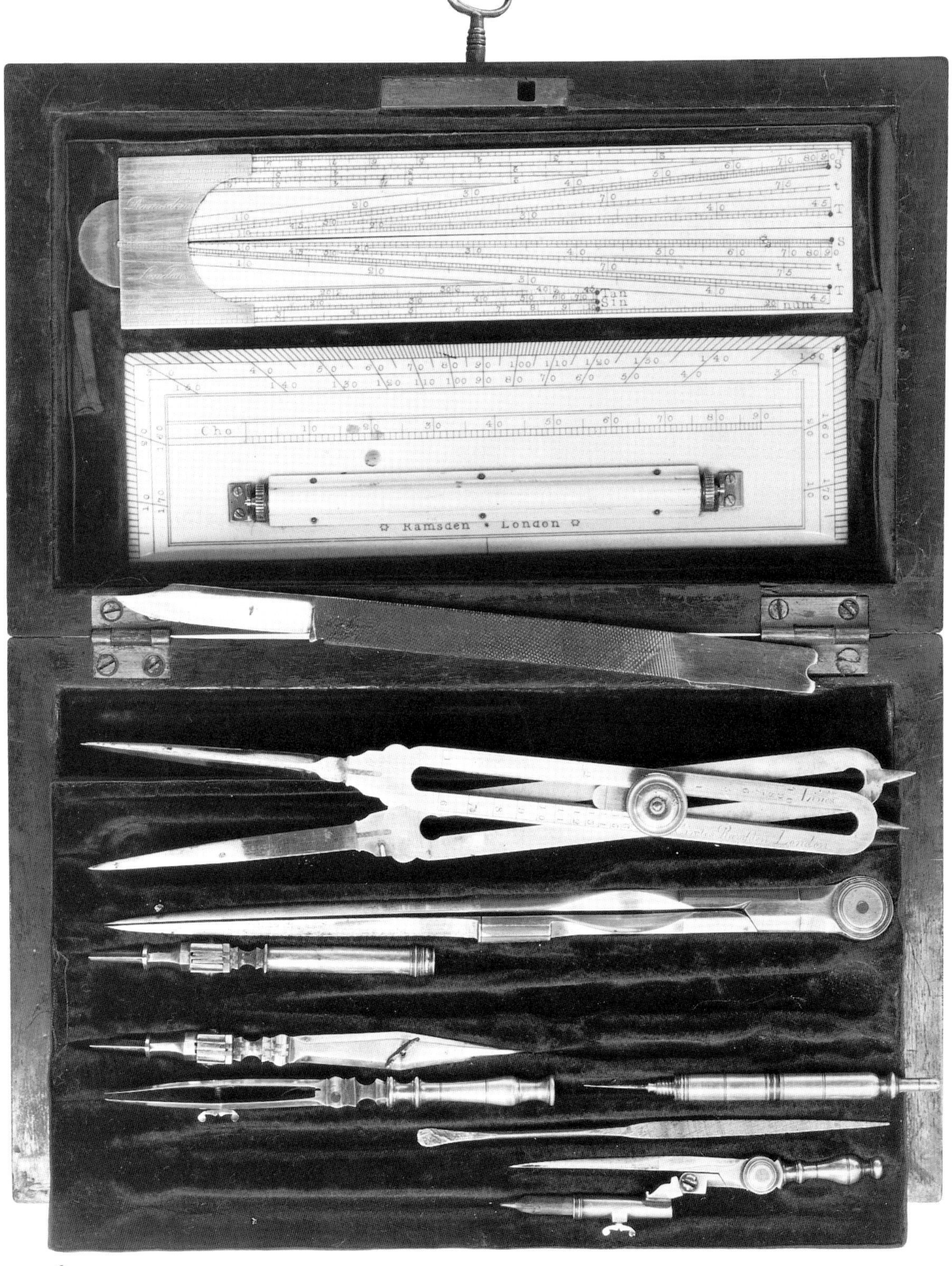

161B

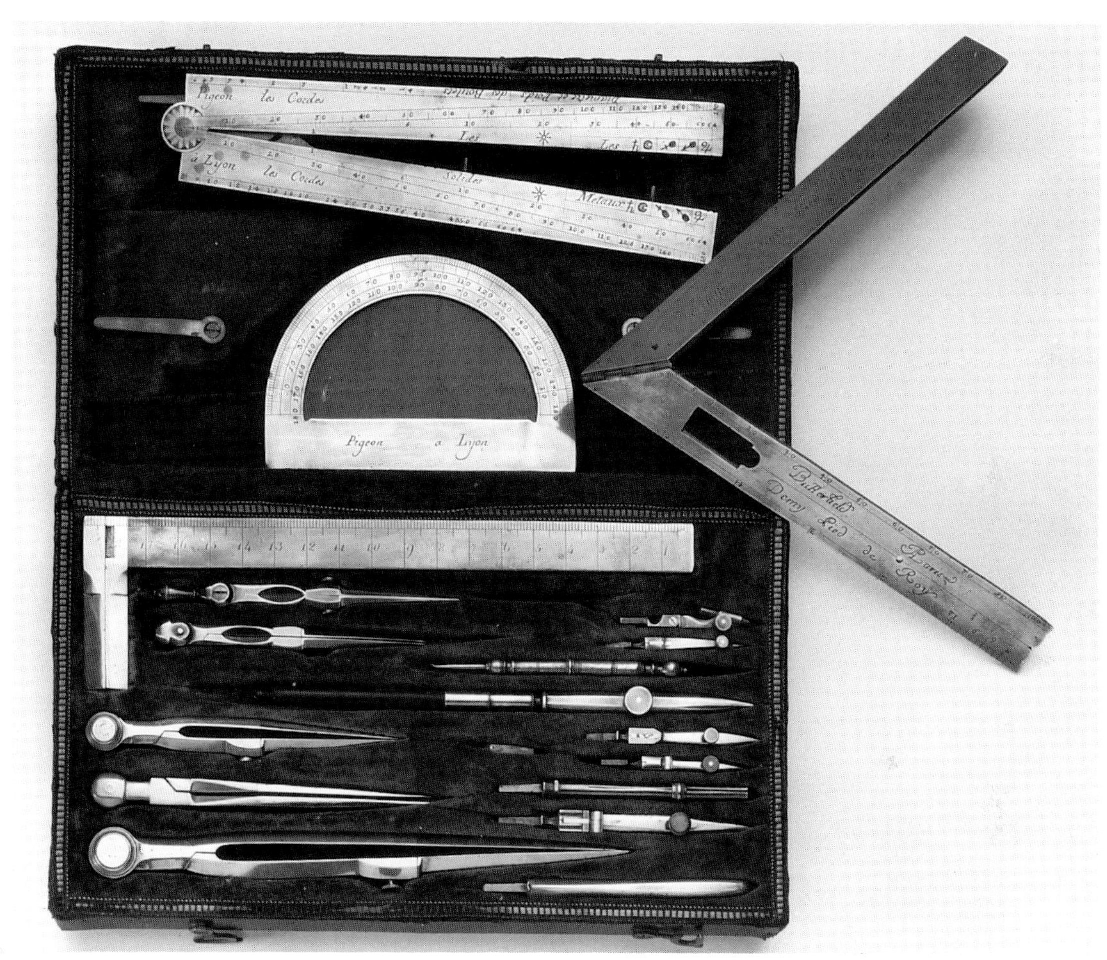

162

[161B] Case of drawing instruments by Jesse Ramsden, London, in a mahogany box lined with green velvet, containing silver items. These comprise: (bottom) a pair of 6 in. compasses with inserts for ink and pencil, a small pair of bows, a pair of proportional compasses, a ruling pen with protracting pin provided within the handle, a knife combined with file and key-screwdriver; (top) 6-inch ivory sector with arched hinge, an ivory small rolling parallel ruler combined with rectangular protractor and some scales. Late 18th century. Case: $7\frac{1}{2} \times 4\frac{1}{2}$ in (190×115 mm). *Science Museum, London.*

[162] A flat case of drawing instruments, some signed 'Pigeon à Lyon', covered in black leather, lined with velvet with gilt braid to edges, and closed by means of brass clasps. The brass instruments include a sector, a semi-circular protractor, a rule fitted with a gauge, a pair of compasses with inserts for ink and pencil, a ruling pen with an ebony handle and a separate pricker. Shown with an odd Butterfield folding square (not part of set). French. c.1800. *Clemens Riefler Collection, Nesselwang, West Germany.*

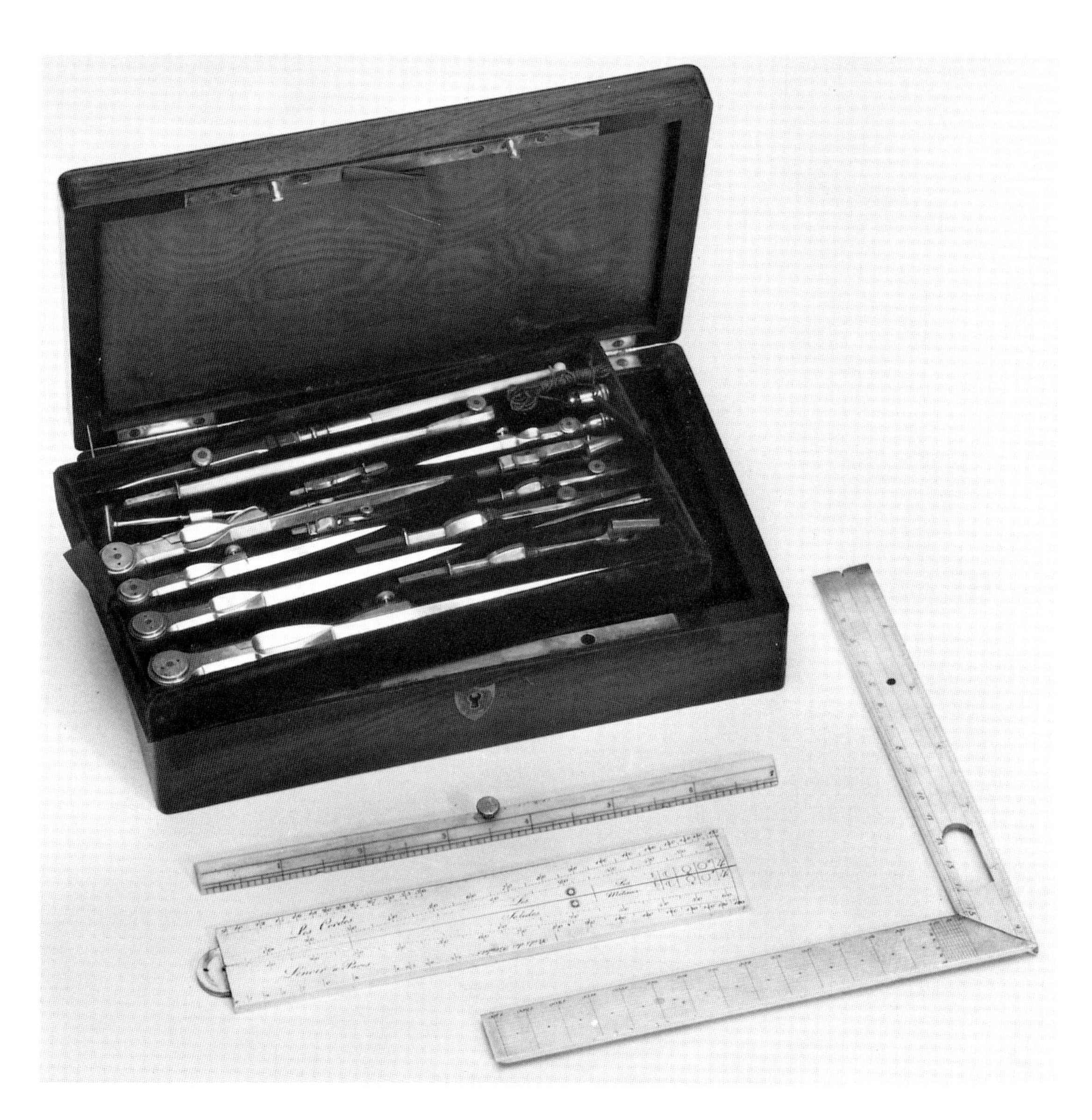

[163] A mahogany case, the tray lined with velvet and the lid with silk. The set of drawing instruments of silver includes two pairs of dividers, large and bow compasses, a ruling pen, an ivory rule for inches and centimetres, a sector and a protractor signed 'Lenoir à Paris', and a folding square graduated with metric and inch scales with an aperture for the plumb-bob usually provided in French cases. Case: $8\frac{1}{4} \times 5$ in (210×127 mm). *c.*1810. *Private collection.*

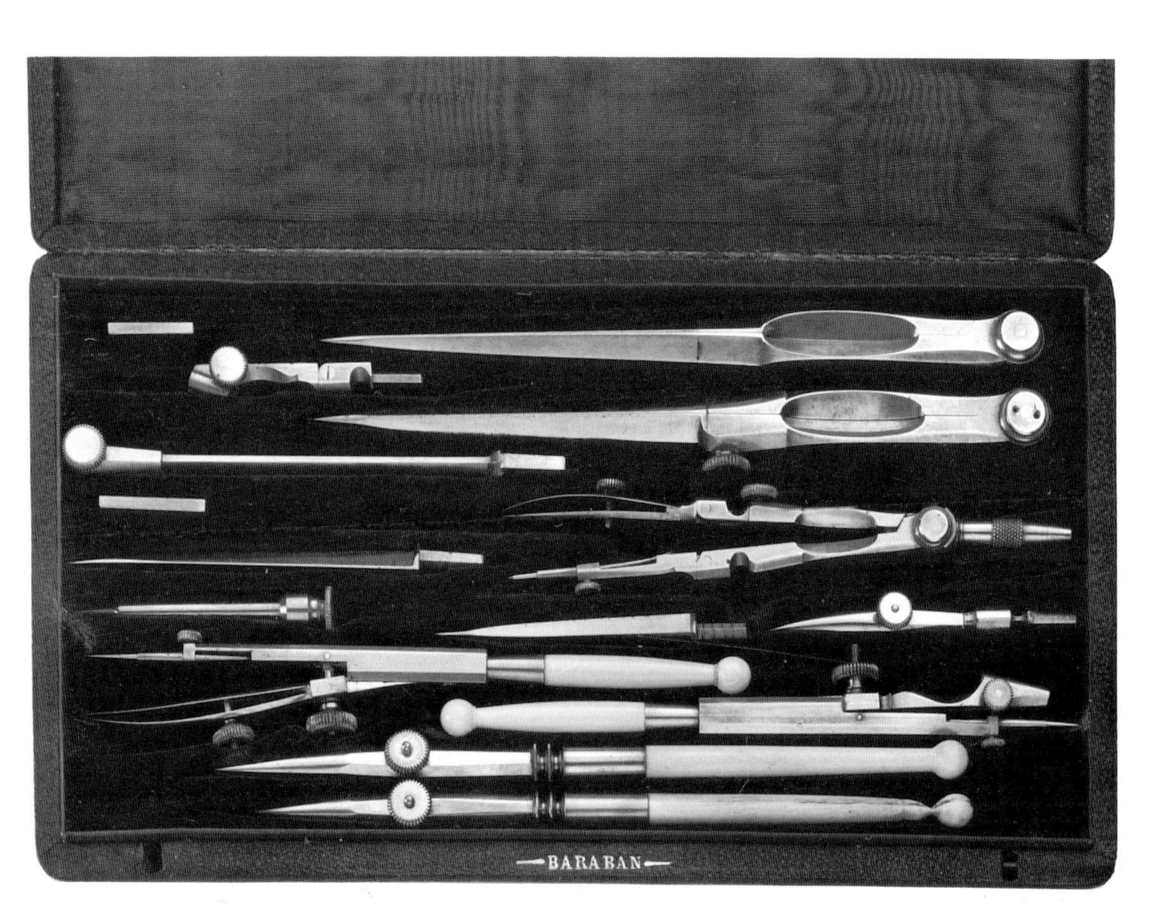

[164] A flat leather-covered case with a bolt fastener, the inside frame marked – BARABAN – . This small set of drawing instruments comprises: a large pair of dividers, compasses with inserts for pencil and crayon and an extension piece, a pair of small bows with burled handle, a large pump compass with ivory handles, one for ink and one for pencil, two fine ruling pens both with ivory handles, and a pin-head compass. French. *c.*1870. *Clemens Riefler Collection, Nesselwang, West Germany.*

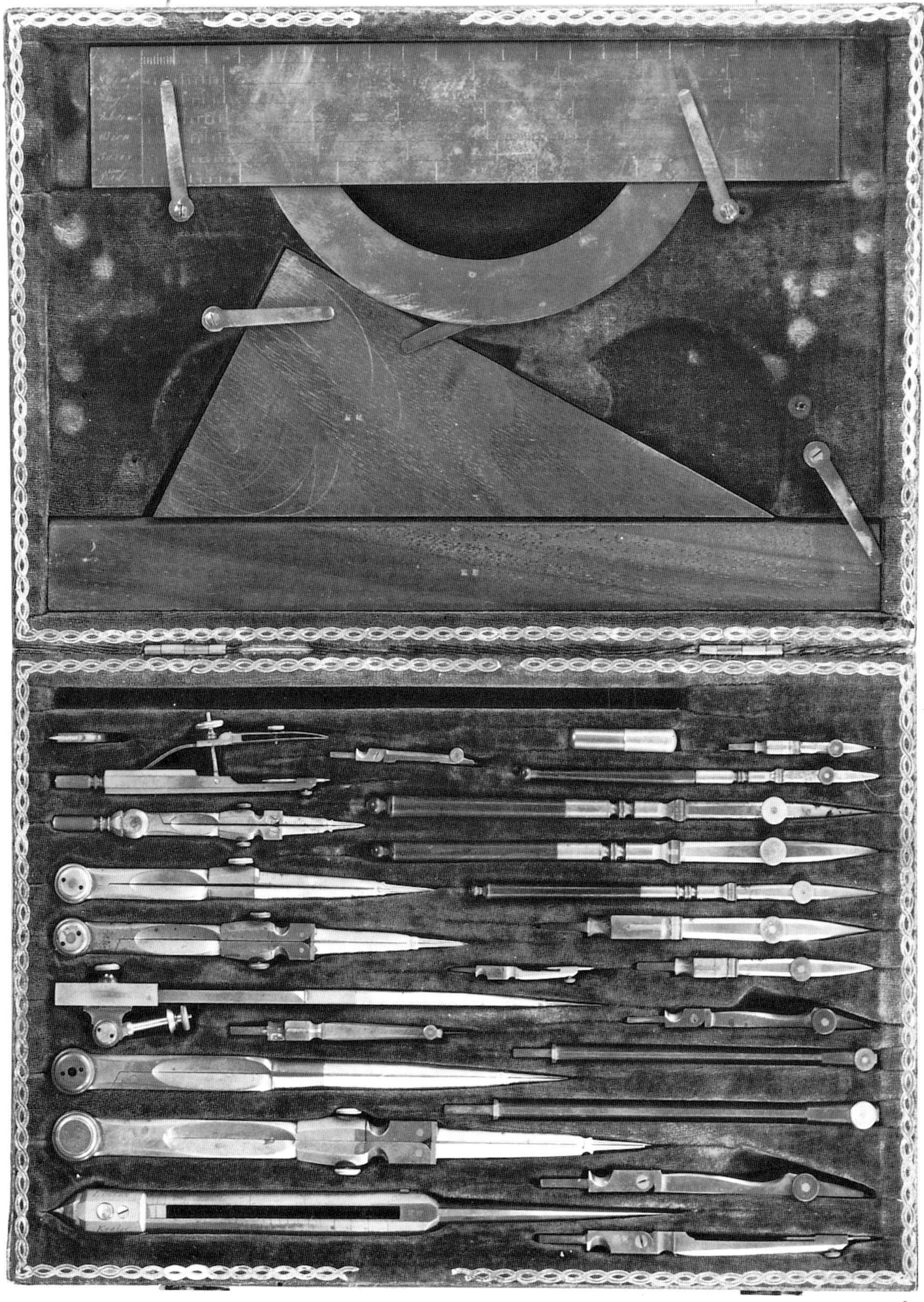

165

[165] Leather-covered flat case of mass-produced high-quality drawing instruments made by Kern, of nickel-plated brass. The main tray is lined with velvet and braid and fitted with a wide range of ruling pens with ebonized handles: large dividers, large compasses with inserts for ink and pencil and extension pieces, a pair of proportional compasses, small bow compasses and their inserts, small bows with handle and a pump compass. The lid contains a ruler, a comparative scale rule, a protractor and a triangle, all made of hardwood. Swiss. *c.*1900. *Kern & Co Collection, Aarau, Switzerland.*

[166] A modern set of high-quality drawing instruments by Riefler in a leather-covered wooden case with rounded corners, lined in velvet. The design is still based on the cylindrical pattern patented by Sigmund Riefler in 1877. This neat set comprises proportional compasses, three ruling pens and wheel pen, a pump compass, a set of three spring bows, and large and medium compasses with their inserts and extension pieces. Note the largest ruling pen has index marking for standard line widths. 1983. *Clemens Riefler Collection, Nesselwang, West Germany*

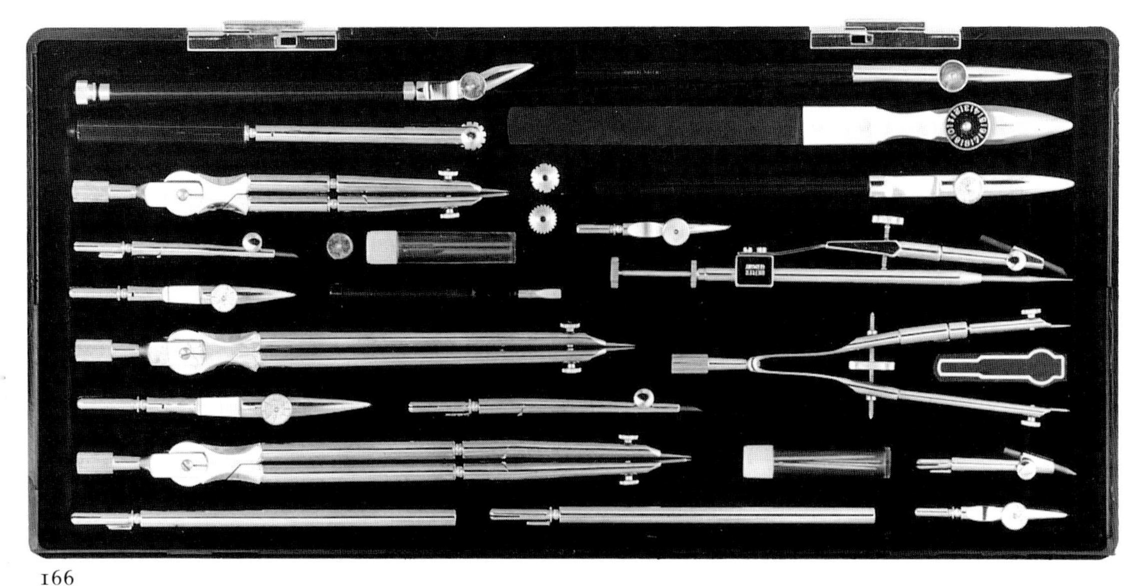

166

[167] Medium case of drawing instruments in rosewood, with a lining of watered silk in the lid which is marked in gold: 'W. H. Harling, Mathematical Instrument Manufacturer, 47 Finsbury Pavement, London'. The lift-out navy blue velvet lined tray contains electrum instruments including a set of three spring bows, medium bows, ruling pens, large compasses and their inserts, and Swiss pattern beam compass fittings. In the lower section is an ivory sector, a rectangular protractor combined with drawing scales and an ivory parallel rule with parallel links. Case: $9\frac{1}{2} \times 7$ in (240×180 mm). *c.*1900.
Blundell Harling Collection, Weymouth.

[XVI] Set of brass instruments in a flat leather-covered case lined with natural chamois. In addition to the usual compasses and ruling pen, the case includes a brass scale, a protractor, a set-square and an ebony parallel rule together with a water-colour dish and a small palette. Italian, mid-18th century. *Alessandro Ubertazzi Collection, Milan.*

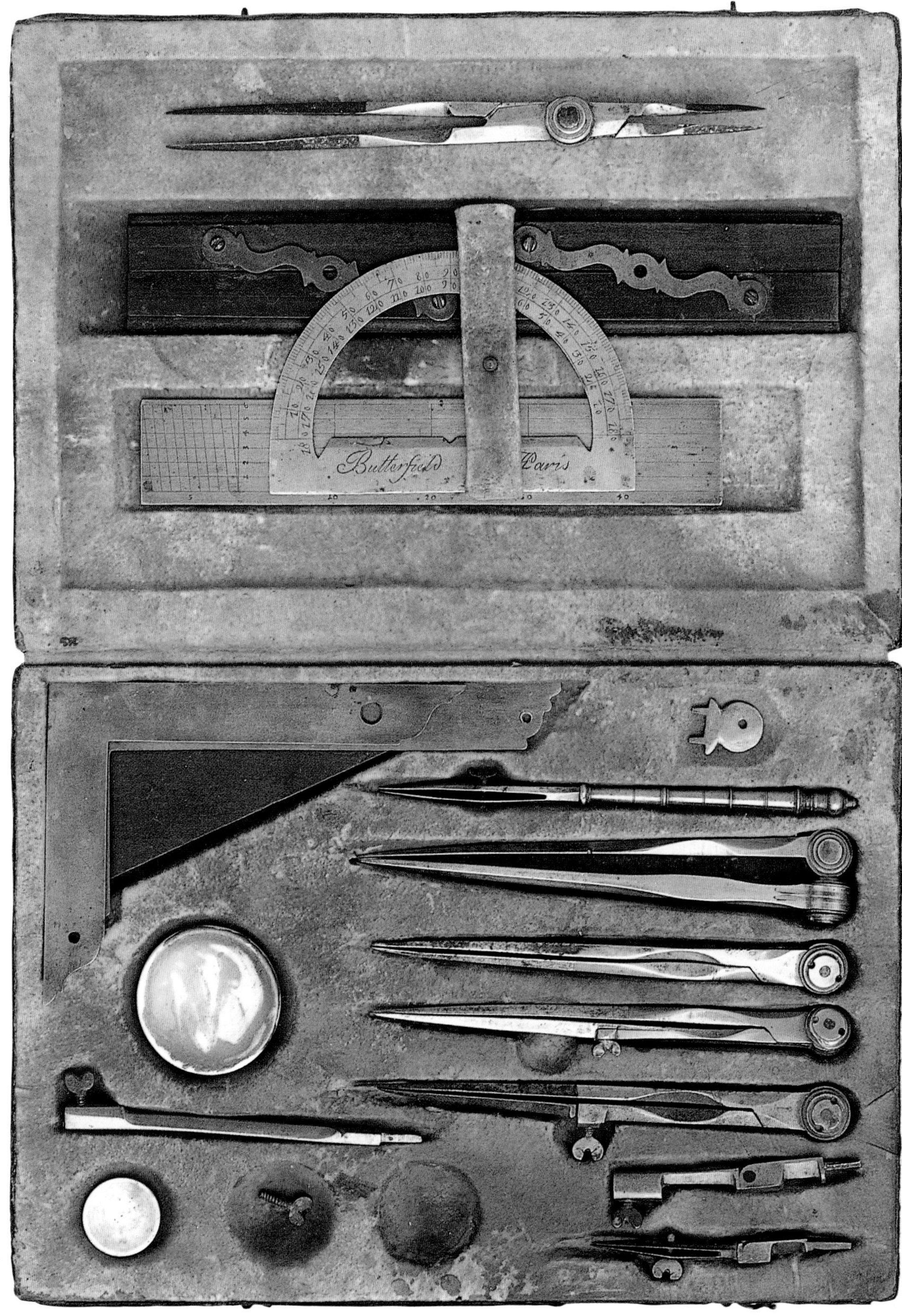
Butterfield Paris

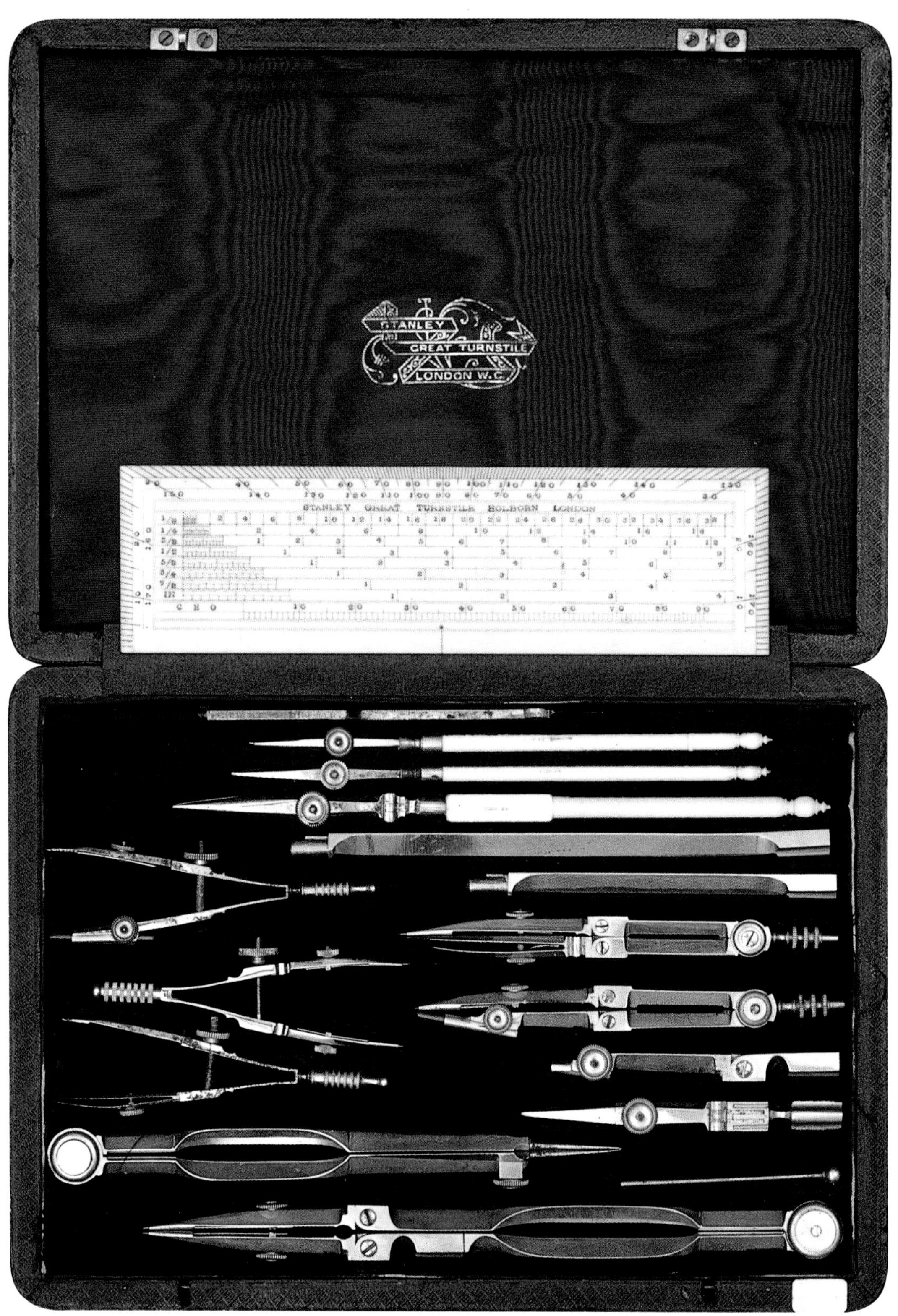
STANLEY
GREAT TURNSTILE
LONDON W.C.
STANLEY GREAT TURNSTILE HOLBORN LONDON

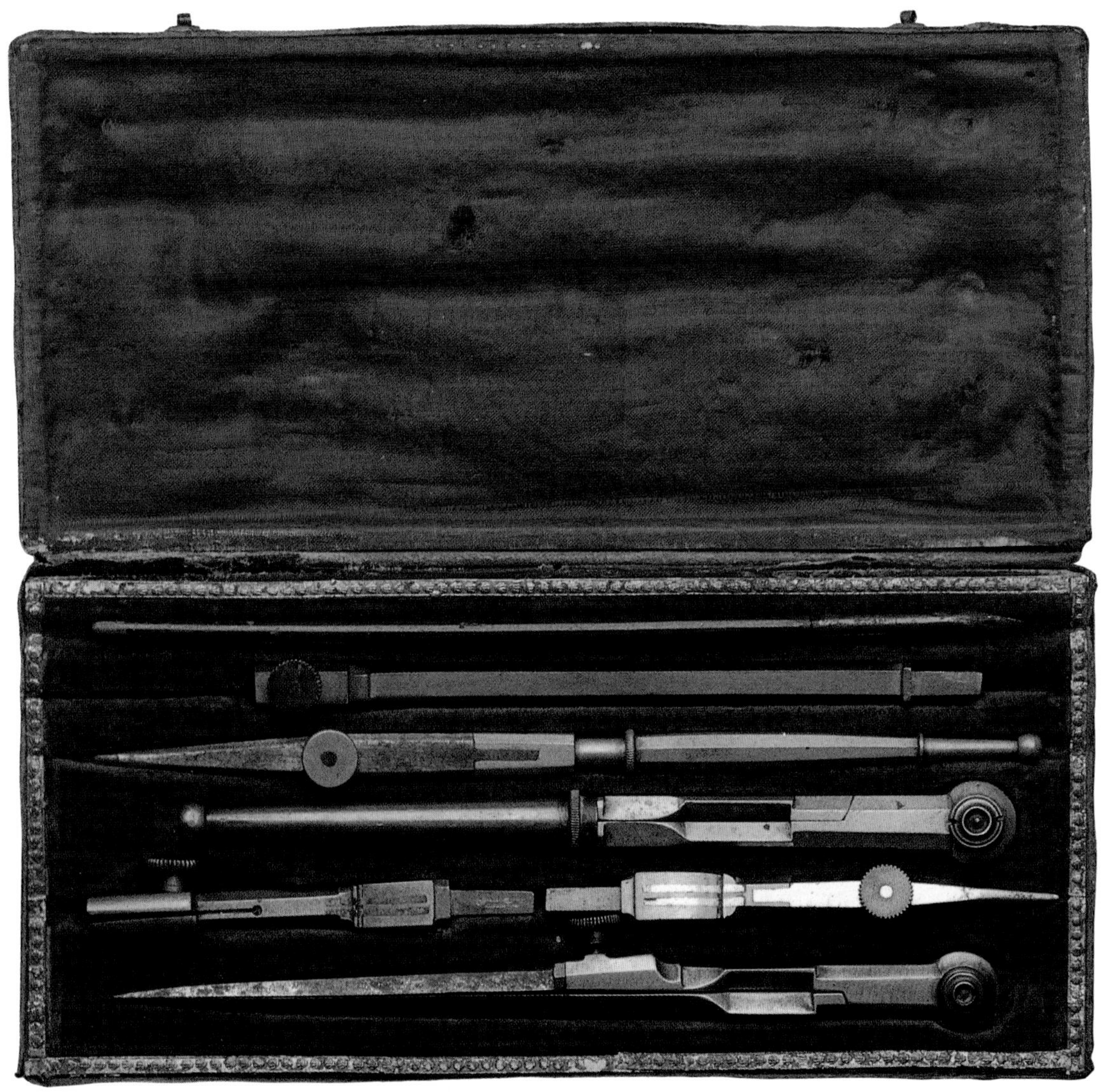

XVIII

[XVII] Large flat leather-covered wallet case with spring clip fastening which contains a full set of drawing instruments. The gilt-stamped trademark on the watered silk lining of the lid reads STANLEY GREAT TURNSTILE LONDON W.C. The ivory 6-inch scale/protractor is inscribed STANLEY GREAT TURNSTILE HOLBORN LONDON. Note the pens of three sizes, the large pair of compasses, the hair dividers, the medium bows and set of three spring bows, the extension piece and the adjustment tool. Case: 8 × 6 × 1 in (200 × 150 × 25 mm). Late 19th century. *Andrew Alpern Collection, New York.*

[XVIII] Small flat leather-covered case, the tray lined with velvet, the lid in purple satin, containing a small set of compasses and a ruling pen such as used by students and engineering draughtsmen. Note the joint to the compasses and the sheath. Made by Carlo Bordogna, Milan. *c.*1840. *Alessandro Ubertazzi Collection, Milan.*

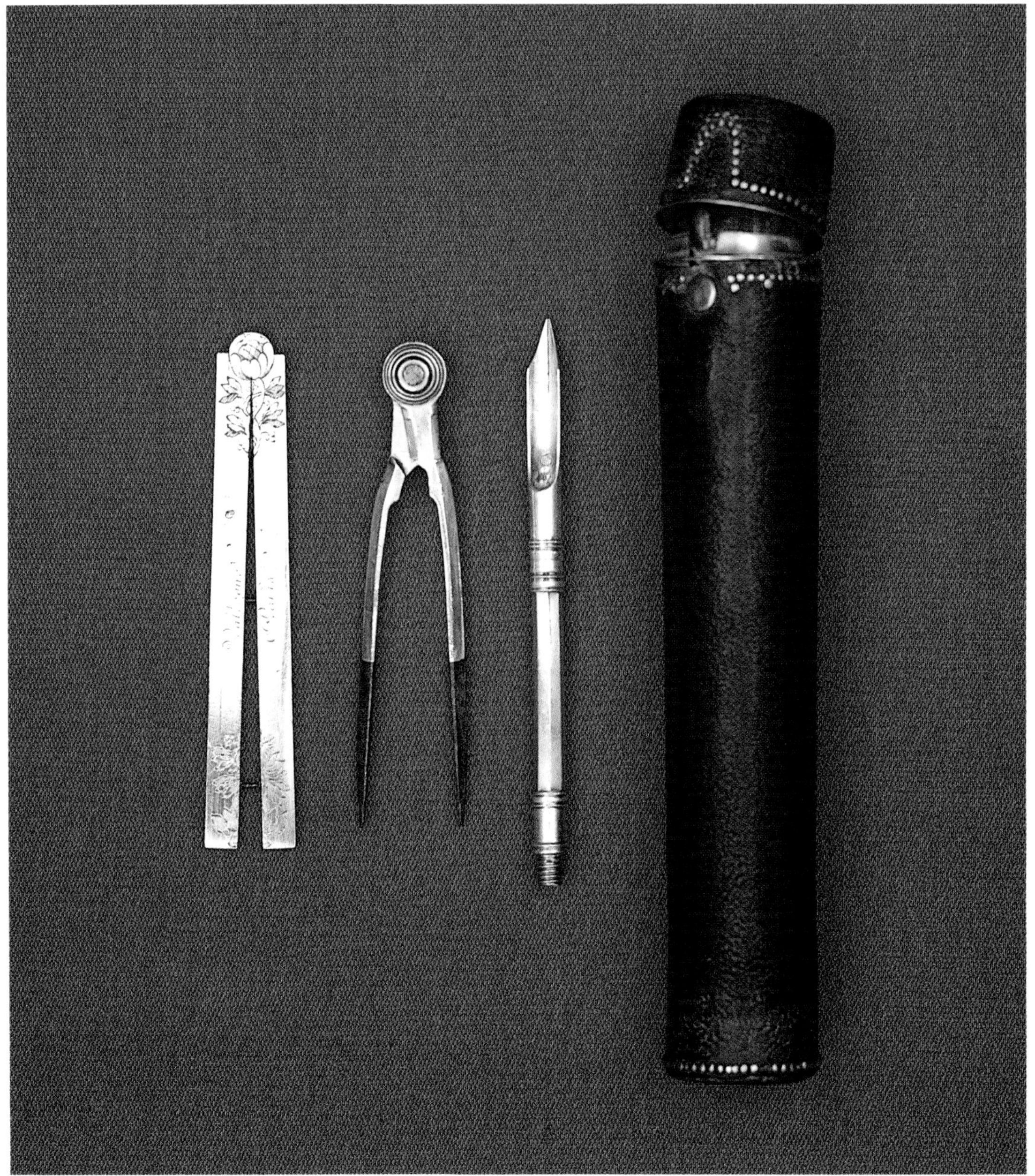

XIX

[XIX] A set of miniature drawing instruments contained in the brown leather-covered handle, with silver nail-head trimming, of a French walking stick. This small set comprises: a silver folding rule with foliate engraved decoration, a silver writing pen, a pair of dividers inscribed 'Demi-Pied du Roi Vallogne Paris'. It lacks the pencil-holder and the screw-on cap for the quill pen. Case: 6 × 1 in diameter (150 × 25 mm). 18th century. *Andrew Alpern Collection, New York.*

Pocket cases

Pocket cases were made to be carried on the person and were sometimes referred to as 'gentlemen's travelling cases'; they ranged in size from 4 to 7 in (100 to 175 mm). They were similar to each other in their external apperance, but there was considerable variety in their contents with great ingenuity employed to provide a wide choice of instruments in a compact space.

By the seventeenth century it was customary to make small hide leather cases, sometimes with stamped gilt decoration, with a selection of drawing instruments stacked vertically. There are examples in the Musées Royaux d'Art et d'Histoire in Brussels and the Museo di Storia della Scienza in Florence. From 1700 onwards pocket cases were generally made of wood covered externally with leather or fishskin often with brass or silver mounts; they were fitted with specially shaped slots to take the various instruments vertically and were usually arranged with a clip-top. However, many French cases can be found with simple slip-over lids; especially to large cases. By 1800 more economical cases were available made of cardboard covered with fishskin or morocco leather.

In 1709 Nicolas Bion (1652–1723) illustrated pocket cases in three sizes: 6, 4½ and 3 *pouces* or inches. By 1723 Edmund Stone (1700–68), in his translation of Bion, included a plate which contrasted English and French designs for pocket cases. The English case is shown to be oval and tapered whereas the French case is rectangular with sharp corners and is set back in size below the line of the lid [129].

Very few examples of Bion's pocket cases survive but a small fishskin covered case containing gold instruments was in the collection of Sir John Finlay, the Scottish collector, and on loan to the Royal Scottish Museum until 1962. A similar 4 in (100 mm) case by Bion, but covered in green fishskin, is shown in [168]. An excellent example of a larger pocket case is one by the highly skilled English instrument maker, Thomas Tuttell (fl.1695–1702) *c.*1700 [169]. It is remarkable that the delicately engraved instruments all fit into the plain black fishskin case which gives no hint of the highly decorated items within. Several similar black fishskin pocket cases of varying sizes were made by Richard Glynne in the early eighteenth century. Like Tuttell he was an accomplished engraver. One example of a large pocket case by Glynne shows an influence from French design since it has angular corners and is set back below the lid [170]. This case contains silver instruments and has a decorated parallel rule with protractor, a combination found in several cases of this period. Another interesting pocket case by Glynne which contains gunner's callipers among the brass instruments, is now in the Museum of the History of Science, Cambridge. John Rowley (fl.1698–1728) also made black fishskin pocket cases in various sizes; a giant 12 in (305 mm) version by him can be seen in the same Museum. Thomas Wright (*c.*1686–1748), who succeeded Rowley in 1728, also contributed pocket cases; one for a military user containing drawing instruments in silver [X]. Another renowned London maker, Thomas Heath, made pocket cases to several designs, using various materials for both the instruments and the cases. These varied in size from miniature to medium and large. The contents of a typical small fishskin-covered case by Heath, all brass instruments, are shown in detail [171]. Another example of a large late-eighteenth-century fishskin case is one sold by Benjamin Martin (1704–82) [XI].

The principal French instrument makers made similar pocket cases, and there are surviving examples by such makers as Chapotot, Butterfield, Lemaire, Huber and others dating to before 1750, followed by Quillet and Baradelle. Leather covered vertical cases were more popular in France and continued to be so until *c.* 1830, often made quite large – 8 in (200 mm) high – with a slip-on lid or a leather tongue-flap instead of a hinged lid. The pattern of French instruments is usually less advanced than that of English cases of the same period; the French ruling pens are sometimes rather coarse, arranged either double-ended or with a crayon holder to the reverse end; the compasses are often to what Bion called the 'German' pattern.

Sharkskin or leather treated to simulate it was a very popular finish for English pocket cases from the early eighteenth century to the early nineteenth century. There are numerous examples in the principal Museum collections in Britain by many well-known London makers such as Thomas Heath, Heath & Wing, the Adams workshop, Dollond, Troughton, Cary and Elliott, and several by these and other lesser known makers appear in the sale-rooms. A first-rate example containing a full set of silver instruments is a case by Dollond dating from the early nineteenth century [XII]. Another case of similar date, by Nairne and Blunt, contains brass instruments and would have been considerably cheaper.

The shell of special tortoises, particularly the hawk-bill turtle, had been used for encasing objects or as an inlay for decorative work since *c.*1640. Pocket cases encased in this highly decorative but fragile material can be found dating to the early eighteenth century. There are French examples by Pierre Lemaire (fl.

1735–60), and one unusual pocket case by him, which contains silver instruments, has a hinged base which reveals an ink-well [172]. A case containing a small set of silver instruments made by Edward Nairne *c.*1774 can be seen in [XIII]. Tortoise-shell continued to be used during the period 1800–40 for pocket cases by William Elliott (1807–1849), Charles A. Schmalcalder (fl.1808–38) and several other London makers.

A wide variety of small pocket cases, or 'etuis', as they are often called, $5 \times 1\frac{1}{2}$ in or $4\frac{1}{2} \times 1\frac{1}{2}$ in (125×38 mm or 115×32 mm) in size, was made to hold only a basic set of three to six drawing instruments. The set usually comprised a pair of compasses with alternative inserts for ink and pencil, a scale and sometimes a ruling pen and small bow compasses. From the late eighteenth century the provision of a double-hinged holder for the pen and pencil inserts in these small cases was quite common. From the mid-eighteenth to the mid-nineteenth century small cases were made by the principal English makers covered in shagreen, fishskin or lizard skin (sometimes dyed chartreuse green). Others were made of tortoise-shell. A late-eighteenth-century case by Whiford in shagreen with silver mounts [XIV] can be contrasted with a simpler early-nineteenth-century example by Troughton [XV]. (Note the ivory scale with both inch and metric divisions, unusual for an English case.)

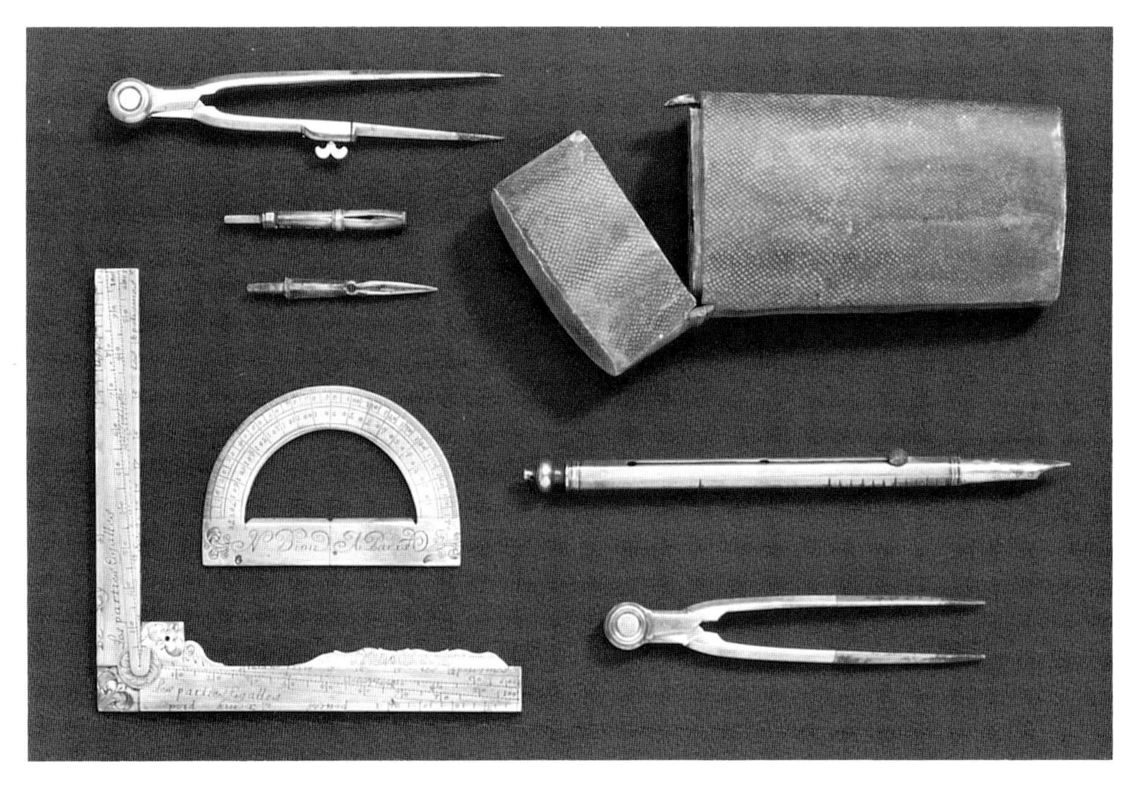

[168] A pocket set of drawing instruments to a small green rayskin-covered case with flip-top and silver release button, containing silver items: a sector $3\frac{1}{2}$ in (90 mm) combined as set square hinged to stay open 90° and 180° also divided as scale rule, a $2\frac{1}{4}$ in (55 mm) protractor inscribed 'N Bion A Paris', a pair of compasses of 'German pattern' with points and inserts for ink and pencil (note the pen with goat's foot groove for ink), a pair of dividers $3\frac{1}{8}$ in (80 mm), and a holder for crayon with a retractable quill pen with scale divisions to case as Bion Pl.IX, items (A), (C), (D), (E), and (F). Early 18th century. Case: Height 4 in (98 mm).
Science Museum, London.

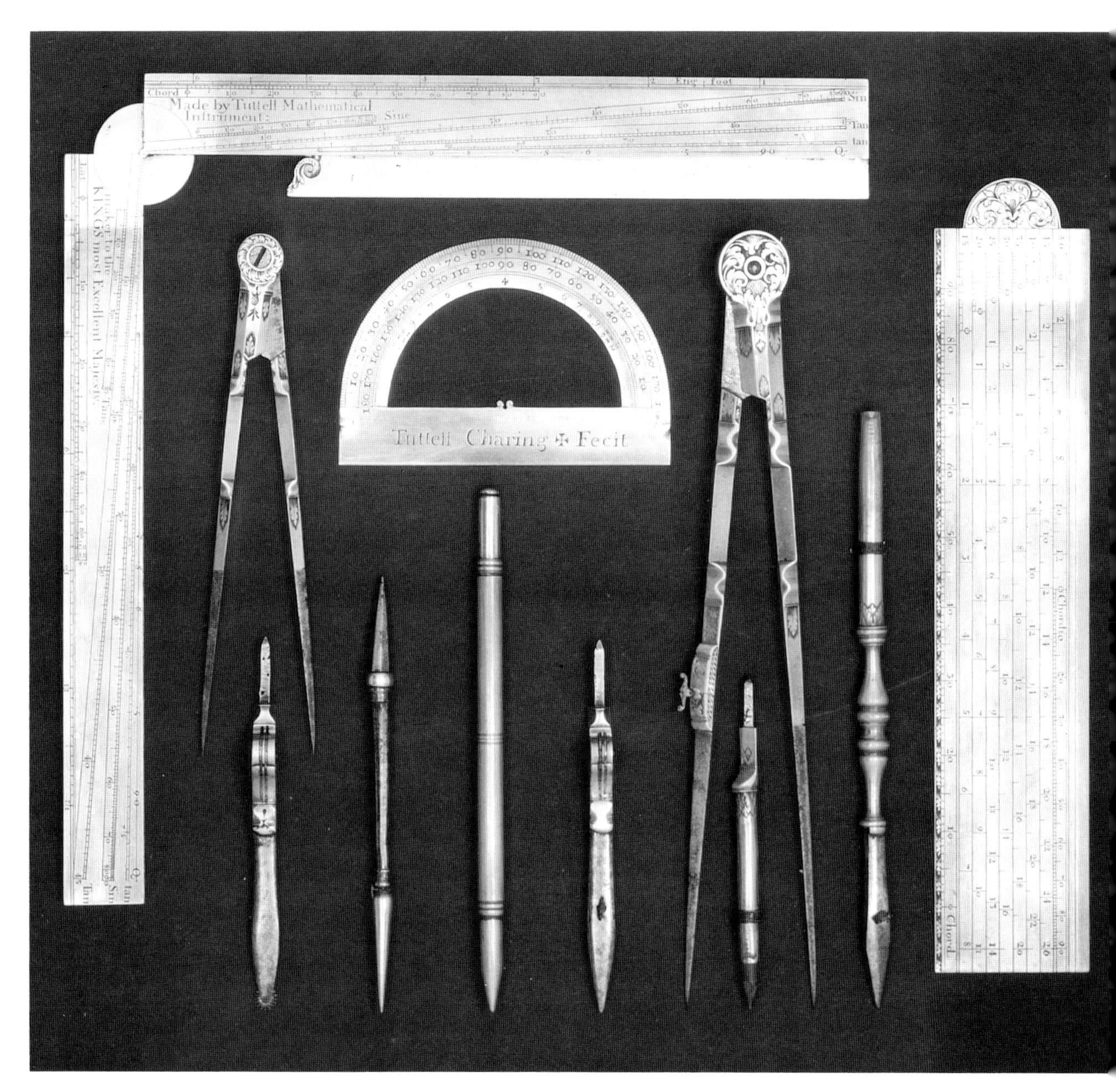

[169] A pocket set of drawing instruments to a black fishskin-covered wooden case. The sector is inscribed 'Made by Tuttell Mathematical Instrument: maker to the KING's most Excellent Majesty'. Many of the brass instruments are finely engraved and decorated with a foliate design, and the set includes a sector with a small ledge to one arm, a plotting scale with diagonal scale to the reverse side, a semi-circular protractor inscribed 'Tuttell Charing X fecit', a pair of dividers, a pair of large compasses with inserts for ink and pencil and dotting wheel, a pricker with a stylus at the reverse end, a tracer with a blunt point, and a drawing pen with a crayon-holder at the reverse end. Note the fine hand-cut wing screws on the pen and the compasses. Height $7\frac{1}{8}$ in (182 mm). *c.*1700. *Private collection.*

[170] Black fishskin-covered case mounted with silver designed on the French pattern with a set-back below lid and angular corners. This case contains silver drawing instruments, some signed 'R. Glynne fecit', and includes a sector with small nibs to one arm, a plotting scale with line of chords on one side and diagonal scales on the reverse, a pair of compasses with inserts for ink, pencil and dotting pen, a pair of dividers and a parallel rule with scissored links combined with a protractor. English. *c.*1730. *Museum of the History of Science, Oxford.**

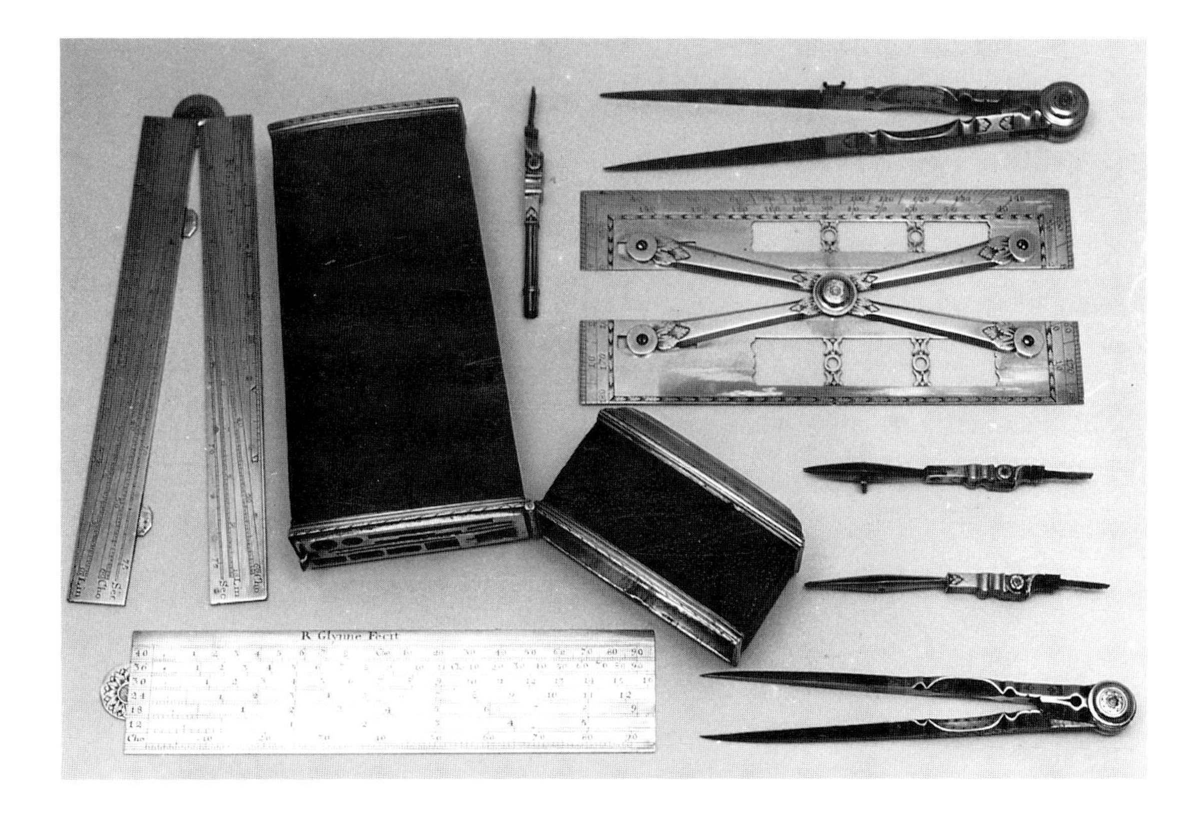

[171] A small pocket case covered in black fishskin with the brass instruments which it contains. The 4-inch sector is signed 'T. Heath fecit' and has a third arm to act as brace. The set also includes a pair of dividers, a pair of compasses and inserts for ink and pencil, a pair of small bows with turned handle, a ruling pen with turned handle shown with the pricker unscrewed, and a small pencil with brass mount used as a tracer and for easy extraction from the vertical case. English. Mid-18th century. *Science Museum, London.*

172

[172] A tortoise-shell pocket case mounted with silver. The set includes a silver sector signed 'Le Maire fils à Paris', a horn *aide-mémoire*, a pair of dividers and a ruling pen containing a pricker. It is remarkable for the travelling inkstand, complete with screw-on cap, fitted to the bottom of the case. Case: $5\frac{1}{4}$ in (135 mm). Mid-18th century. *Private collection.*

[173] Flat wallet case with elaborately tooled decoration on the maroon leather-covered wooden case, which contains a small set of nickel silver drawing instruments. Under the flap inside the lid is an ivory parallel rule and a scale marked 'Holtzapffel & Co., 64 Charing Cross' with scales for fractions of an inch. Case: $5\frac{1}{4} \times 3\frac{1}{4} \times 1$ in (133 × 83 × 25 mm). Early 19th century. *Andrew Alpern Collection, New York.*

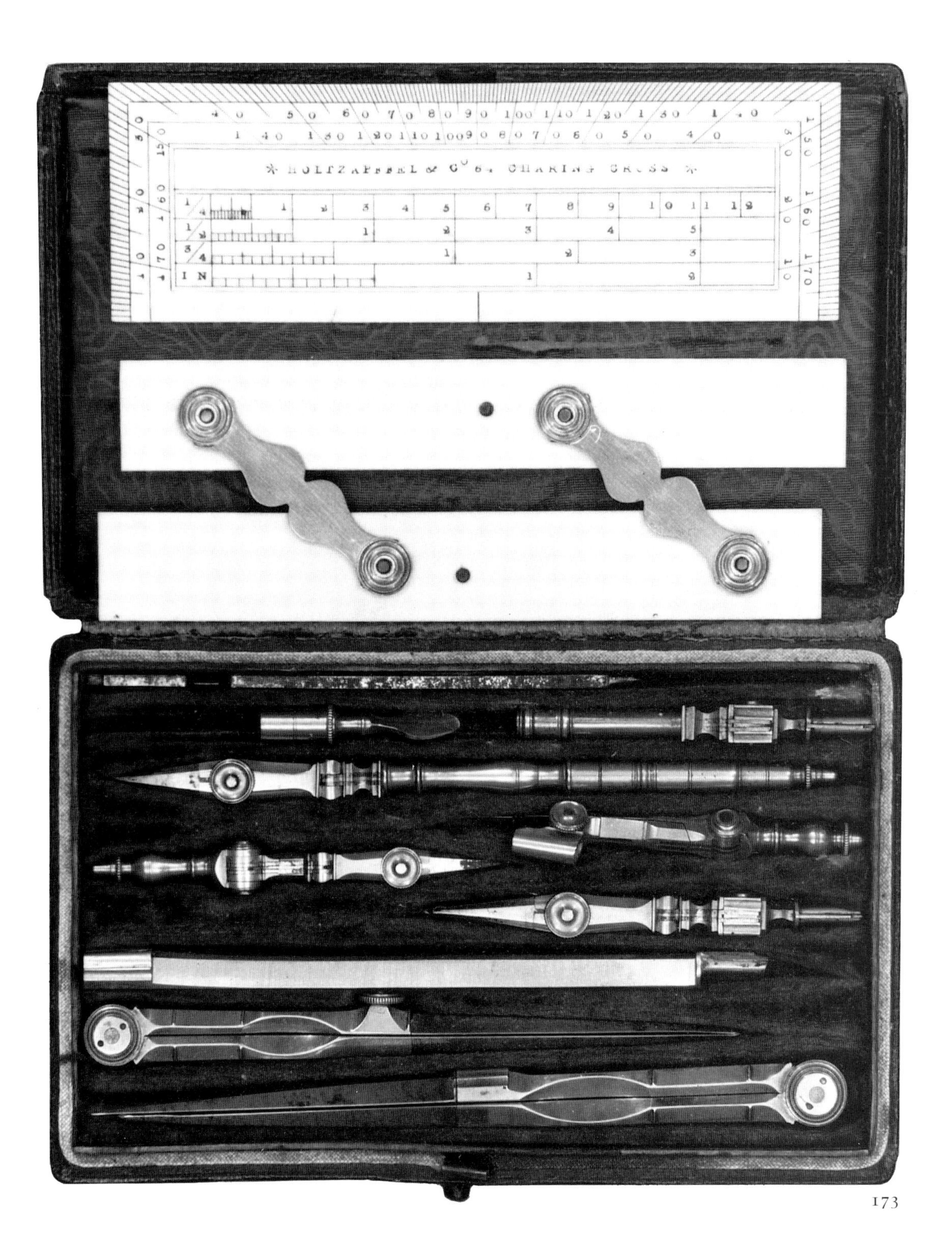

173

[174] A complete miniature set of instruments for drawing and writing shown with the cylindrical case. The case is covered in black fishskin decorated with silver nails, and there is an inkwell in its base. The set includes a pair of dividers of the 'German' pattern described by Bion, a crayon-holder, two silver quill pens and a small folding rule inscribed 'Demi Pied De Roy'. French. Case: 5 in (125 mm) long. Early 18th century. *Gustav and Margarete Thorban Collection, West Germany.*

Flat wallet cases

After 1800, flat wallet cases were introduced, of polished hardwood or leather-covered wood, $5\frac{1}{2} \times 3\frac{1}{2}$ in (140×90 mm) and only $\frac{3}{4}$–1 in (19–25 mm) thick. During the late nineteenth century some were made to this design in France covered in black leather and scored with a diamond pattern. An English version which dates to *c.*1830 by Holtzapffel [173], is a precursor of many cases made by W. F. Stanley. The latter firm introduced a larger flat compact case in the late nineteenth century which held a complete set of drawing instruments [XVII]. W. F. Stanley continued to offer these leather-covered flat cases until the middle of the twentieth century; an illustration appeared in their 1925 catalogue for such cases in two sizes to take either their $4\frac{1}{2}$ or 6 in (115 or 152 mm) instruments.

Small cases containing only compasses and their inserts together with a ruling pen were made in Milan, such as the example from Carlo Bordogna's workshop made between 1830 and 1850 [XVIII]. Similar small sets were made in Britain for the use of students and technical draughtsmen.

[175] Invitation card designed by Rex Whistler for the RIBA Centenary Conference in London, 1934. *British Architectural Library, London.*

Unusual objects containing drawing instruments

Diminutive sets of drawing instruments were made as mementoes arranged in miniature cases or were sometimes incorporated into unusual objects. There is a fake spy-glass of *c.*1690 in the collection of the National Maritime Museum at Greenwich which contains miniature drawing instruments to one end and an ink-pot to the other. Another version includes an ink-pot, this time in a French cylindrical case [174].

During the late eighteenth century and early nineteenth century walking sticks with special fittings became quite popular. They were known as 'gadget canes' or *cannes à système*. Seemingly plain canes hid drinking flasks, snuff-boxes, swords, guns, musical instruments, measuring rules and, less commonly, drawing instruments. A fine example from a French walking stick appears in [XIX]. This device is known as a 'Baradelle' in France, after the maker who is supposed to have invented the design. The English architect and collector, Sir John Soane (1753–1837) owned a walking stick which contained a folding measuring rule in the Malacca cane and a small set of drawing instruments housed in the hollow hardwood handle, complete with a magnetic compass set in the screw-on cap.

It has not been possible to include a greater number of the interesting variety of instrument cases made during the period covered by this book. For instance the early seventeenth century tooled hide cases, sometimes provided with thong leather shoulder straps for easier transportation; the many eighteenth century *étuis* which included a basic set of drawing instruments together with the more usual demountable cutlery and folding scissors; the Dutch and Milanese small student draughtsman's sets which continue to have, well into the nineteenth century, compasses and dividers provided with the traditional octagonal ball-joints which originated in the sixteenth century.

Finally this book has tried to avoid illustrating composite sets; many appear in the sale rooms. In several museums there are examples of interest because the items are by several known makers. It is always essential to assess whether rogue items have been introduced and if they are of similar date. Those sets which have seen considerable use for drawing often have damaged joints and points to compasses and dividers and the ruling pens are taken out and subsequently lost. There are fortunately still many fine sets appearing with dealers and in the sale rooms; but it is always worth examining each instrument carefully before assuming the date or country of origin.

Select Gazetteer of museum collections

Austria

Kunsthistorisches Museum, Burgring 5, A 1010, VIENNA

Österreichisches Museum für angewandte Kunst, Stubenring 5, A 1010, VIENNA

Belgium

Musées Royaux d'Art et d'Histoire, Parc du Cinquantenaire 10, BRUSSELS, B 1040

Czechoslovakia

National Technical Museum, Kostelni 42, 17078 PRAGUE 7

France

Musée des Arts Décoratifs, Pavillon de Marsan, 107–09 rue de Rivoli, 75001 PARIS

Musée du Louvre, Palais du Louvre, 75001 PARIS

Musée National de la Renaissance, Château d'Ecouen, 95440 ECOUEN

Musée National des Techniques (formerly Conservatoire National des Arts et Métiers), 292 rue Saint-Martin, 75003 PARIS

Observatoire de Paris, 61 avenue de l'Observatoire, 75014 PARIS

Federal Republic of Germany

Deutsches Museum, Museuminsel 1, 8000 MUNICH 22

Germanisches Nationalmuseum, Weinmarkt 1, 8500 NUREMBERG

Staatliche Kunstsammlungen Kassel, Bruder Grimmplatz 5, 3500 KASSEL 1

Staatliche Museen Preussischer Kulturbesitz, Kunstgewerbemuseum, Tiergartenstrasse 6, D-1000 BERLIN 30

Museum für Kunst und Gewerbe, Steintorplatz 1, 2000 HAMBURG 1

German Democratic Republic

Staatlicher Mathematisch-Physikalischer Salon, zum Zwinger, 8010 DRESDEN

Great Britain

The British Architectural Library: Drawings Collection, Royal Institute of British Architects, 21 Portman Square, LONDON W1H 9HF

British Museum, Great Russell Street, LONDON WC1B 3DG

Museum of the History of Science, Broad Street, OXFORD OX1

Museum of London, London Wall, LONDON EC2Y 5HN

National Army Museum, Royal Hospital Road, Chelsea, LONDON SW3 4HT

National Maritime Museum, Greenwich, LONDON SE10 9NF

Royal Museum of Scotland, Chambers Street, EDINBURGH EH1 1JF

Science Museum, South Kensington, LONDON SW7 2DD

Whipple Museum of the History of Science, Free School Lane, CAMBRIDGE CB2 3RH

Italy

Museo di Storia della Scienza, Piazza dei Giudici 1, 50122 FLORENCE

Università degli Studi di Padova, via Marzolo 8, 35131 PADUA

Netherlands

Museum Boerhaave, Steenstraat 1a, 2312 BS LEYDEN

Universiteitsmuseum, Bilstraat 166, 3507 LA UTRECHT

United States

Adler Planetarium, 1300 Lake Shore Drive, CHICAGO 60605

Metropolitan Museum of Art, New York City, 5th Avenue, 82nd Street, NEW YORK 10028

National Museum of History and Technology, Smithsonian Institution, WASHINGTON DC 20560

Select bibliography

Early reference works
(arranged chronologically)

BESSON, Jacques
Theatrum instrumentorum, Orleans, 1569

Théatre des instrumens mathématiques et mécaniques, Lyons, 1579

POMODORO, Giovanni
Geometria prattica, Rome, 1603

FURTTENBACH, Joseph
Mechanische Reissladen, Augsburg, 1644

BION, Nicolas
Traité de la construction et principaux usages des instrumens de mathématiques, Paris, 1709; La Haye 1723

DOPPELMAYR, Johann Gabriel
Weitere Eröffnung der neuen mathematischen Werkschule, Nuremberg, 1717

STONE, Edmund
The Construction & Principal Uses of Mathematical Instruments (English translation of Bion's *Traité*), London, 1723 (revised edition with appendix on English instruments, London, 1758: this edition in facsimile, The Holland Press, London, 1972)

LEUPOLD, Jacob
Theatrum arithmetico-geometricum, Leipzig, 1723

PENTHER, Johann Frederik
Praxis geometriae, Augsburg, 1732, 1755 and 1788

WEBSTER, William
Description & Use of a Complete Set or Case of Pocket Instruments, London, 1739

ADAMS, George, the Elder
Micrographia illustrata, London, 1746 (the supplement lists mathematical instruments)

ROBERTSON, John
Treatise of such Mathematical Instruments as are usually put into a Portable Case, London, 1747

DIDEROT, Denis and d'ALEMBERT, J. L.
Encyclopédie ou dictionnaire raisonné des sciences, des arts et des métiers, Paris, 1751–80

Encyclopédie méthodique (see Plates, Vol. III), Panchoucke, Paris, 1788–91

MARTIN, Benjamin
Description & Use of a Case of Mathematical Instruments, London, 1771

ADAMS, George, the Younger
Geometrical and Graphical Essays, London, 1791 (revised editions issued by W. and S. Jones in 1797, 1813 and 1823. German edition issued in 1775).

BARROW, John
Description of Pocket Magazine Cases of Technical Drawing Instruments, London, 1792

REES, Dr Abraham
The new Cyclopaedia or Universal Dictionary of Arts & Sciences, London, 1802–19

BREWSTER, David
The Edinburgh Encyclopaedia, Edinburgh, 1808–30

STUDER, Johann Gottfried
Beschreibung der verschiedenen Zeichnen . . . und Vermessungs Instrumente, Dresden, 1811

Encyclopaedia Metropolitana, London, 1817–45

NICHOLSON, Peter
Architectural Dictionary, London, 1819

SIMMS, Frederick
A Treatise on the Principal Mathematical Drawing Instruments, London, 1834

BRADLEY, Thomas
Practical Geometry, London, 1836

HEATHER, J. F.
A Treatise on Mathematical Instruments, London, 1849

STANLEY, W. F.
A Descriptive Treatise on Mathematical Drawing Instruments, 1866, 1868, 1873, 1888

Twentieth-century works

BAYNES, Kenneth and HUGH, Francis
The Art of the Engineer (Lutterworth Press), London, 1981

BOBINGER, Maximilian
Alt-Augsburg Kompassmacher (Hans Rosler), Augsburg, 1966

BONELLI, Maria L. Righini
Antique Instruments in the Museum of the History of Science, Florence (Arnaud), Florence, 1980

BOOKER, P. J.
A History of Engineering Drawing (Chatto and Windus), 1963 (reprinted with amendments (Northgate), London, 1979)

BRACHNER, Alto (ed.).
G. F. Brander 1713–1783 (Deutsches Museum), Munich, 1983

BROWN, Joyce
Mathematical Instrument-Makers in the Grocers' Company 1688–1800 (Science Museum), London, 1979

CALVERT, H. R.
Scientific Trade Cards in the Science Museum Collection (Science Museum), London, 1971

CHALDECOTT, John A.
Handbook of the King George III Collection of Scientific Instruments (Science Museum), London, 1951

CLERQ, Peter R. de
Nineteenth-century Scientific Instrument-Makers (edited papers of 4th Scientific Instrument Symposium; German nineteenth century Instrument-Makers by Alto Brachner (Museum Boerhaave), Leyden, 1985)

DAUMAS, Maurice
Les instruments scientifiques aux XVIIe et XVIIIe siècles (Paris), 1953 (translated into English by Mary Holbrook with an English title *Scientific Instruments of the Seventeenth and Eighteenth Centuries and their Makers)* (Batsford), London, 1972

DICKENSON, H. W.
A brief history of draughtsman's instruments, Transactions of the Newcomen Society 27 (1949–50), pp 73–84

DREIER, Franz Adrian
Winkelmessinstrumente, Exhibition catalogue of the Kunstgewerbemuseum, Berlin, 1979

FELDHAUS, F. M.
Die Geschichte des technischen Zeichnens (F. Kuhlmann), Wilhelmshaven, 1953 (2nd revised edition by E. Schriff, issued by the same publisher in 1959, is available in English in the American monthly *Graphic Science*, October 1960 to May 1963)

GILLE, Bertrand
Les Ingénieurs de la Renaissance (Hermann), Paris, 1964 (available in English as *The Renaissance Engineers* (Lund Humphries), 1966)

GROTZSCH, Helmut.
Dresden Mathematisch-Physikalicher Salon (E. A. Seemann), Leipzig, 1978

HAMBLY, Maya
Drawing Instruments: their History, Purpose and Use for Architectural Drawings, exhibition catalogue, Heinz Gallery (Royal Institute of British Architects Drawing Collection) London, 1982

MACKENSON, Ludwig von
Die erste Sternwarte Europas mit ihren Instrumenten und Uhren: 400 Jahre Jost Bürgi (Callwey), Munich, 1979

MICHEL, Henri
Les instruments des sciences dans l'art et l'histoire (Albert de Visscher), Brussels, 1966 (English edition translated by F. R. and R. E. W. Maddison as *Scientific Instruments in Art and History*, Barrie & Rocliff, London, 1967

MILBURN, John R.
Benjamin Martin 1704–1782, a biography (Noordhoff International Press), Leyden, 1976; a supplement to this biography, London, 1986: *Retailer of Sciences* (Vade-Mecum Press), London, 1978.

NEDOLUHA, Alois
Kulturgeschichte des technischen Zeichnens (Blätter fur Technikgeschichte 19–21, 1957–59), Vienna

ROTA, Italo and UBERTAZZI, Alessandro
Galeria degli Strumenti, an exhibition catalogue, Galleria del Desegno, Milan Triennale, 1979

SCOTT-SCOTT, Michael
Drawing Instruments 1850–1950 (Shire Publications), 1986

STANLEY, W. F. (Revised by Tallack)
Drawing and Mathematical Instruments, E. and F. N. Spon, London, 1925

STARCK, Georg
Die Entwicklung des deutschen Reisszeug Industrie (Universitätsverlag von Rob. Posts), Leipzig, 1925

TAYLOR, E. G. R.
Mathematical Practitioners of Tudor and Stuart England (Cambridge University Press), 1954

Mathematical Practitioners of Hanoverian England (Cambridge University Press), 1966

TURNER, Anthony
Early Scientific Instruments: Europe 1400–1800 (Philip Wilson/Sotheby's), London, 1987

TURNER, Gerard L'E.
Nineteenth-century Scientific Instruments (Sotheby Publications), London, 1983.

ZINNER, Ernst
Deutsche und Niederländische astronoomische Instrumente des 11–18 Jahrhunderts (C. H. Beck), Munich, 1956

Photographic acknowledgements

Grateful acknowledgement is made to the following for supplying photographs and for permission to reproduce them (references are to illustration numbers, Roman numerals denoting Colour Plates):

Adler Planetarium, Chicago: 73
Andrew Alpern, New York: 40, 71
Gil Amiaga, New York: II, IV, VIII, XI, XII, XIII, XIV, XV, XVII, XIX, 147, 156, 173
Blundell Harling, Weymouth: 103, 113, & 167
Bonhams, London: 8
Paul Breman, London: 20, 23
British Museum, London: 74, 145
British Architectural Library, London: V, 2A, 2B, 6, 9, 14, 17, 27, 28, 41, 63, 67, 87, 93, 102, 118, 135, 138, 154, 175
Geremy Butler, London: 49, 64, 99, 101A, 102, 119
Faber-Castell, Germany: 45, 48, 50
Christie's, South Kensington: 78, 115, 116, 117B, 130
John Cook, Oxford: 101A
Corinium Museum, Cirencester: 51
Deutsches Museum, Munich: 15, 153
Norman Foster Architects, London: 9
Germanisches National Museum, Nuremberg: 36, 59, 117A
David Gray, London: 70, 101B, 119
Haff, Germany: 42, 66, 77, 86, 124, 157
Angelo Hornak, London: I
Jesus College, Cambridge: 150
Kern & Co, Switzerland: IX, 56A, 165
Kunstgewerbemuseum, Berlin: 158
Mansell Collection, London: 12
Mathematisch-Physikalischer Salon, Dresden: 38, 52, 121
Museo di Storia della Scienza, Florence: 19, 132, 149, 159
Museum für Kunst und Gewerbe, Hamburg, 39A
Museum of the History of Science, Oxford: 1, 76, 80, 83, 112, 134, 146, 148, 150, 170
Museum of London: 34
Phillips, Blenheim Street, London: 85B
RIBA Drawings Collection, London, *see* British Architectural Library, London
Clemens Riefler, West Germany: 56, 58, 61, 68, 69, 79, 162, 164, 166
Trustees of the Science Museum Library, London: 20A, 21, 22, 24, 30, 31, 32, 33, 38, 54, 83, 95, 105, 110, 143
Trustees of the Science Museum, London: 10, 75, 82, 85A, 88, 90, 91, 92, 114, 128, 133, 142, 151, 152, 161B, 168, 171
Michael Scott-Scott, Dartmouth: 120
Sotheby's, London: VI, X, 60, 62, 81, 100, 109, 130, 153, 155, 161A, 169, 172
Staatliche Kunstsammlungen, Cassel: 122
Gustav Thorban, West Germany: 25, 26, 131, 174
Alessandro Ubertazzi, Milan: III, VII, XVI, XVIII, 56, 149A
Board of Trustees of the Victoria and Albert Museum, London: 160
Whipple Museum of the History of Science, Cambridge: 137
Dr Berthold Wolpe, London: 29, 89, 141
Yale University Art Gallery, Connecticut: 1

Index

Page numbers in *italic* refer to illustrations; references to colour plates are shown in **bold** type

Aarau, Switzerland, 29
Abraham, A. (workshop), 29
Académie des Sciences, Paris, 23, 131
Ackermann, Rudolph (firm), *168*
Adam, Robert, 142
Adams, Dudley, 27
Adams, George, the Elder, 27–8, 30, 51, 89; architectonic sector, 137, 139, *140*; perspectograph, 145; magazine cases, 161, *167*; *Micrographia illustrata*, *47*
Adams, George, the Younger, 27; compasses, 69, *72*; helicograph, 95, *97*; large radius curves, 101; set squares, 105; parallel rule, 111, *112*; protractors, 120, *123*; triangular compasses, 125; proportional compasses, 128; pantograph, 131; perspectograph, *148*; cases, 154, 185; *Geometrical and Graphical Essays*, 47, *48*, *112*, 131, 144, *148*, *endpapers*
Adie, Alexander, 132
Adie, Patrick, 133, 145
Airy, Sir George B., 94
Alberti, Leone Battista: *De re aedificatoria*, 35, 95; *Della pittura*, 144
Alleaume, Jacques, of Paris, 24
Allen, Elias, 24
Alteneder, Theo, 30
Amsler, Jacob, 29
angles: measuring, 120–2
Apollonius, of Perga, 99
Archbutt, J. & W.E. (firm), 67, *124*, 161, *169*, 173
architectural drawing, 17–18
Army and Navy Stores, London, 31
Augsburg, 20–1, 69

Babylon, 19
Baker, Charles, *110*, 120
Baraban (French company), 54, 173, *181*
Baradelle, Jacques, of Paris, 173, 185; walking stick, 193
Barrow, John: *Description of Pocket and Magazine Cases of Technical Drawing Instruments*, 47, 49, 69, 128
Bartholomew's (map-makers), 132
Bate, R.B. (*later* Potter of Poultry), 28, 130, 132
Baumann, Hans, 65
Baynes, K. and Pugh, F.: *the Art of the Engineer*, 54
Beach and Co, London, *80*
Berge, John, 113, *138*
Besson, Jacques, 23; *Theatrum instrumentorum*, 35–6, 128
bevels, 107
bi-centrolinead, 145
Billmeir, S.A., 54
Bion, Nicolas, 24, 28; pocket cases, 57, 185, *186*; fountain pen, 61; pencils, 66; compasses, 69, 82, 125; elliptical trammel, 89; set squares, 105; scales, 115; protractor, 120, *121*; proportional compasses, 128; pantograph, 130; *Traité de la construction et les principaux usages des instruments de mathématiques*, 25, 37, *38*, 39; translations, 37, 41, *134*, 135, 144, *146*, *147*
Bird, John, 28
Blätter für Technikgeschichte (journal), 54
Bleuer, John, 47
blue-prints, 127
Blundell Harling (company), 30, 77, *111*, 120, 161
Blunt, Thomas, 27, 185
Bonnier de la Mosson, of Paris, 25
Booker, P.J.: *A History of Engineering Drawing*, 54
Bordogna, Carlo: flat case, **Pl. XVIII**, 193
Bosse, Abraham, 144
bows, spring, **Pl. II**
Bramer, Benjamin, 41, 144, *146*
Brander, Georg Friedrich, 28, 48, 116, *124*, 125
Brander & Hoeschel, of Augsburg, 116
Brewster, Sir David: *Edinburgh Encyclopaedia*, 49, 52, 53, 66, 75, 89, 99, 127, 132, 145
British Standards, 17
British Thornton (company), 31
Brookes, 104
Brown, Joyce: *Mathematical Instrument Makers in the Grocers' Company*, 24
Brunelleschi, Filippo, 19, 144
Bruti, Revisi: *Archiesto per formar con facilità li cinque ordini d'architettura*, 137, 139
Buckland, William, *frontispiece*
Builder, The (magazine), 30
Bürgi, Jost, 21, 23, 128, 144
Burstow, Edward, 92
Butterfield, Michael, 24, 57, 115, *136*, 185
Byzantine Empire, 19

callipers, 88, *88*

Campbell, Colen: *Vitruvius Britannicus*, 12
Canivet, of Paris, 28, 105, *107*, 156
Caran d'Ache (company), 68
cartography, 17, 20
Carver, Isaac, *138*
Carwitham, Thomas: *Description and Use of an Architectonic Sector*, 137
Cary, William (firm), *85*, 101, 120, 130; cases, 154–6, 185
cases of drawing instruments:
—crucifix-shaped, 153, *153*
—French inlaid rosewood, **Pl. VIII**
—flat, **Pls IX, XVI, XVII, XVIII**
—magazine, **Pl. VII**, 161, *162–72*
—medium-sized, 173, *174–84*
—pocket, **Pls X, XI, XII, XIII, XIV, XV**, 185–6, *186–90*
—presentation, **Pl. VI**, 156, *157–9*
—wallet, *191*, 193
—walking-stick, **Pl. XIX**, 193
Cassel, 21
catalogues of instruments, 54
Cattaneo, Giovanni, **Pl. VII**
Cattaneo, Luigi, 65
centrograph, 101
centrolinead, 51, 145, *150*
Cerceau, Jacques Androuet de, 36, 144
Chambers, Ephraim: *Cyclopaedia*, 48, 75, 82, 89
Chapotot, Louis & son, of Paris, 24, 28, 57, 185
Chard, R. A. E.: case, *155*
Charlemagne, Emperor, 35
Chaulnes, Duc de, 25, 119
Chorez, Daniel, 24
circles, 69–88
Clement, Joseph, 91
clinograph, 110
Coffin, E., *17*
Cole, Benjamin, Senior, 26, *106*
Cole, Benjamin, Junior, 26
Cole, Humphrey, 23
compasses, 19, 69–70, *70–3*
—beam, **Pl. III**, 23, 75–6, *80*, *81*; triangular, 124, *125*
—bow, 81, *82*
—cylindrical, 88
—drop-bow, 81–2
—elliptical, 23, 89, *92*
—folding and pocket, *83*, 84
—hair, 75
—Napier, *83*, 84
—pillar, *83*, 84
—pump, 81
—quick-set, 32, *74*, *75*
—reversible, *84*
—screw, 72
—spring-bow, 81, *82*
—Swiss, *83*, 84
—triangular *see* dividers, three-legged
—triangulation, 21
—tubular, 84
—tubular beam, *80*,
—turn-about, 37, 70, 82, *82*, 84
—volute, 95, *97*
—wing, **Pl. I**, 72, *76*, *77*
computer-aided draughting systems (CAD), 17, 33
conchoid curves, 99–101
conchoidograph, 101, *101*
Conté, N. J., 66
copying, 125–7
Coradi (firm), 99
Culpeper, Thomas, 115, *116*, *138*, *139*
curves, 89–101
—conchoid, 99–101
—free, 101, *104*
—hyperbolic, 99
—irregular ('French'), 101–4, *102–104*
—large-radius, 101
—parabolic, *98*, 99
—spiral, 95–9, *96*

Danfrie, Philippe, 23
Daumas, Maurice: *Les instruments scientifiques au XVII et XVIII siècles*, 54
'dead drawing', 11
delineators, 145, *149*
della Francesca, Piero *see* Piero della Francesca
Demainbray, Dr Stephen, 25
Desargues, Gérard, 99
Descartes, René, 99
d'Este family, 21
Diagraphe, Le, 144
Diderot, Denis and Alembert, Jean Le Rond d': *Encyclopédie*, *14*, 48, 131, *131*
Didyma, near Miletus: Temple of Apollo, 19
Digges, Leonard: *A Geometrical Practice named Pantometria*, 22, 36, 120
Digges, Thomas, 22, 36
dividers, 36, 36, 69, *70–2*, 73, *78–79*, 84–5, *85–6*, *114*, 125, *endpapers*
—hair (*or* spring), 75
—pillar, *85*
—screw, 72
—single-handed, 84
—spacing, 85, *87*
—three-legged (triangular compasses), 84–5, *124*, 125
—turn-about, 82, *82*
—wing, 72, *76*
Dollond, Peter, 13; cases, **Pl. XII**, 154, 185
Dollond, P. & J., 47
Donkin, Bryan: pen, *52*
Doppelmayr, Johann Gabriel, 28, 41
dotting pen *see* wheel-pens
drawing scales *see* scales
Drechsler, Georg, *166*
Dubreuil, Jean: *La perspective pratique*, *14*, 113
Dürer, Albrecht, 35, *58*, 89; *Unterweysungen der Messung*, 144

Eckhardt, A. G., 113
Ecobra (company), 29, 32
Edinburgh Encyclopaedia *see* Brewster, Sir David
Egypt, ancient, 19
eidographs, 132–3, *133*

electrum *see* German silver
Elliott, William (*later* Elliott & Sons; *then* Elliott Brothers), 28, 101, 116, 120, *126*, 130; cases, 154, 156, 161, *171*, 173, 185–6
ellipses, 89–95
ellipsographs, **Pl. V**, *53*, 89–90, *90–5*, 94–5
elliptical trammels *see* trammels, elliptical
Encyclopaedia Metropolitana, 49–50
encyclopaedias, 48–51
Encyclopédie *see* Diderot, Denis; Alembert, Jean Le Rond d'
Encyclopédie méthodique, *26*, 48–9
English, E. W., 145
engraving, 13–14, 20
enlarging and reducing, 127–8, 130
erasing and erasers, 66
Ertel (workshop), of Munich, 29
Esser, Hermann, 30
Esser, Ludwig, 29
étuis *see* cases, pocket
Euclid, 19
Euler, Leonard, 156

Faber-Castell (company), 33, 64–6, 68, *68*, 70, 120
Faber, A. W., 66, *67*, 68
Faber, Kaspar, 66
Farey, Cyril Arthur, 145
Farey, John, Senior, 89
Farey, John, Junior: ellipsograph, **Pl. V**, *53*, 89–90, *91*, *93*; perspective drawings, 14; illustrates encyclopaedias, 49, *50*, *52*, *53*, 89–90, 105; compasses, 70, 75, 81; on 'Ovals', *93*, 94; and large radius curves, 101; tee-square, 113; triangular compasses, 125; tracers, 127; pantograph, 131; delineator, 145, *149*
Feldhaus, F. M., 61; *Geschichte des technischen Zeichnens*, 54; *Die Technik der Vorzeit*, 54
Finlay, Sir John, 185
Finney, James, 91, *92*
flutes (columnar), 99, *100*
Fortin, Nicolas, of Paris, 28
Foster, Norman, *18*
France: measurement in, 116
Frisius, Gemma, 120
Furttenbach, Joseph: *Mechanischer Reissladen*, 36, 40

Galileo Galilei, 25; *Le operazioni del compasso geometrico e militare*, 36, 135
Gallard, Petrus, *176*
Gavard, J. D. C., 132, 144
Gemini, Thomas, 22
German silver (electrum), 28
Gesner, Conrad: *De omni rerum fossilium genere*, 66
Giorgio Martini, Francesco di, 11, *12*
Glynne, Richard, 26, 105, 111, 173, 185, *188*
Goldmann, Nicholas, 41; *Tractatus de stylometris*, 142, *143*
goldsmiths, 19
Gourdin, of Paris, 89, *90*
graphite, 65–6
graphomètres, 24
Graphos drawing pen, 64, *64*
Greatorex, Ralph, 24
Greece, ancient, 19
Grocers' Company, London, 24, 26–7
Gudea (Babylon), 115
Gunter, Edmund, 24; *Description and Use of the Sector*, 36, 135
Gunter's scales, 115
Gwilt, Joseph: *Principles of Architecture*, *100*

Habermel, Erasmus, 21, 156
Haff, Gebrüder (company), 29, 32–3, 51, 61; US imports from, 30; catalogues, 54; specialist drawing pens, *63*; compasses, 72, *74*, 77, *81*, 82; spacing dividers, 85, *86*; ellipsographs, 94, *95*; proportional compasses, 130, *130*; cases, 156, 161, *172*
Haff, Thomas, 29
Halden, John & Co, 31–2; catalogues, 54, 161
Halfpenny, William: *Magnum in Parvo*, 44, 142
handbooks, 41, 44
Harling, W. H., 30–2, 54, 156; cases, 161, 173, *184*
Harris, William, 130
Haselberger, Lothar, 19
hatching, 11–13
Hayes, Walter, 24
Haywood's parallel rule, *112*
Hearne, George, 26, 173, *177*
Heath, Thomas, 27, 44, 75, 84, 89, 101, 111, 120, 137, 142; cases, 185, *189*
Heath & Wing, 121, *122*, 131, 185
Heather, J. F.: *Mathematical Instruments*, 51
helicographs, 47, 95, *97*
Henrion, Denis, of Paris, 24
Heron of Alexandria, 127
Hicks, John, 94
hinges, 23
Hogarth, William, 139
Holbein, Hans: portrait of Kratzer, *22*
Holtzapffel, Charles, 119–20, *191*, 193
Honnecourt, Villard de *see* Villard de Honnecourt
Hood, Thomas: *The Making & Use of the Geometrical Instrument called a Sector*, 36, 135
Hooke, Robert, 23, 89
Hoppus, Edward, *106*
Huber, of Paris, 185
hyperbolic curves, 99

inks, 57, 64
Ionic order, *141*
isograph (bevel), 107
Isograph technical pen, 64

Johnson, H., 97, *98*
Jolicar, 61
Jones, Thomas, 85, *87*
Jones, W. & S. (firm), 27–8, 47; compasses, 69, *72*, 128; ellipsographs, 90; protractors, 122; pantograph, *132*

Kepler, Johann, 21
Kern, Joseph (company), of Aarau, 29, 32–3, 61; cases, **Pl. IX**, 156, 161, 173, *182*; catalogues, 54; technical pens, 64; compasses, 72, *73*, 82; proportional compasses, 130
Keuffel & Esser (company), of USA, 104, *104*

Keuffer, William, 30
Kinwest pattern set square, 110
Kirby, Joshua: *Description of the Correct Use of an Architectonic Sector*, 137, 139
knuckle-joints to compasses and dividers, 75
Kovac, J., 64
Kratzer, Nicolas, *22*, 23
Kremsmunster monastery, Austria, 25
Kuhlmann, F. (company), of Wilhelmshaven, 54

Lanci, Baldassare, 21
Langley, Batty: *The City and Country Builder's & Workman's Treasury of Designs*, *14*, 44, 96, *141*
Langlois, Claude, 28, 131, 173
laser plotters, 33
Le Clerc, Sebastian, 144
Lee-Guiness (company), 32
Lemaire, Jacques, 28
Lemaire, Pierre, 28, 185, *190*
Le Muet, Pierre: *Manière de bastir*, 41
Lencker, Hans: *Perspectiva*, 36, *36*
Lennel, of Paris, 28, 173
Lenoir, Etienne, of Paris, 28, 105, 173, *180*
Leonardo da Vinci, 35, 75, 98–9, 128, 144
Lequeu, Jean-Jacques: *Nouvelle méthode appliquée aux principes élémentaires du dessin*, *16*, 105, 113
Leupold, Jacob: *Theatrum arithmetico geometricum*, 41, 69, *71*, *102*, *107*, 113, 135
Lind, James, 145
Linex (company), 120
London, 23–6, 28, 30–2
Lowry, Wilson, 49, *92*
Lusuerg, Domenicus, 25, 57, 75, 84, 89; case, **Pl. VI**, 156
Lusuerg, Jacobus, 25, 57; case, 156
Lyle, D., *97*
Lyons, Edward D., 145

Malie, Thomas, 137
Marabu (company), 114, 120
Marquois scales, 119, *155*, 156
Mars range (of pens), 64–5
Martin, Benjamin, 27; pocket case, **Pl. XI**, 185; pantograph, 131; *Description & Use of a Case of Mathematical Instruments*, 47
Martini, Francesco di Giorgio *see* Giorgio Martini, F. di
Maudesley, Henry, 91
Mayline (company), 114
Mazzoleni, Marcantonio, 25
measuring, 115–123
Medici family, 21
Medici, Cosimo de', 21
metre and metric system, 116, 119
Michel, Henri: *Les instruments des sciences dans l'art et l'histoire*, 54
'micronorm' pens, 64
Milanese set (and case), 125, 128, 156, *157*, *161*
miniature instruments, **Pl. XIX**, *174*
Mordan & Company, 67
More, Sir Thomas, 23
Morgan, Francis, 26
Mosson, Bonnier de la *see* Bonnier de la Mosson
Moxon, James, 41, 51
Moxon, Joseph, 105, 130; *Description of Mathematical Instruments*, 89, 125; *Mathematical Dictionary*, *41*; *Mathematics made Easie*, 37; *Mechanick Exercises*, 41
Munster, Sebastian, 120

Nairne, Edward, 27, 66; case, **Pl. XIII**, 173, 185–6
Napier compasses, *83*, 84
Nasmyth, James, 94, *94*
needle-points to drawing instruments, 70
Newman (firm), *168*
Newsam, Bartholomew: case, 125, 128, *152*, *160*
Niceron, Jean F., 41, 144, *146*; *Thaumaturgis opticus*, 144
Nicholson, M. A., *150*
Nicholson, Peter, 14, 49, 99, *100*, 101; invents centrolinead, 145, *150*; *Architectural Dictionary*, 51; *The Carpenter's and Joiner's Assistant*, 51; *Five Orders of Architecture*, 51, 99; *New Practical Builder*, *150*; *Practical Builder & Workman's Companion*, 51, 116, *118*; *Student Instructor*, 101
Nicomedes, 99
North, Sir Roger, 23, 88, 105, 156, *162–5*
Norton & Gregory (company), 32
Nuremberg, 20–1, 29, 69

Olympia (company), 32
Ordnance Survey drawings, 14
Orléans, Duc d', 25, 28
orthogonal drawing, 11, 20
ovals, 93, 94
ox-gall, for colours and inks, *62*, *169*

Pain, William: *The Builder's Companion & Workman's General Assistant*, 44, 142
Palladio, Andrea, 11, 12, 34, 125, 139
Panckoucke, Charles Joseph, 48
pantographs, 24, 36, 130–2, *131*, *132*
parabolagraph, 99, *99*
parabolic curves, *98*, 99
parallel motion rules, 113–14
parallel rules, 11, 111, *112*, 113, *114*, 121; double, 111, *112*
Paris, 23–4
patternbooks, 41, 44
Payne, J., 99, *99*
Peacock's Delineator, 145
Peale, Charles Willson: *frontis.*
pencils, black-lead, 47, 65–6, *66*; propelling, 65, 67–8; hardness, 66–7; technical, 68, *68*; clutch (or drop-action), 68; fine-line, 68
Penrose & Bennett (firm), 95
pens, drawing, *or* ruling, 11, 47, 57–8, *58–60*; specialist, 58, 61, 63
—curved, 62
—fountain, 61–4
—goat-foot, 57
—Micronorm, 64
—plotter, 65
—rail or road, 62

—technical (continuous ruling), 32–3, 61, *62*, 64, *64*, 65, *65*
—wheel-pen, 11, 57, 61, *62*
Pentel (company), 68
Penther, Johann Friedrich, 105, 120; *Praxis geometriae*, 41, *42*, *43*
Pepys, Samuel, 24, 130
perspective drawing, 13–14, *15*, 24, 36, *36*, 144–50
perspectographs, 144–5, *146–8*
Pettus, Sir John, 65
Philpott, Mr, *168*
Piero della Francesca, 144
Pigeon, of Lyon, *179*
plane-tables, 11
plumb-level, *106*, *107*
pocket-cases *see* cases
Pomodoro, Giovanni, 105; *Geometria prattica*, *34*, *35*, 36, 66, 69
Pompeii, 19, *20*, 69, 88, 128
Pope, Alexander, 25
Potter, J. D., 132
Potter of Poultry *see* Bate, R. B.
pouncing and pounce boxes, 124, *157*
Pricke, Robert, 41
prickers (protracting pins), 57, 125
printing, 20
Prontograph pen, 64
proportional compasses: fixed and variable, 23–4, 126, 127–8, *128–30*; Stone's, 37
proportions, 20, 134–43
protracting pins *see* prickers
protractors, 107, *117*, 120–1, *121*, *122*, 123; Vernier, *110*; combined scale, 121; folding arm, 121–2

Quillet, of Paris, 105, *173*, 185

Rahne, Peter, *136*
Ramsden, Jesse, 27–8, 75, 113, 119, 161, 173, *178*
Rapidograph tubular ink drawing pen, 64, *64*
ratio, 134–43
Redfern, George: presentation case, *169*
reducing *see* enlarging and reducing
Rees, Abraham, 48; *New Cyclopaedia*, 49, *50*, 75, 90, 93, 94, 99, 125, *149*
Reeves & Sons (company), 31, *103*, *114*
Renaissance, 20–3
Renaud-Tachet, of Paris, **Pl. VIII**
Richter, E. O. (*later* VEB Kombinat), 29, 32, 51, 54
Riefler, Clemens (company), 29; wing compasses, *77*; turnabout compasses, *82*; catalogues, 54; compasses, 70, 72, *72*, 75, 82, *82*; elliptical trammels, 89, *90*; proportional compasses, 130; cases, 156, 161, 173, *183*
Riefler, Sigmund, 29, 32–3, 51, 59, 173, *183*
Riepe, Wilhelm, 64
Roberson, of Long Acre, *169*
Robertson, John: *A Treatise of such Mathematical Instruments as are usually put into a Portable Case*, 44, 46, 111, 127, 128, 161
rods, architectural proportional, 142, *142*, *143*
rolling parallel rule, *110*, 113
Rome, ancient, 19, *20*, 69, *70*, 105
roof pitches, 105
Rotring (company), *18*, 33, 64, *64*, 114
Rowley, John, 26, *88*, 128, *130*, 185
Rowney (company), 31, 67
Royal Society of London, 23, 144
rules, 11, 107, *107*, *108*, 110, *110*, 111
—parallel, 11, 111, *112*, 113, *114*, 121
—parallel motion, 113–14
—rolling parallel, *110*, 113
—scale, 115–16, *117–19*, 119–20, *121*
ruling, 105–14
Ryther, Augustin, 23

Sainsbury Centre for Visual Arts, University of East Anglia, Norwich, *18*
St Gallen monastery, Switzerland, 35
Salmon, William: *Palladio Londinensis*, 44, 113, *114*
scale rules and boards, 115–16, *117–19*, 119–20, *121*
scales, 16
—cased set, **Pl. IV**
—drawing, 115–16
—Gunter's, 115
—Marquois, 119–20, *155*, 156
—proportional, 115
—Vernier, 120, 122, 128
Scamozzi, Vincenzo, 35
Scarlett, Edward: trade card, *45*
Scheiner, Christopher: *Pantographice*, 36, 130, *131*
Schissler, Christoph, 21, 57, 89, 92, 120; presentation case, 156, *158–9*
Schissler, Hans Christoph, 21
Schmalcalder, Charles A., 186
Schwenter, Daniel, 61; *Mathematische und philosophische Erquickungsstunden*, 37
Scott, Benjamin, 26–7
sectograph, 85, *87*
sectors, 24, 36, 113, *116*, 134–7, *134–8*; architectonic, 137–42, *139*, *140*
semi-elliptical trammel, 89, *167*
Serlio, Sebastiano, 35, 41, 144
set squares, 11, 105, *106*, 107, *108*, *109*; adjustable, 107, 110, *110*, *111*, 121; Marquois, *155*
Sevin, Pierre, 24, 28
Sforza family, 21
Short, James, 28
Simms, F. W.: *Treatise on Principal Mathematical Instruments*, 51
Simms, William, 26
Sirigatti, Lorenzo: *Practice of Perspective*, 47
Sisson, Jeremiah, 44, 75
Sisson, Jonathan, *116*
slide-rules, 137
slopes and batters, 105
Smythson, Robert, 11, 12, *12*, *13*
Soane, Sir John, 193
Speckle, Daniel: *Architectura*, 128
spiral curves, 95–9, 96
Spong, John, 24, 130
squaring, 105–14
Staedtler (company), 33, 64–5, 68, 70, 120

Stanley, W. F.: spring bows, **Pl. II**; cased set of scales, **Pl. IV**; flat case, **Pl. XVII**; company established, 30, 32; trade label, *30*; premises, *33*; catalogues, 54, 161; compasses, 70, 75, *83*,125; elliptical trammels, 89; ellipsographs, 92, *92*; curved templates, 94; and spiral curves, 97; curves, 99, 101, *101*, 104; adjustable set squares, 107, 110, *110*; parallel rules, 113; tee-square, 113; parallel motion rules, 113; drawing scales, 119–20; protractors, 122; needle-holders, 124; proportional compasses, 126, 128; and tracers, 127; pantograph, 132; eidograph, 133, *133*; and centrolinead, 145; sets and cases, 156, 161, *170*, 173, 193; *Mathematical Drawing Instruments*, 51, 92, 99
Steward, J. H., Ltd, 32, 54
Stolle, Heinrich, 21, 156
Stone, Edmund, 37, 44, 82, 128, *134*, 135, 185
straight lines, 57–68
Stuart, James, 142
Studer, Johann Gotthelf, 125; *Mathematical Instruments for Measuring and Drawing*, 47–8
Sturm, Leonard, 41
stylus, 11, 19, 57
Suardi, Giambattista, 53
Surçou, of Paris, 105
surveying, land, 11, 17, 22

Talos, son of Pedrix, 69
tee-squares, 105, 113, *114*
templates, 94, 101, *102*
textbooks, 51, 54
TG-1 pens, 64, 65
Thirty Years' War, 21
Thornton, A. G. (company), 30–2, 54, 110, 156, 161, 173
TK-matic pencil, 68
tracers, 127, *127*
tracing paper, 124, 127
trade cards, 44, 45
trammels, elliptical, 23, 89, 90
Trechsler, Christoph, the Elder, **Pl. I**, 21, *174*
Trechsler, Christoph, the Younger, 21
Trevithick, Richard, 14
triangulation, 11
Troughton, Edward, 26
Troughton, John, 26
Troughton (firm; *later* Troughton & Simms), **Pl. XV**, 28, 94, *94*, 122, 154, 185–6
tubular beam compasses *see* compasses
Turner, Anthony: *Early Scientific Instruments, 1500–1800*, 54
Turner, Gerard L'E.: *Nineteenth-Century Scientific Instruments*, 44, 54
Tuttell, Thomas, 24, 26, 37, 41, 89, 115; cases, 185, *187*

Ulm, 20
United States of America, 30
Utrecht, 25

Vernier, Paul: scales, 120, 122, 128
Vignola, Jacopo Barrozzi, il, 35
Villard de Honnecourt, 11, 69
Vitruvius, 20; *De architectura*, 35, 95
Voit, Johann Peter: *Comprehensive description of useful arts*, 27
volutes, 95, 96, 97
volutor, 97, *98*
Vries, Jan Vredeman de, 12; *Perspective*, 15, 144

Wagner, Günther, 64
walking-sticks, **Pl. XIX**, 193
Wallace, William, 132
Ware, Isaac, 47
Watkins, J. & W., 47
Watkins & Hill, 28
Watt, James, 14, 144–5, *148*
Webster, William, *Description and Use of a Complete Set or Case of Pocket Instruments sold by J. Sisson*, 44
weights and splines, 101, 104, *104*
West, Miss A. (*later* A. W. West & Sons), 32
wheel-pens, 11, 57, 61, 62
Whiford, T.: pocket case, **Pl. XIV**, 186
Whipple Museum of the History of Science, Cambridge, 26
Whistler, Rex: design, *193*
Whitwell, Charles, 23
Wholes and halves, *121*, 128
Wing, Tycho, 27, 120
Winsor & Newton (company), 31
Wolf (company), 67
Wren, Sir Christopher, 23–4, 41, 144, *147*
Wrench, Edward, *168*
Wright, Thomas, **Pl. X**, 26, 111, 121, 185

yard-sticks, 115

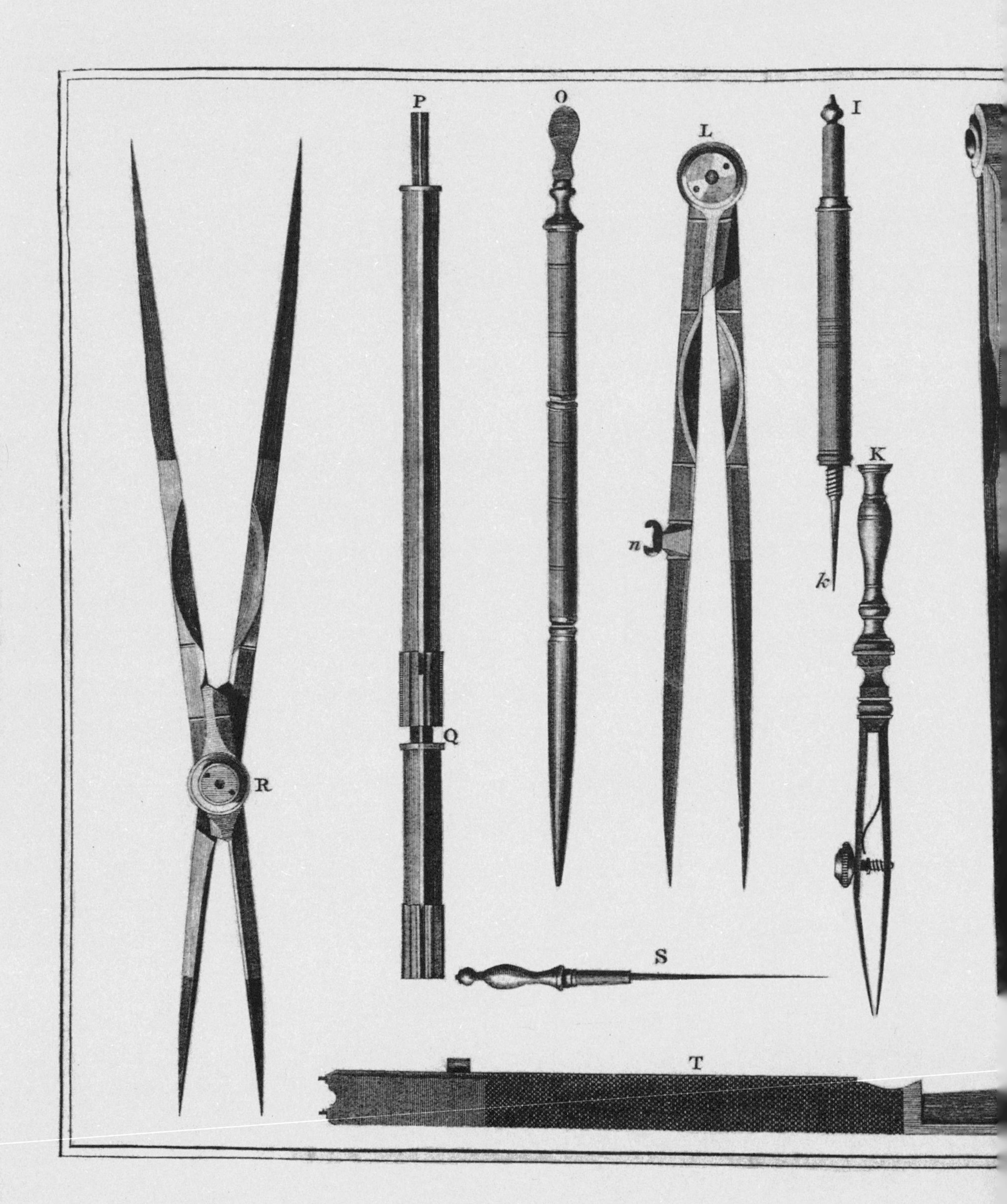
P
O
L
I
R
Q
n
k
K
S
T